Ready Notes

for use with

Chemistry

The Molecular Nature of Matter and Change

Third Edition

Martin S. Silberberg

Prepared by
Cathrine E. Reck
Indiana University

Boston Burr Ridge, IL Dubuque, IA Madison, WI New York San Francisco St. Louis
Bangkok Bogotá Caracas Lisbon London Madrid
Mexico City Milan New Delhi Seoul Singapore Sydney Taipei Toronto

McGraw-Hill Higher Education

A Division of The ***McGraw-Hill*** *Companies*

Ready Notes for use with
CHEMISTRY: THE MOLECULAR NATURE OF MATTER AND CHANGE, THIRD EDITION.
MARTIN S. SILBERBERG

Published by McGraw-Hill Higher Education, an imprint of The McGraw-Hill Companies, Inc., 1221 Avenue of the Americas, New York, NY 10020.

This book is printed on acid-free paper.

2 3 4 5 6 7 8 9 0 QPD QPD 0 9 8 7 6 5 4 3

ISBN 0-07-247580-3
www.mhhe.com

Chapter 1

Chemistry: The Molecular Nature of Matter and Change

Third Edition

Martin S. Silberberg

Physical Change vs. Chemical Change

A

B

The Physical States of Matter

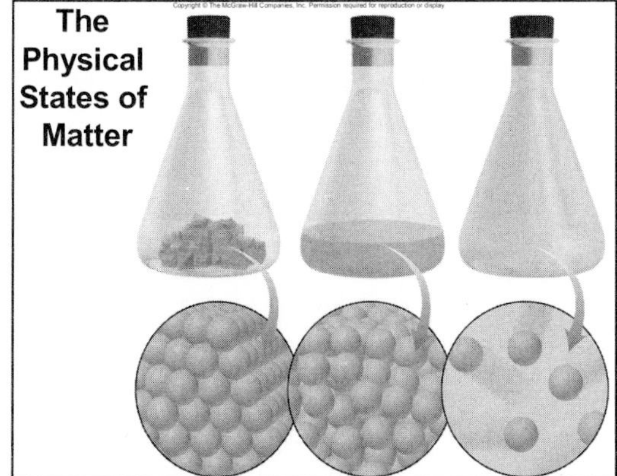

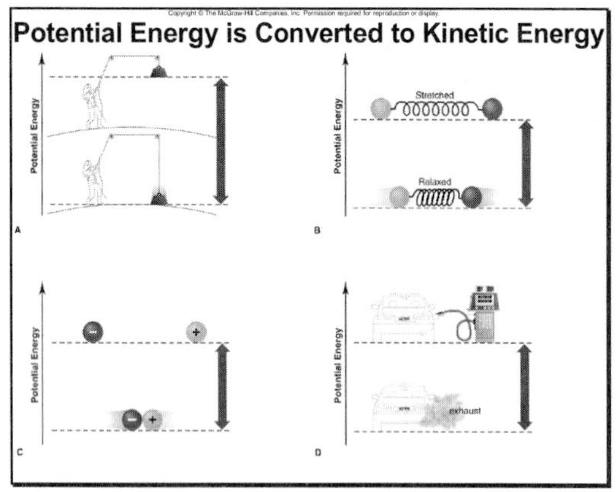

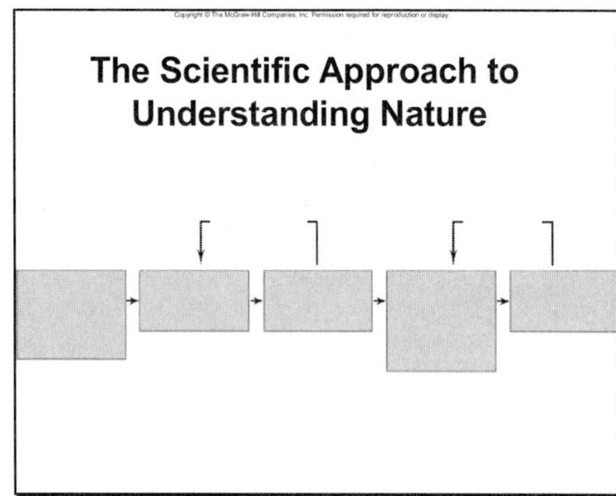

Table 1.2 SI Base Units

Physical Quantity (Dimension)	Unit Name	Unit Abbreviation
Mass	kilogram	
Length	meter	
Time	second	
Temperature	kelvin	
Electric current	ampere	
Amount of substance	mole	
Luminous intensity	candela	

Table 1.3 Common Decimal Prefixes Used with SI Units

Prefix*	Prefix Symbol	Meaning: Number	Meaning: Word	Multiple†
tera	T	1,000,000,000,000		
giga	G	1,000,000,000		
mega	M	1,000,000		
kilo	k	1,000		
hecto	h	100		
deka	da	10		
—	—	1		
deci	d	0.1		
centi	c	0.01		
milli	m	0.001		
micro	μ	0.000001		
nano	n	0.000000001		
pico	p	0.000000000001		
femto	f	0.000000000000001		

*The prefixes most frequently used by chemists appear in bold type.

†Many of the calculations you'll perform involve numbers written in exponential notation, which include a multiple written as a power of 10. If you are not familiar with this method of expressing numbers or just need a review, be sure to read Appendix A.

Table 1.4 Common SI-English Equivalent Quantities

Quantity	SI	SI Equivalents	English Equivalents	English to SI Equivalent
Length	1 kilometer (km)		0.6214 mile (mi)	
	1 meter (m)		1.094 yards (yd) 39.37 inches (in)	
	1 centimeter (cm)		0.3937 inch	
Volume	1 cubic meter (m^3)		35.31 cubic feet (ft^3)	
	1 cubic decimeter (dm^3)		0.2642 gallon (gal) 1.057 quarts (qt)	
	1 cubic centimeter (cm^3)		0.03381 fluid ounce	
Mass	1 kilogram (kg)		2.205 pounds (lb)	
	1 gram (g)		0.03527 ounce (oz)	

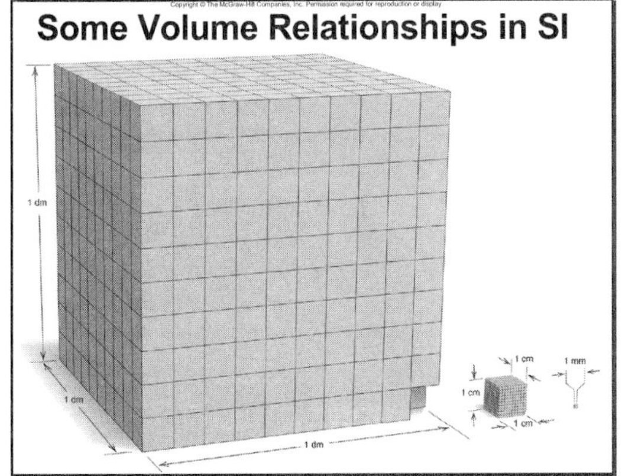

Common Laboratory Volumetric Glassware

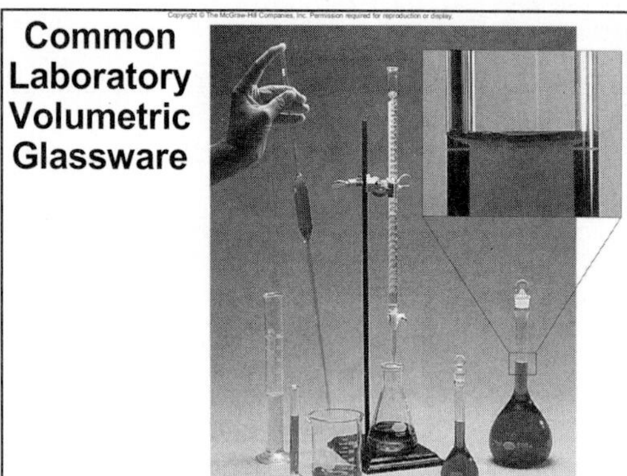

Some Interesting Quantities of Length (A), Volume (B), and Mass (C)

10^{12} m
10^{9} m
10^{6} m
10^{3} m (km)
10^{0} m (m)
10^{-3} m (mm)
10^{-6} m (μm)
10^{-9} m (nm)
10^{-12} m (pm)
A Length

10^{24} L
10^{21} L
10^{18} L
10^{15} L
10^{12} L
10^{9} L
10^{6} L
10^{3} L
10^{0} L
10^{-3} L
10^{-6} L
10^{-9} L
10^{-12} L
10^{-15} L
10^{-18} L
10^{-21} L
10^{-24} L
10^{-27} L
10^{-30} L
B Volume

10^{24} g
10^{21} g
10^{18} g
10^{15} g
10^{12} g
10^{9} g
10^{6} g
10^{3} g
10^{0} g
10^{-3} g
10^{-6} g
10^{-9} g
10^{-12} g
10^{-15} g
10^{-18} g
10^{-21} g
10^{-24} g
C Mass

Table 1.5 Densities of Some Common Substances*

Substance	Physical State	Density (g/cm^3)
Hydrogen		
Oxygen		
Grain alcohol		
Water		
Table salt		
Aluminum		
Lead		
Gold		

*At room temperature (20°C) and normal atmospheric pressure (1 atm).

Some Interesting Temperatures

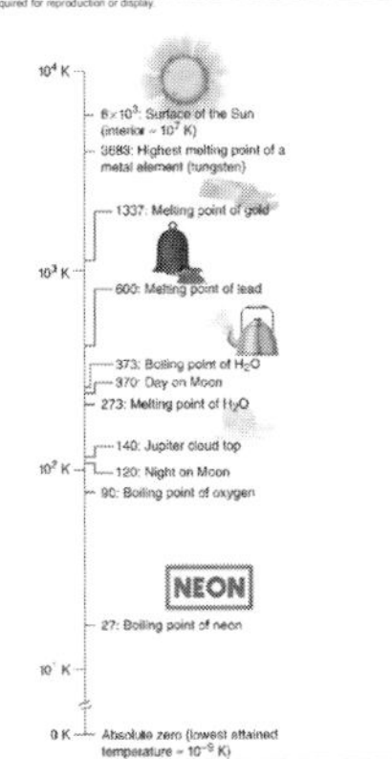

The Freezing Point and Boiling Point of Water in the Celsius, Kelvin (absolute), and Fahrenheit Temperature Scales

Temperature Relationships

$$T\text{ (in °C)} = T\text{ (in K)} - 273.15 \qquad (1.3)$$

$$T\text{ (in °F)} = \tfrac{9}{5}T\text{ (in °C)} + 32 \qquad (1.4)$$

$$T\text{ (in °C)} = [T\text{ (in °F)} - 32]\tfrac{5}{9} \qquad (1.5)$$

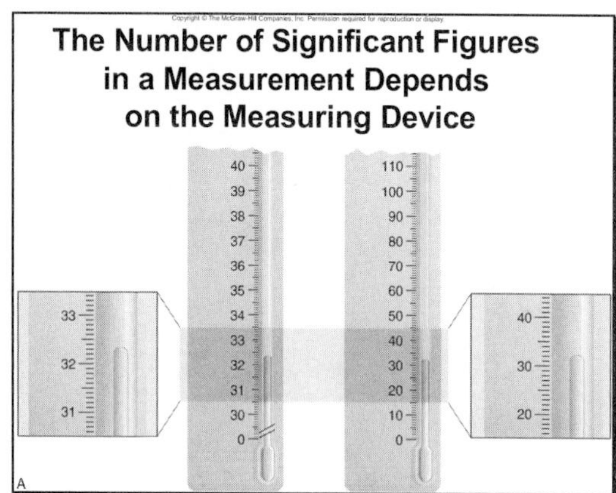
The Number of Significant Figures in a Measurement Depends on the Measuring Device
A

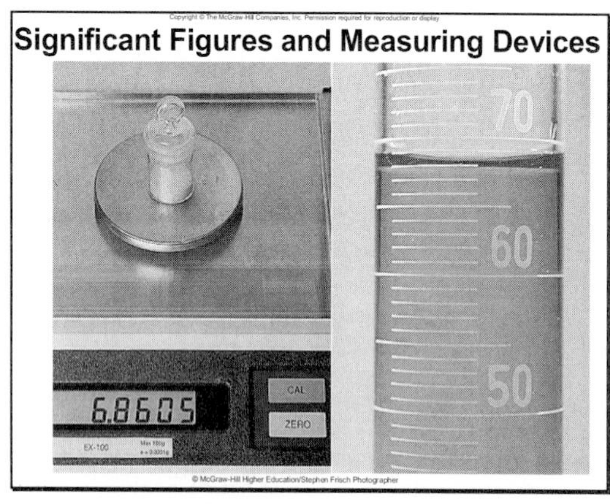
Significant Figures and Measuring Devices
6.8605
CAL
ZERO
70
60
50

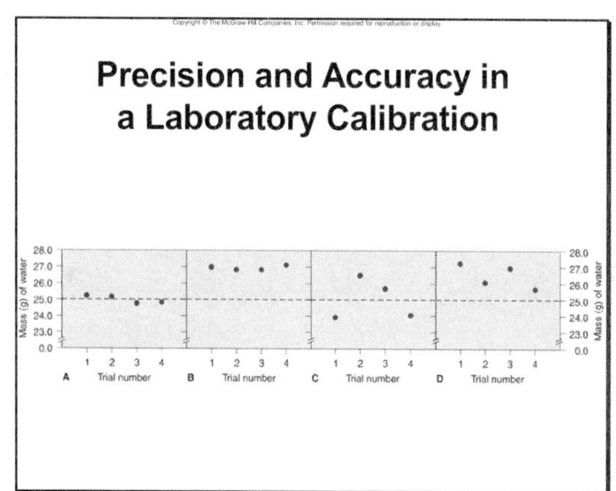
Precision and Accuracy in a Laboratory Calibration
Mass (g) of water
Trial number
A
B
C
D

Chapter 2

Chemistry: The Molecular Nature of Matter and Change

Third Edition

Martin S. Silberberg

Elements, Compounds, and Mixtures on the Atomic Scale

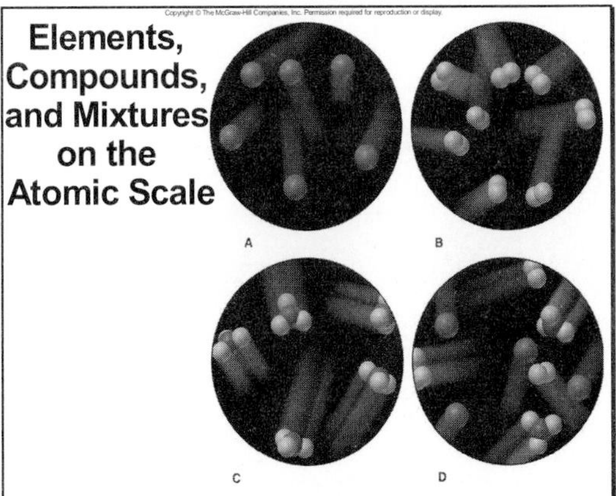

Table 2.1 Some Properties of Sodium, Chlorine, and Sodium Chloride

Property	Sodium	+	Chlorine	⟶	Sodium Chloride
Melting point	97.8°C		−101°C		801°C
Boiling point	881.4°C		−34°C		1413°C
Color	Silvery		Yellow-green		Colorless (white)
Density	0.97 g/cm^3		0.0032 g/cm^3		2.16 g/cm^3
Behavior in water	Reacts		Dissolves slightly		Dissolves freely

The Law of Mass Conservation: Mass Remains Constant During a Chemical Reaction

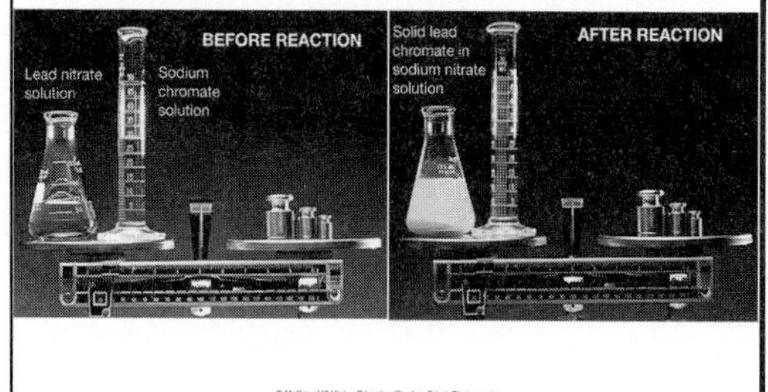

Meaning of Mass Fraction and Mass Percent

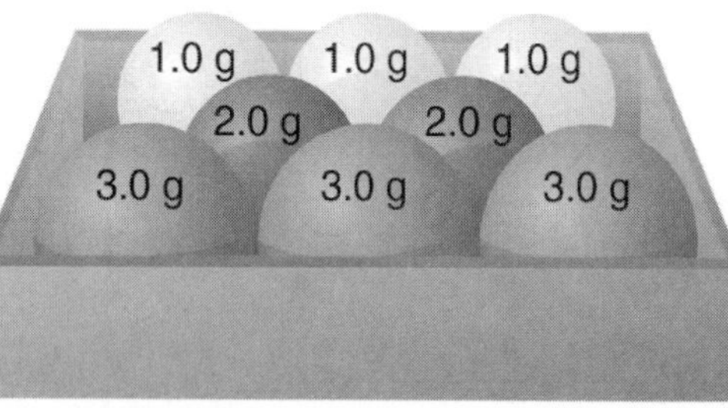

The Atomic Basis of the Law of Multiple Proportions

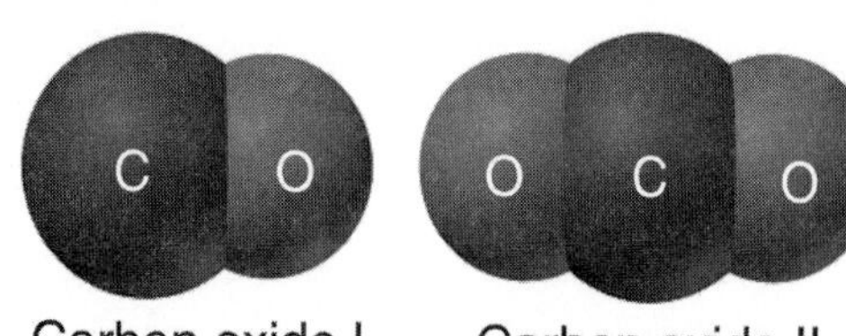

Carbon oxide I (carbon monoxide)

Carbon oxide II (carbon dioxide)

Experiments to Determine the Properties of Cathode Rays

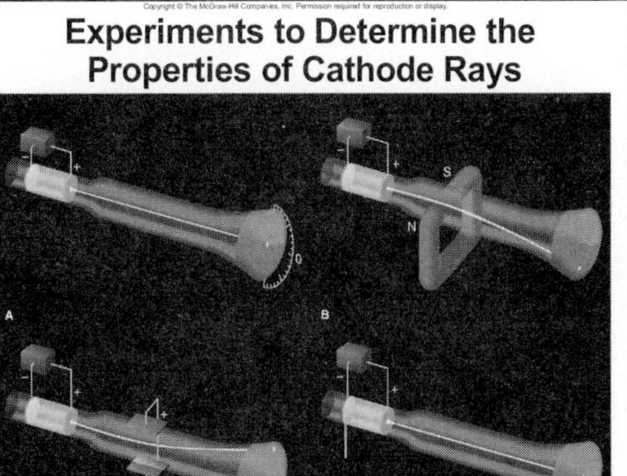

Millikan's Oil-drop Experiment for Measuring an Electron's Charge

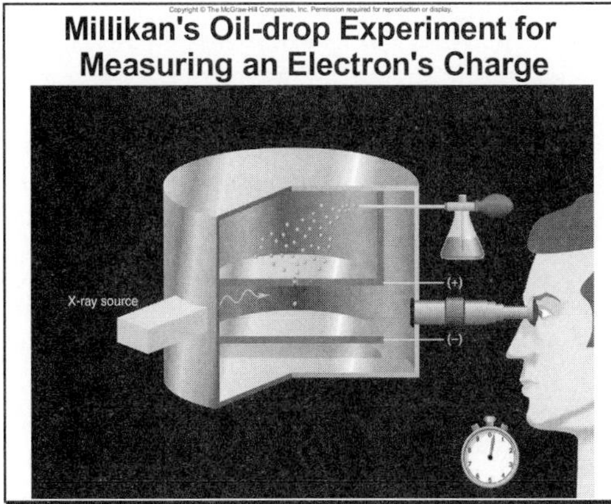

Rutherford's α-Scattering Experiment and the Discovery of the Atomic Nucleus

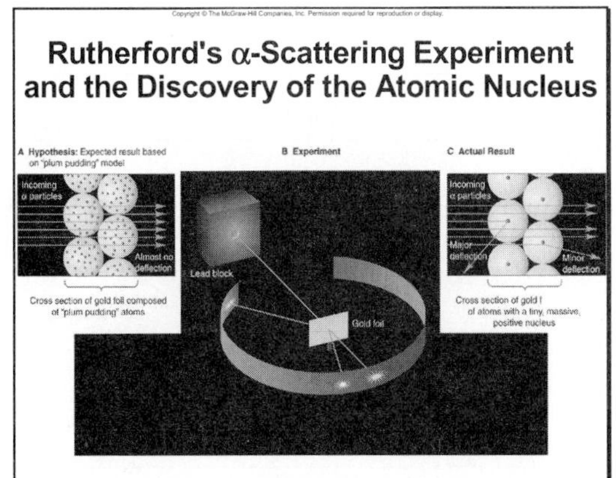

General Features of the Atom

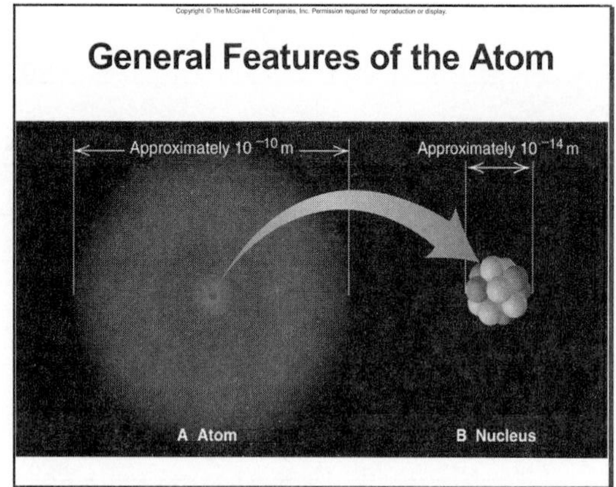

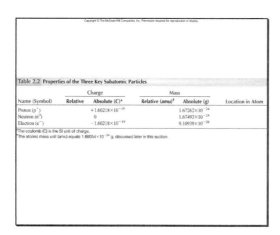

Table 2.2 Properties of the Three Key Subatomic Particles

	Charge		Mass		
Name (Symbol)	Relative	Absolute (C)*	Relative (amu)†	Absolute (g)	Location in Atom
Proton (p^+)		$+1.60218\times10^{-19}$		1.67262×10^{-24}	
Neutron (n^0)		0		1.67493×10^{-24}	
Electron (e^-)		-1.60218×10^{-19}		9.10939×10^{-28}	

*The coulomb (C) is the SI unit of charge.
†The atomic mass unit (amu) equals 1.66054×10^{-24} g; discussed later in this section.

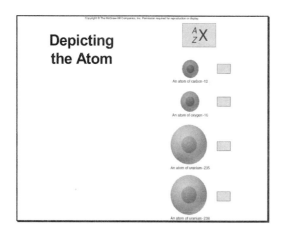

Depicting the Atom

$^{A}_{Z}X$

An atom of carbon-12

An atom of oxygen-16

An atom of uranium-235

An atom of uranium-238

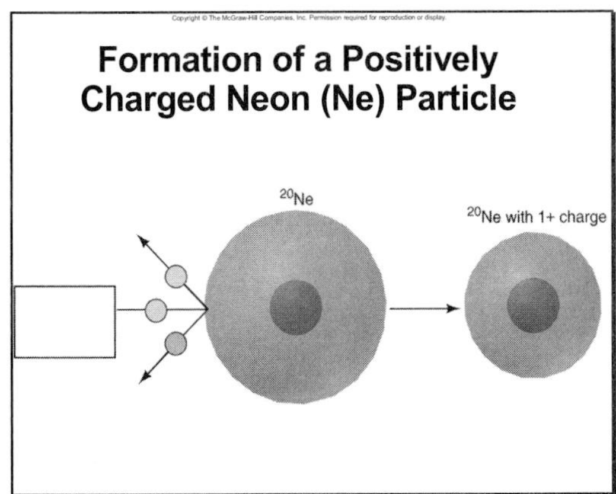
Formation of a Positively Charged Neon (Ne) Particle
^{20}Ne
^{20}Ne with 1+ charge

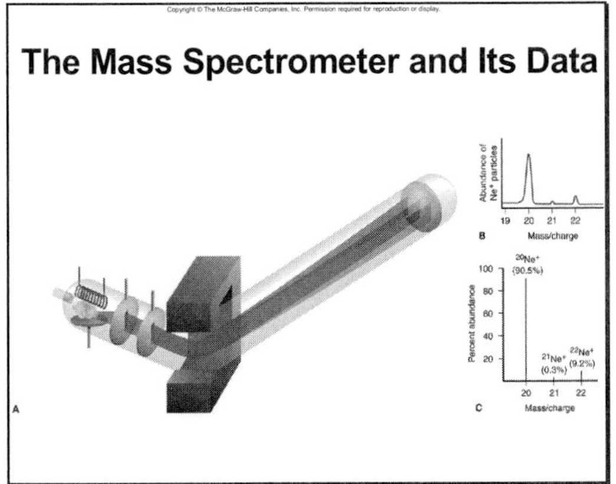
The Mass Spectrometer and Its Data
A
B
C
Mass/charge
Percent abundance
$^{20}Ne^{+}$ (90.5%)
$^{21}Ne^{+}$ (0.3%)
$^{22}Ne^{+}$ (9.2%)

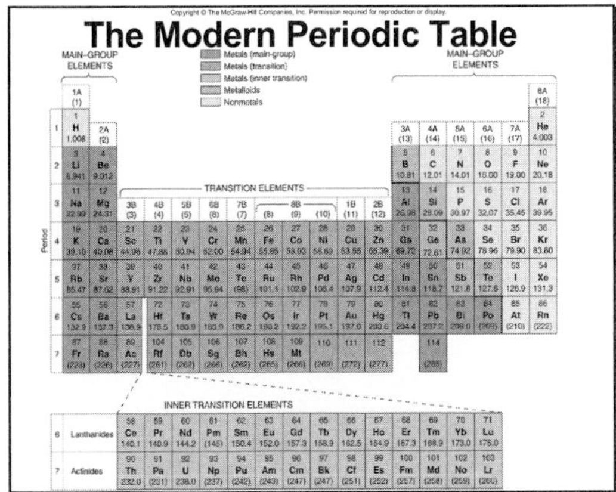
The Modern Periodic Table
MAIN-GROUP ELEMENTS
TRANSITION ELEMENTS
INNER TRANSITION ELEMENTS
Lanthanides
Actinides

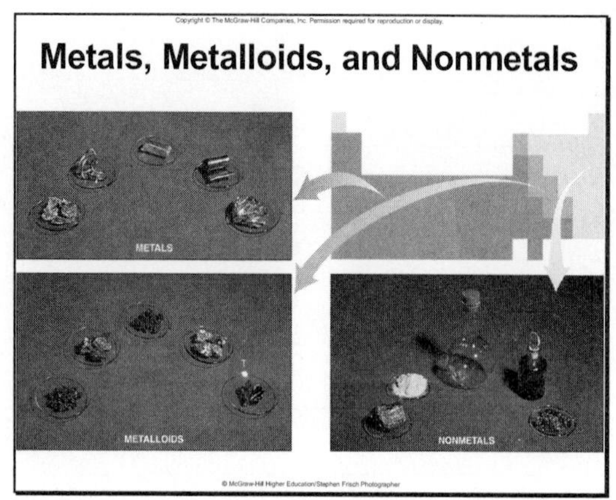
Metals, Metalloids, and Nonmetals
METALS
METALLOIDS
NONMETALS

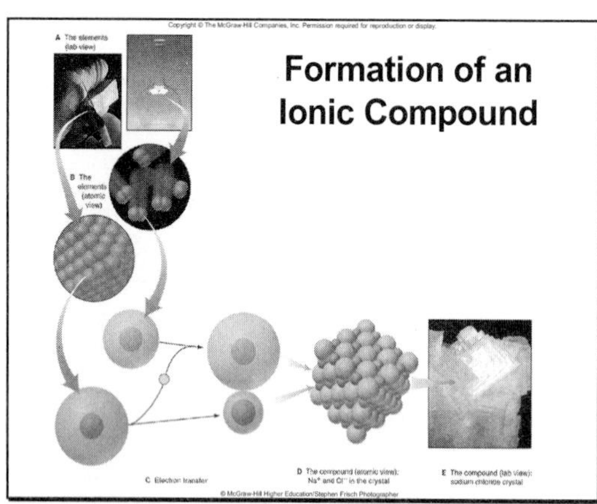
Formation of an Ionic Compound

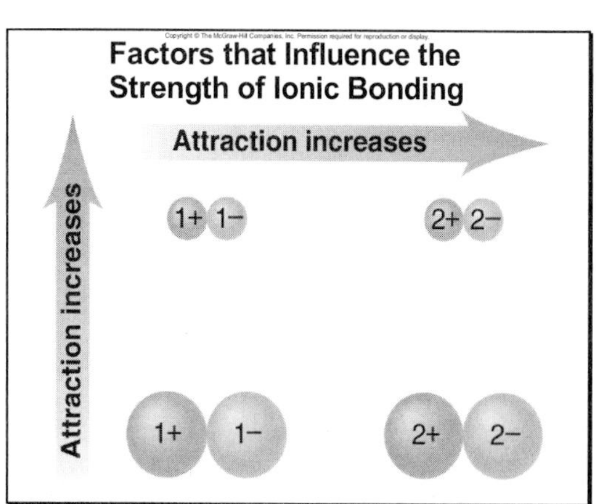
Factors that Influence the Strength of Ionic Bonding
Attraction increases
Attraction increases
1+ 1–
2+ 2–
1+
1–
2+
2–

The Relationship Between Ions Formed and the Nearest Noble Gas

- 5A (15): N^{3-}
- 6A (16): O^{2-}, S^{2-}
- 7A (17): H^-, F^-, Cl^-, Br^-, I^-
- 8A (18): He, Ne, Ar, Kr, Xe
- 1A (1): Li^+, Na^+, K^+, Rb^+, Cs^+
- 2A (2): Mg^{2+}, Ca^{2+}, Sr^{2+}, Ba^{2+}
- 3A (13): Al^{3+}

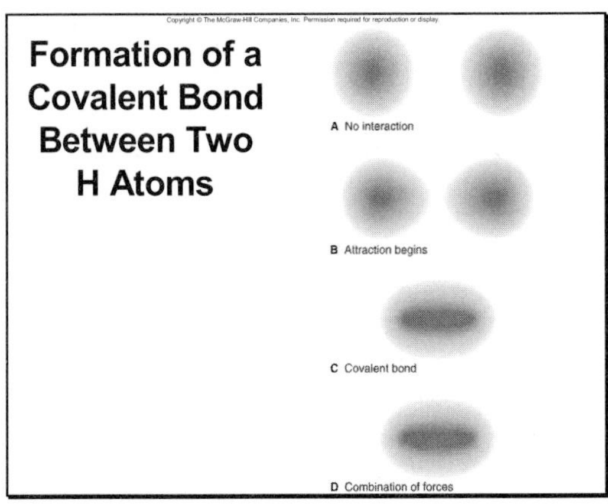

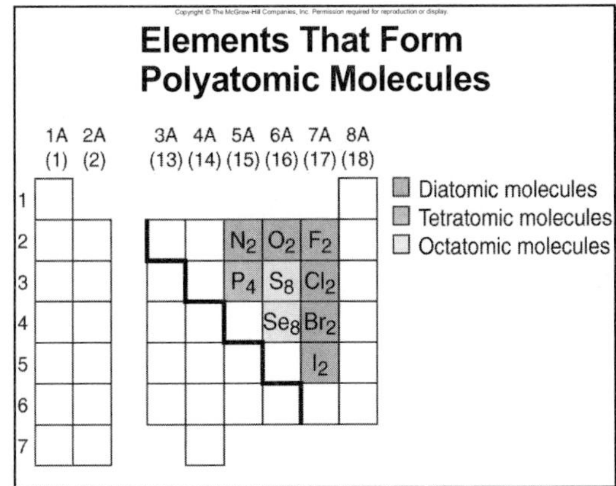

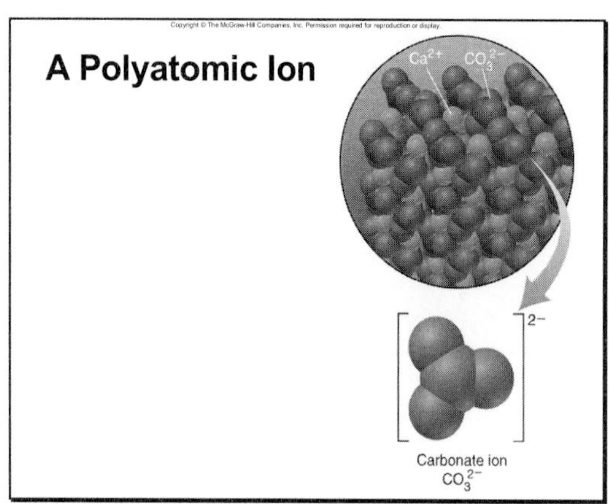

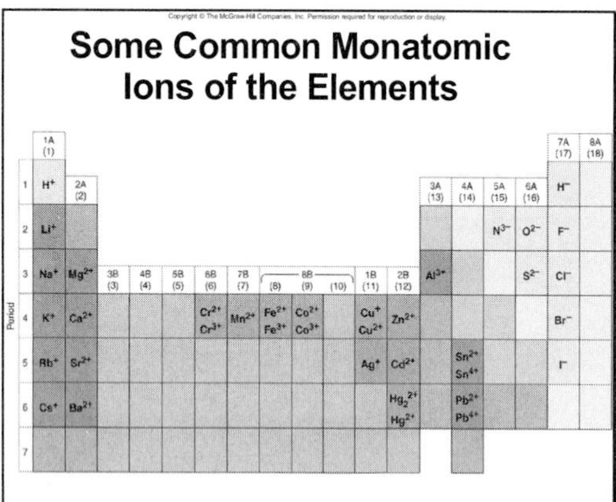

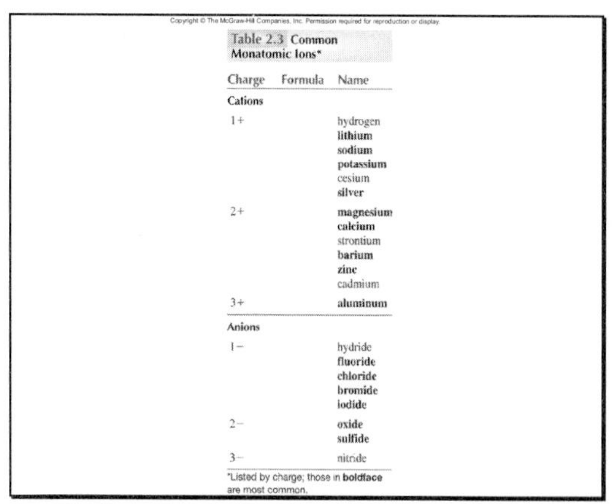

Table 2.3 Common Monatomic Ions*

Charge	Formula	Name
Cations		
1+		hydrogen
		lithium
		sodium
		potassium
		cesium
		silver
2+		**magnesium**
		calcium
		strontium
		barium
		zinc
		cadmium
3+		**aluminum**
Anions		
1−		hydride
		fluoride
		chloride
		bromide
		iodide
2−		**oxide**
		sulfide
3−		nitride

*Listed by charge; those in **boldface** are most common.

Table 2.4 Some Metals That Form More Than One Monatomic Ion*

Element	Ion Formula	Systematic Name	Common (Trivial) Name
Chromium		chromium(II)	chromous
		chromium(III)	chromic
Cobalt		cobalt(II)	
		cobalt(III)	
Copper		**copper(I)**	cuprous
		copper(II)	cupric
Iron		**iron(II)**	ferrous
		iron(III)	ferric
Lead		**lead(II)**	
		lead(IV)	
Mercury		mercury(I)	mercurous
		mercury(II)	mercuric
Tin		**tin(II)**	stannous
		tin(IV)	stannic

*Listed alphabetically by metal name; those in **boldface** are most common.

Table 2.5 Common Polyatomic Ions*

Formula	Name
Cations	
	ammonium
	hydronium
Anions	
	acetate
	cyanide
	hydroxide
	hypochlorite
	chlorite
	chlorate
	perchlorate
	nitrite
	nitrate
	permanganate
	carbonate
	hydrogen carbonate (or **bicarbonate**)
	chromate
	dichromate
	peroxide
	phosphate
	hydrogen phosphate
	dihydrogen phosphate
	sulfite
	sulfate
	hydrogen sulfate (or bisulfate)

*__Boldface__ ions are most common.

Naming Oxoanions

No. of O atoms (increasing ↑)	Prefix	Root	Suffix
	per	*root*	ate
		root	ate
		root	ite
	hypo	*root*	ite

Table 2.6 Numerical Prefixes for Hydrates and Binary Covalent Compounds

Number	Prefix
1	mono-
2	
3	
4	
5	
6	
7	
8	
9	
10	

Table 2.7 The First 10 Straight-Chain Alkanes

Name	Formula
Methane	CH_4
Ethane	
Propane	
Butane	
Pentane	
Hexane	
Heptane	
Octane	
Nonane	
Decane	

All Molecules are Minute, with their Relative Sizes Depending on Composition

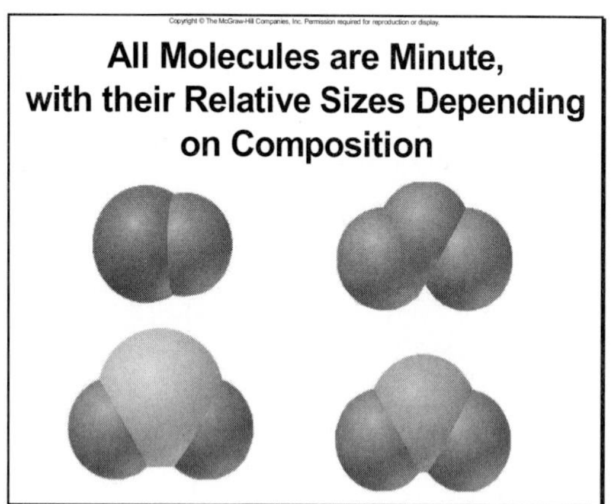

Molecules Are Depicted in a Variety of Useful Ways

H_2O

H:O:H

H–O–H

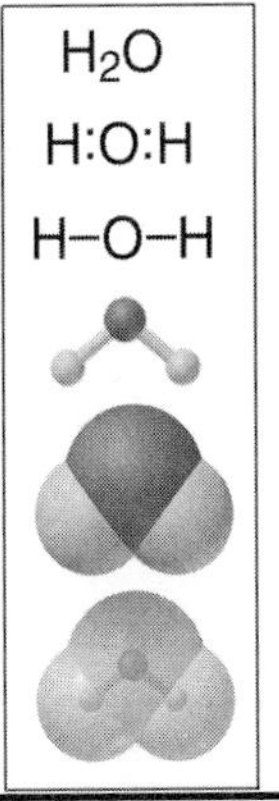

Many Household Items Consist of Somewhat Larger Molecules

Butane (C_4H_{10}, 58.12 amu),

Acetic acid (CH_3COOH, 60.05 amu)

Aspirin ($C_9H_8O_4$, 180.15 amu)

Heme ($C_{34}H_{32}FeN_4O_4$, 616.49 amu)

Very Large Molecules, Called Macromolecules, Can be Synthetic

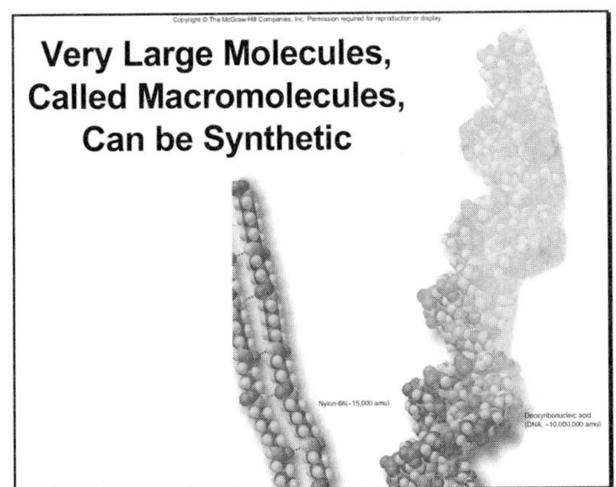

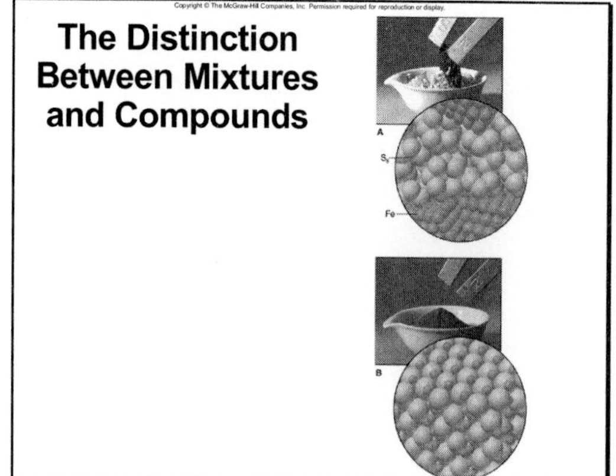
The Distinction Between Mixtures and Compounds
A
B

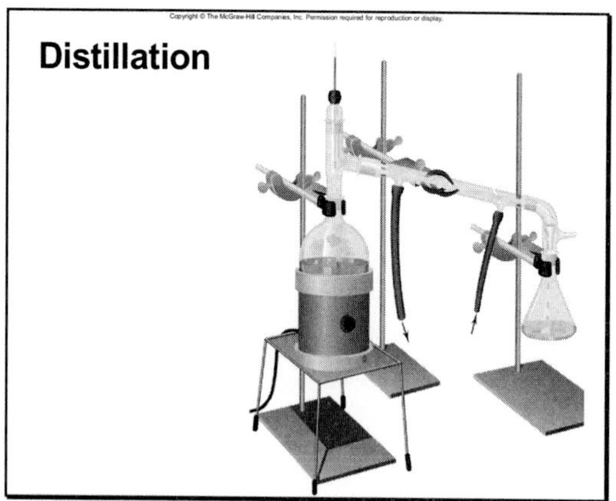
Distillation

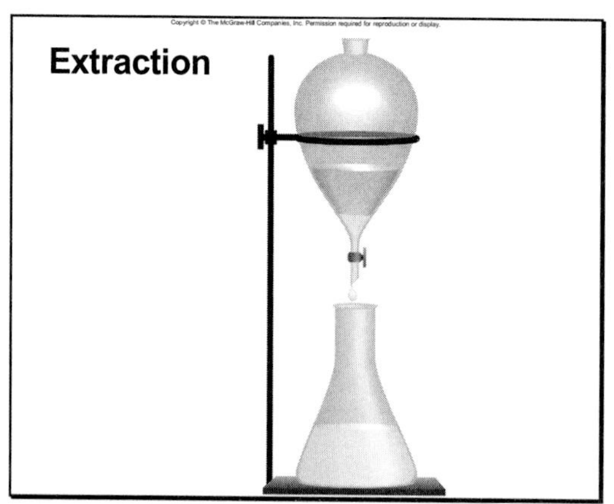
Extraction

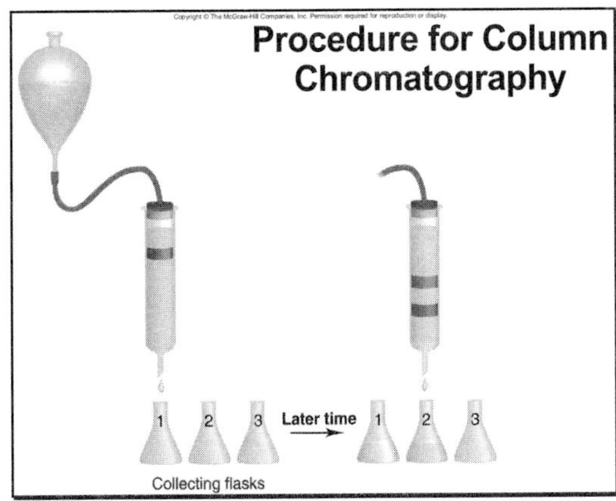
Copyright © The McGraw-Hill Companies, Inc. Permission required for reproduction or display.
Procedure for Column Chromatography
1
2
3
Later time
1
2
3
Collecting flasks

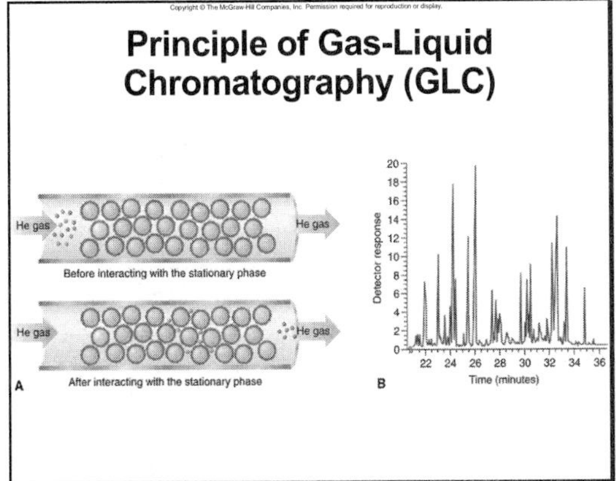
Copyright © The McGraw-Hill Companies, Inc. Permission required for reproduction or display.
Principle of Gas-Liquid Chromatography (GLC)
He gas
He gas
Before interacting with the stationary phase
He gas
He gas
After interacting with the stationary phase
A
Detector response
Time (minutes)
B

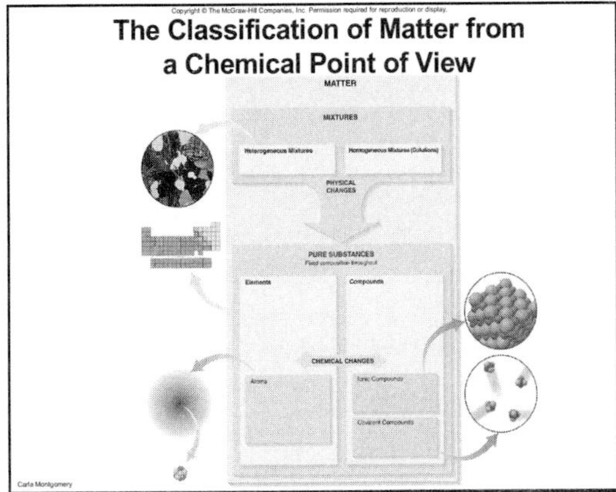
Copyright © The McGraw-Hill Companies, Inc. Permission required for reproduction or display.
The Classification of Matter from a Chemical Point of View
MATTER
MIXTURES
PHYSICAL CHANGES
PURE SUBSTANCES
Elements
Compounds
CHEMICAL CHANGES

Chapter 3

Chemistry: The Molecular Nature of Matter and Change

Third Edition

Martin S. Silberberg

Imagine a Mole of…

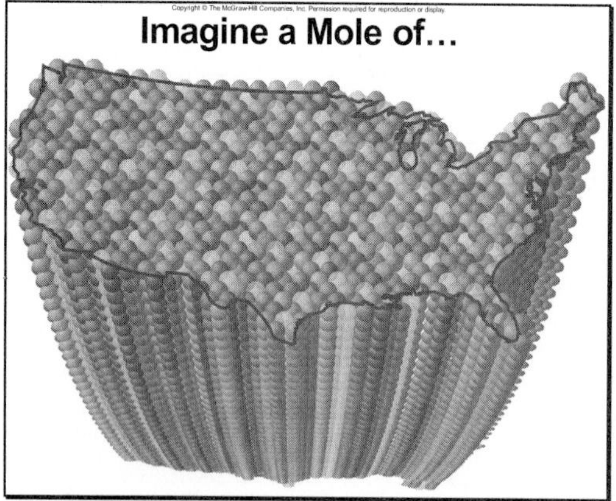

One Mole of Some Familiar Substances

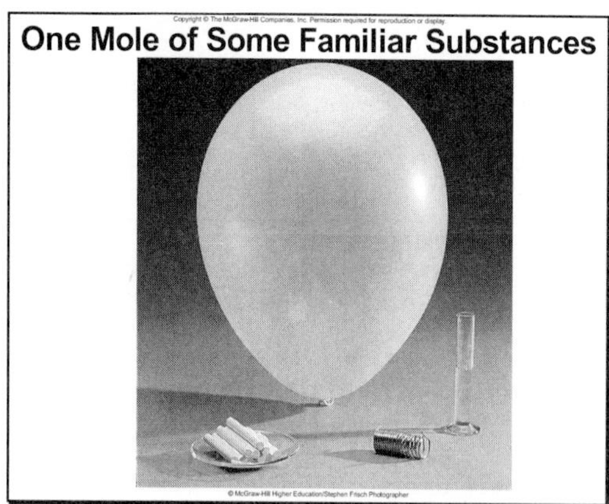

Table 3.1 Summary of Mass Terminology*

Term	Definition	Unit
Isotopic mass	Mass of an isotope of an element	
Atomic mass (also called atomic weight)	Average of the masses of the naturally occurring isotopes of an element weighted according to their abundance	
Molecular (or formula) mass (also called molecular weight)	Sum of the atomic masses of the atoms (or ions) in a molecule (or formula unit)	
Molar mass ($\mathcal{M}$) (also called gram-molecular weight)	Mass of 1 mole of chemical entities (atoms, ions, molecules, formula units)	

*All terms based on the ^{12}C standard: 1 atomic mass unit = $\frac{1}{12}$ mass of one ^{12}C atom.

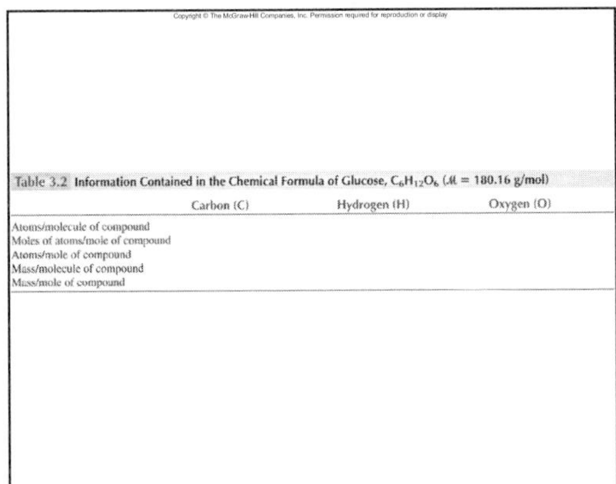

Table 3.2 Information Contained in the Chemical Formula of Glucose, $C_6H_{12}O_6$ ($\mathcal{M}$ = 180.16 g/mol)

	Carbon (C)	Hydrogen (H)	Oxygen (O)
Atoms/molecule of compound			
Moles of atoms/mole of compound			
Atoms/mole of compound			
Mass/molecule of compound			
Mass/mole of compound			

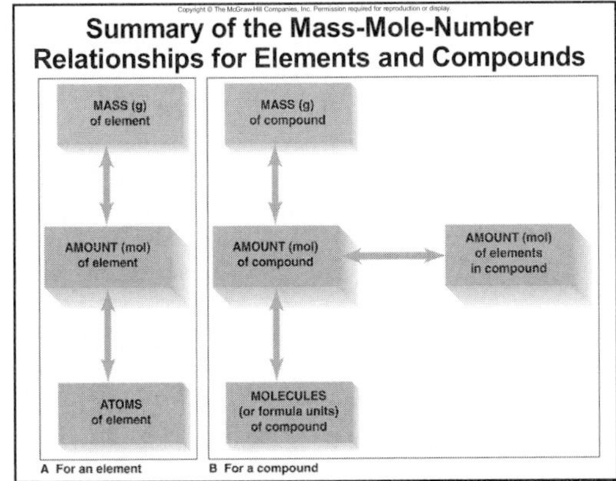

Combustion Apparatus for Determining Formulas of Organic Compounds

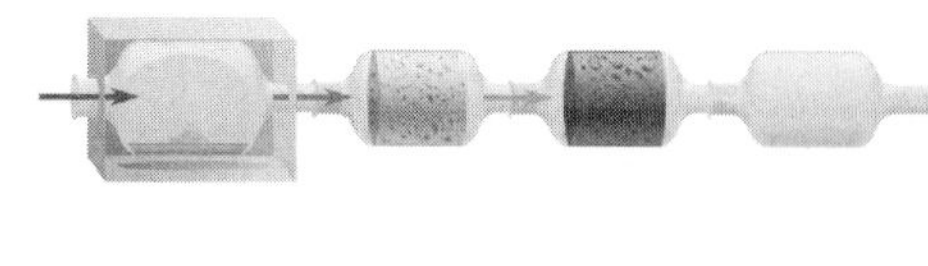

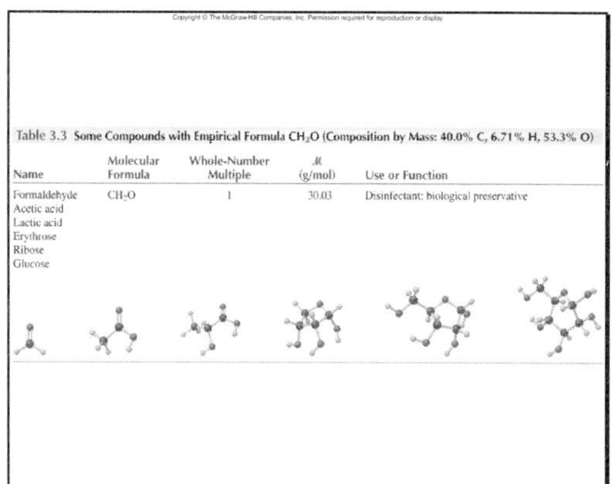

Table 3.3 Some Compounds with Empirical Formula CH_2O (Composition by Mass: 40.0% C, 6.71% H, 53.3% O)

Name	Molecular Formula	Whole-Number Multiple	$\mathcal{M}$ (g/mol)	Use or Function
Formaldehyde	CH_2O	1	30.03	Disinfectant: biological preservative
Acetic acid				
Lactic acid				
Erythrose				
Ribose				
Glucose				

Table 3.4 Two Compounds with Molecular Formula C_2H_6O

Property	Ethanol	Dimethyl Ether
$\mathcal{M}$ (g/mol)		
Color		
Melting point		
Boiling point		
Density (at 20°C)		
Use		
Structural formula and space-filling model	H—C(H)(H)—C(H)(H)—O—H	H—C(H)(H)—O—C(H)(H)—H

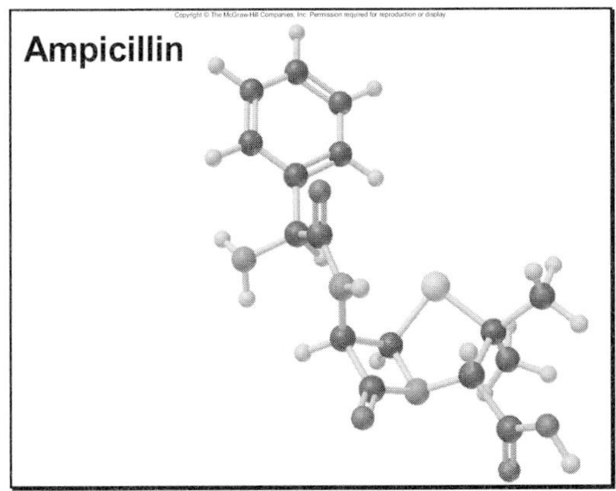
Ampicillin

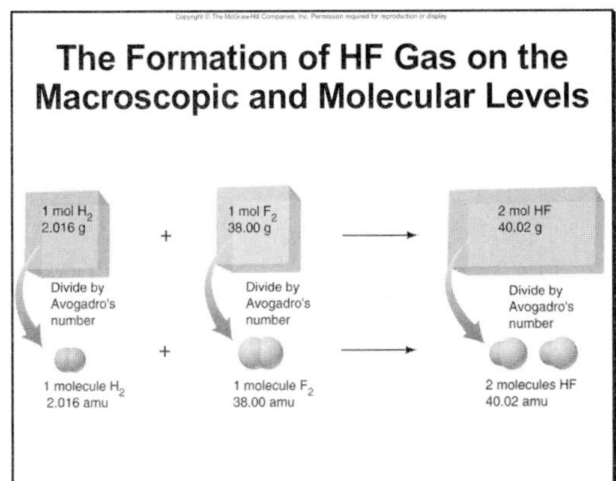
The Formation of HF Gas on the Macroscopic and Molecular Levels
1 mol H2 2.016 g
1 mol F2 38.00 g
2 mol HF 40.02 g
Divide by Avogadro's number
1 molecule H2 2.016 amu
1 molecule F2 38.00 amu
2 molecules HF 40.02 amu

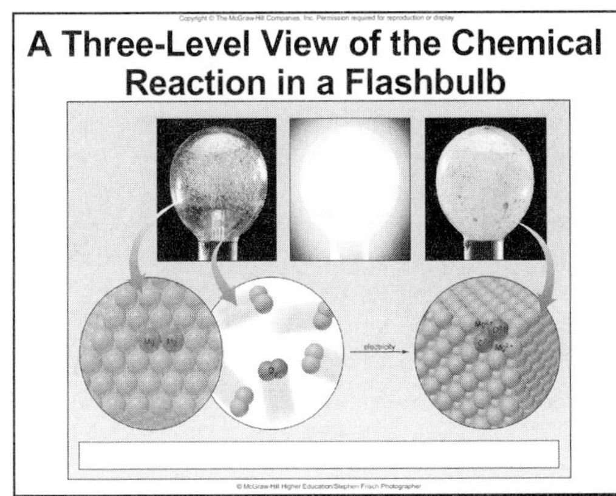
A Three-Level View of the Chemical Reaction in a Flashbulb

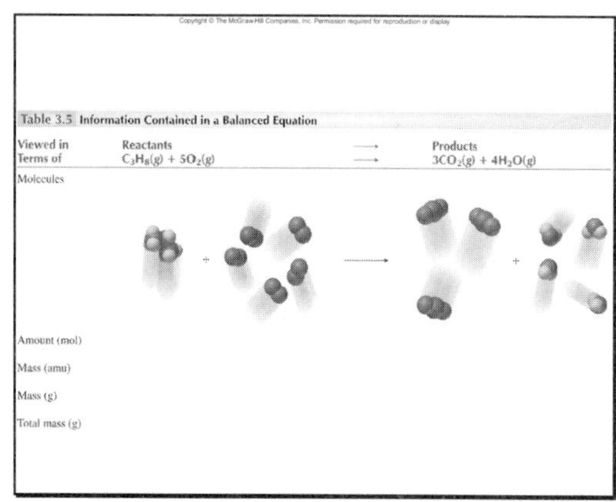

Table 3.5 Information Contained in a Balanced Equation

Viewed in Terms of	Reactants $C_3H_8(g) + 5O_2(g)$	⟶	Products $3CO_2(g) + 4H_2O(g)$
Molecules			
Amount (mol)			
Mass (amu)			
Mass (g)			
Total mass (g)			

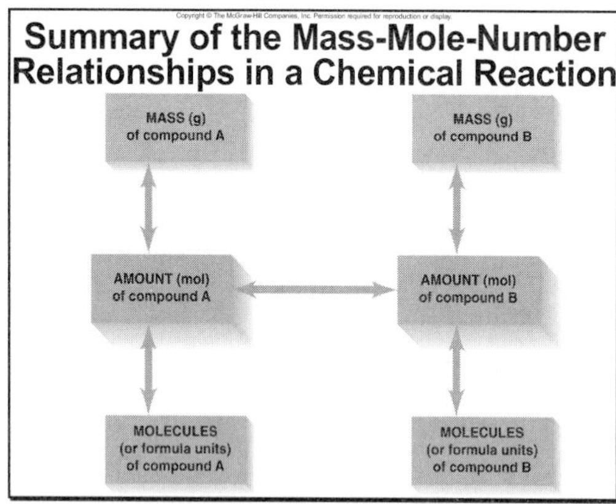

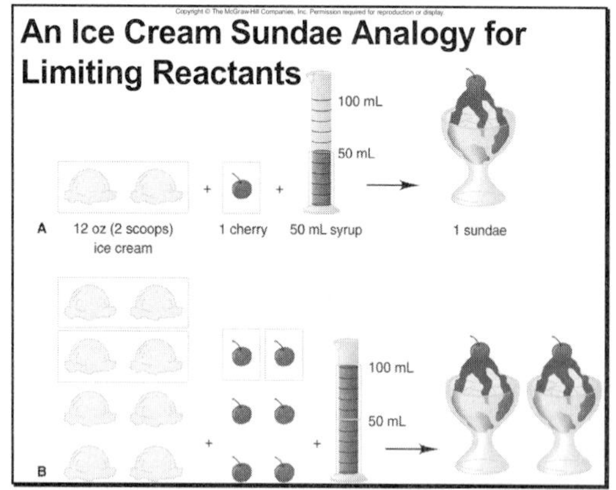

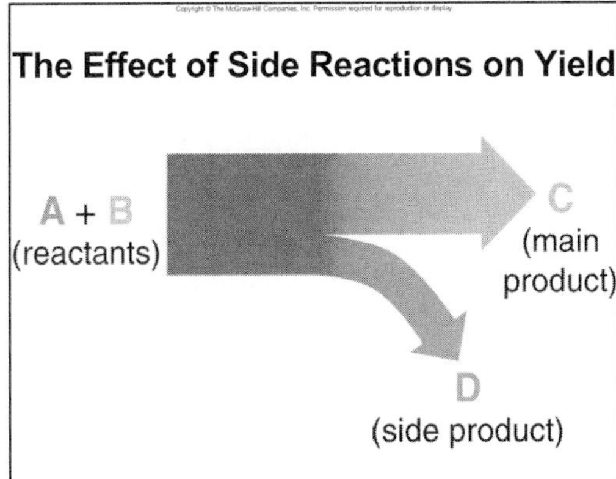

Percent Yield

$$\% \text{ yield} = \frac{\text{actual yield}}{\text{theoretical yield}} \times 100 \qquad (3.7)$$

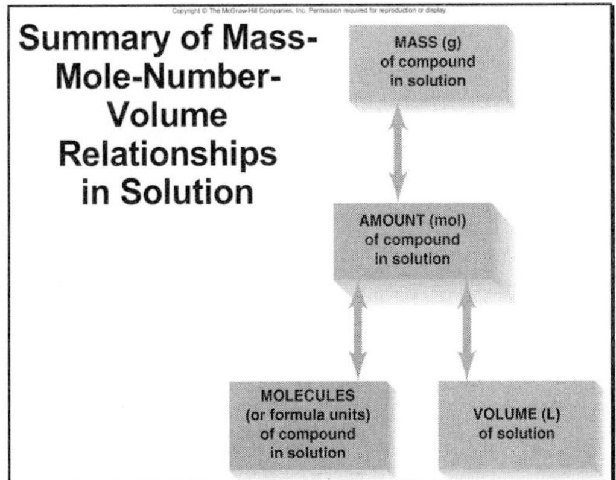

Copyright © The McGraw-Hill Companies, Inc. Permission required for reproduction or display.
Laboratory Preparation of Molar Solutions
A
B
C
D
© McGraw-Hill Higher Education/Stephen Frisch Photographer

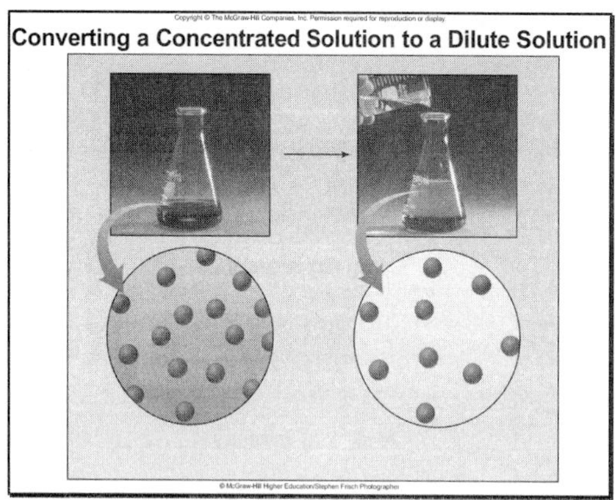
Copyright © The McGraw-Hill Companies, Inc. Permission required for reproduction or display.
Converting a Concentrated Solution to a Dilute Solution
© McGraw-Hill Higher Education/Stephen Frisch Photographer

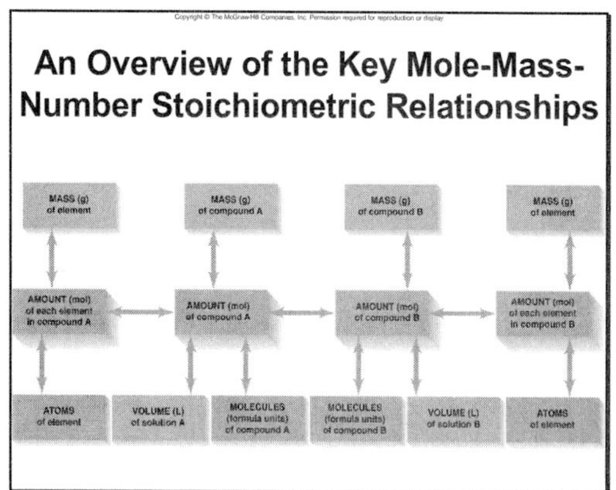
Copyright © The McGraw-Hill Companies, Inc. Permission required for reproduction or display.
An Overview of the Key Mole-Mass-Number Stoichiometric Relationships
MASS (g) of element
MASS (g) of compound A
MASS (g) of compound B
MASS (g) of element
AMOUNT (mol) of each element in compound A
AMOUNT (mol) of compound A
AMOUNT (mol) of compound B
AMOUNT (mol) of each element in compound B
ATOMS of element
VOLUME (L) of solution A
MOLECULES (formula units) of compound A
MOLECULES (formula units) of compound B
VOLUME (L) of solution B
ATOMS of element

Chapter 4

Chemistry: The Molecular Nature of Matter and Change

Third Edition

Martin S. Silberberg

The Electrical Conductivity of Ionic Solutions

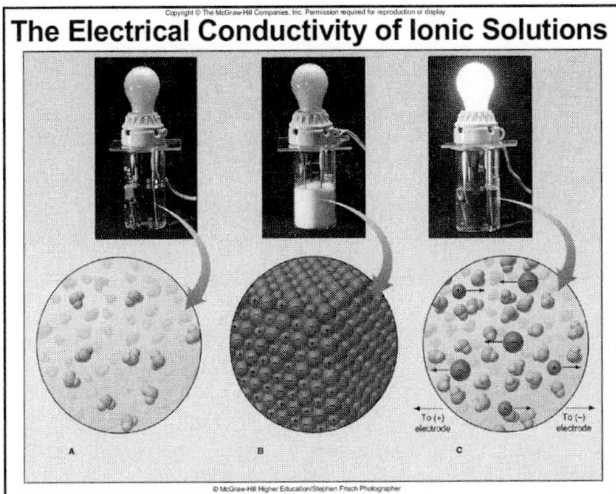

Electron Distribution in Molecules of H_2 and H_2O

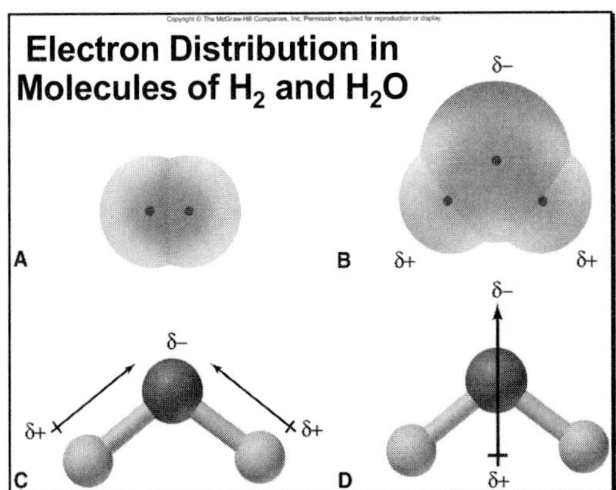

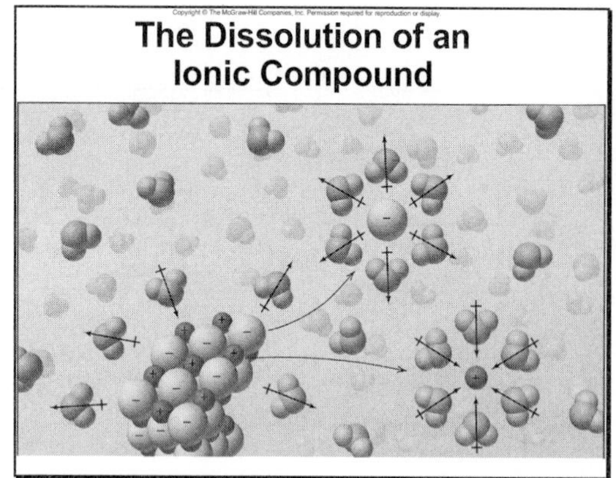
The Dissolution of an Ionic Compound

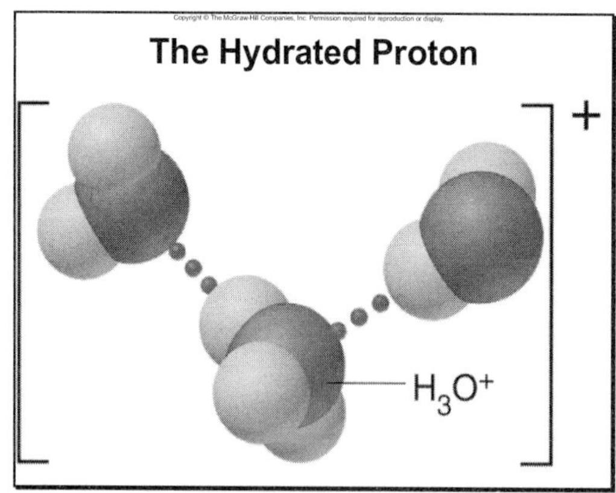
The Hydrated Proton
H_3O^+

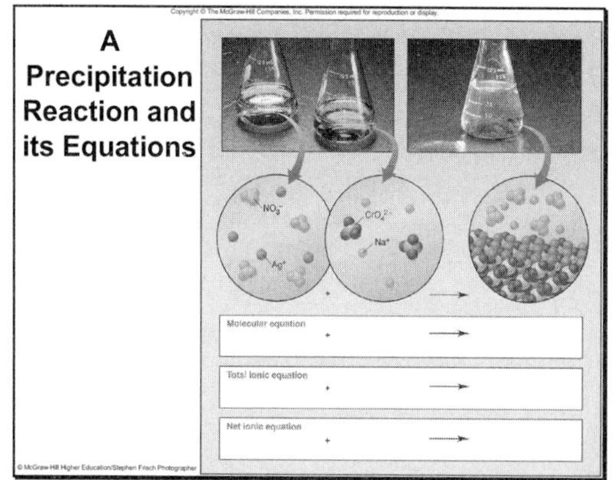
A Precipitation Reaction and its Equations
Molecular equation
Total ionic equation
Net ionic equation

The Reaction of $Pb(NO_3)_2$ and NaI

Copyright © The McGraw-Hill Companies, Inc. Permission required for reproduction or display.

Table 4.1 Solubility Rules for Ionic Compounds in Water

Soluble Ionic Compounds	Insoluble Ionic Compounds
1. All common compounds of Group 1A(1) ions (Li^+, Na^+, K^+, etc.) and ammonium ion (NH_4^+) are soluble.	1. All common metal hydroxides are insoluble, *except* those of Group 1A(1) and the larger members of Group 2A(2) (beginning with Ca^{2+}).
2. All common nitrates (NO_3^-), acetates (CH_3COO^- or $C_2H_3O_2^-$), and most perchlorates (ClO_4^-) are soluble.	2. All common carbonates (CO_3^{2-}) and phosphates (PO_4^{3-}) are insoluble, *except* those of Group 1A(1) and NH_4^+.
3. All common chlorides (Cl^-), bromides (Br^-), and iodides (I^-) are soluble, *except* those of Ag^+, Pb^{2+}, Cu^+, and Hg_2^{2+}.	3. All common sulfides are insoluble *except* those of Group 1A(1), Group 2A(2), and NH_4^+.
4. All common sulfates (SO_4^{2-}) are soluble, *except* those of Ca^{2+}, Sr^{2+}, Ba^{2+}, and Pb^{2+}.	

Copyright © The McGraw-Hill Companies, Inc. Permission required for reproduction or display.

The Behavior of Strong and Weak Electrolytes

Strong electrolyte

Weak electrolyte

© McGraw-Hill Higher Education/Stephen Frisch Photographer

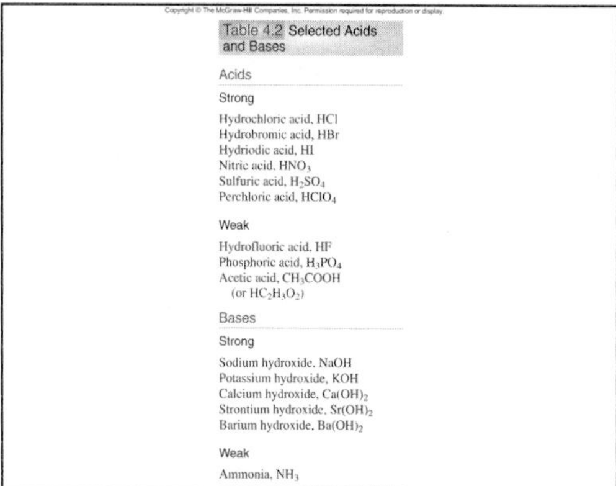

Table 4.2 Selected Acids and Bases

Acids
Strong
Hydrochloric acid, HCl
Hydrobromic acid, HBr
Hydriodic acid, HI
Nitric acid, HNO_3
Sulfuric acid, H_2SO_4
Perchloric acid, $HClO_4$
Weak
Hydrofluoric acid, HF
Phosphoric acid, H_3PO_4
Acetic acid, CH_3COOH (or $HC_2H_3O_2$)

Bases
Strong
Sodium hydroxide, $NaOH$
Potassium hydroxide, KOH
Calcium hydroxide, $Ca(OH)_2$
Strontium hydroxide, $Sr(OH)_2$
Barium hydroxide, $Ba(OH)_2$
Weak
Ammonia, NH_3

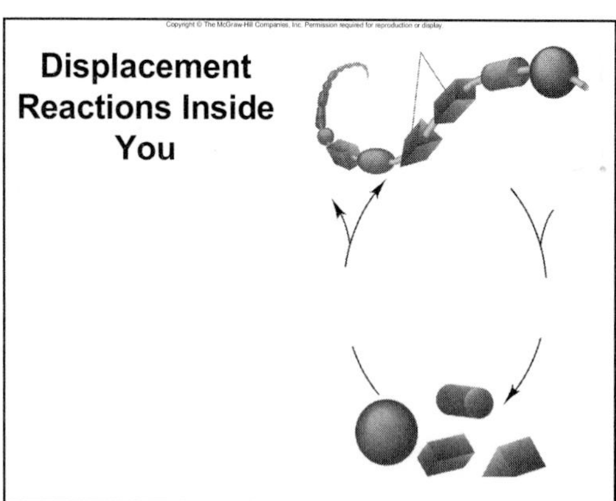

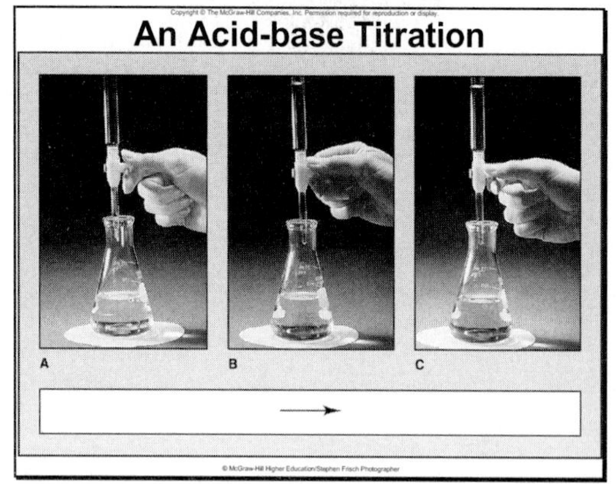

Finding Concentration of an Acid from and Acid-Base Titration

Volume (L) of base
(difference in buret readings)

↓ multiply by M (mol/L) of base

Amount (mol) of base

↓ molar ratio

Amount (mol) of acid

↓ divide by volume (L) of acid

M (mol/L) of acid

An Aqueous Strong Acid-Strong Base Reaction on the Atomic Scale

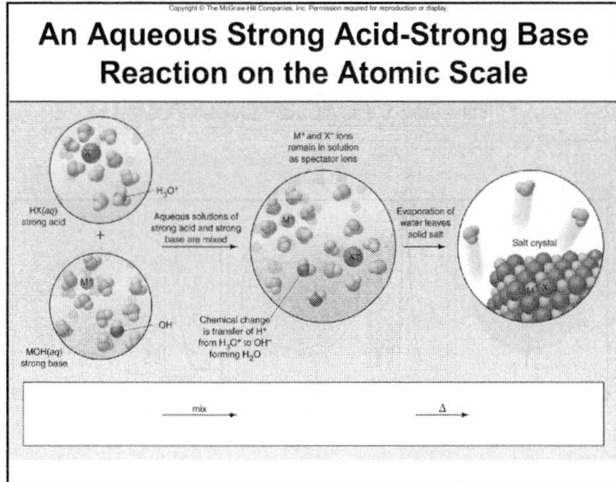

An Acid-Base Reaction That Forms a Gaseous Product

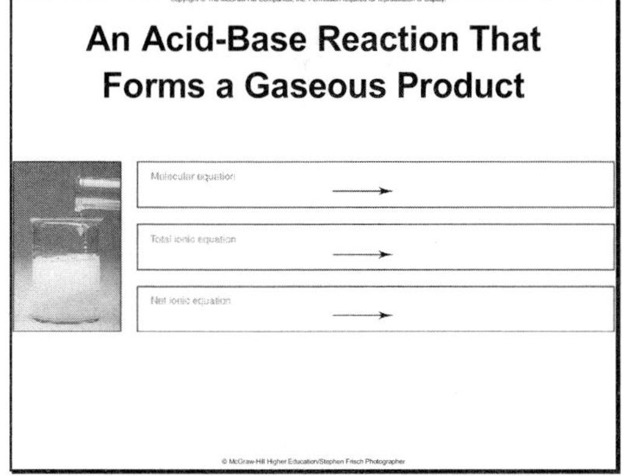

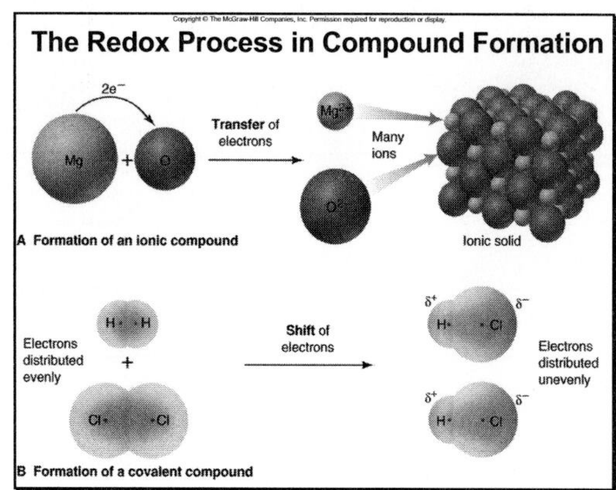

Table 4.3 Rules for Assigning an Oxidation Number (O.N.)

General rules

1. For an atom in its elemental form (Na, O_2, Cl_2, etc.): O.N. = 0
2. For a monatomic ion: O.N. = ion charge
3. The sum of O.N. values for the atoms in a compound equals zero. The sum of O.N. values for the atoms in a polyatomic ion equals the ion's charge.

Rules for specific atoms or periodic table groups

1. For Group 1A(1): O.N. =
2. For Group 2A(2): O.N. =
3. For hydrogen: O.N. =
   O.N. =
4. For fluorine: O.N. =
5. For oxygen: O.N. =
   O.N. =
6. For Group 7A(17): O.N. =

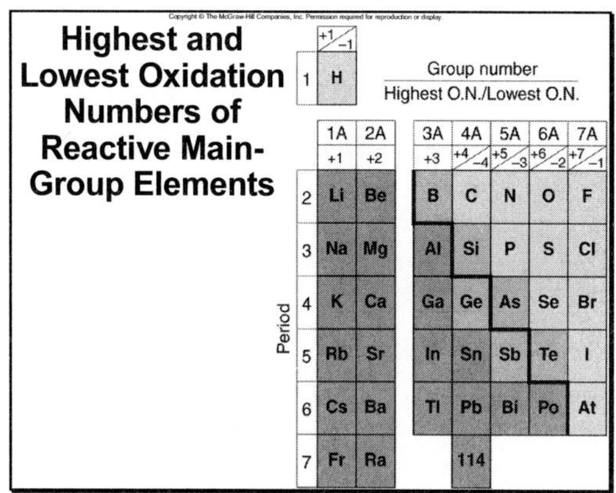

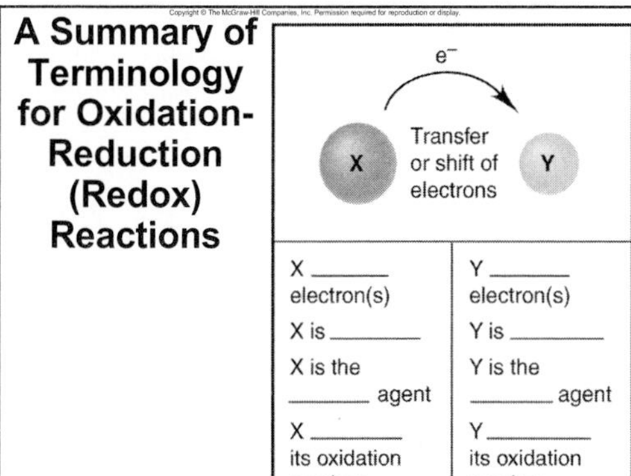
Copyright © The McGraw-Hill Companies, Inc. Permission required for reproduction or display.
A Summary of Terminology for Oxidation-Reduction (Redox) Reactions
e⁻
X
Transfer or shift of electrons
Y
X ______ electron(s)
X is ______
X is the ______ agent
X ______ its oxidation number
Y ______ electron(s)
Y is ______
Y is the ______ agent
Y ______ its oxidation number

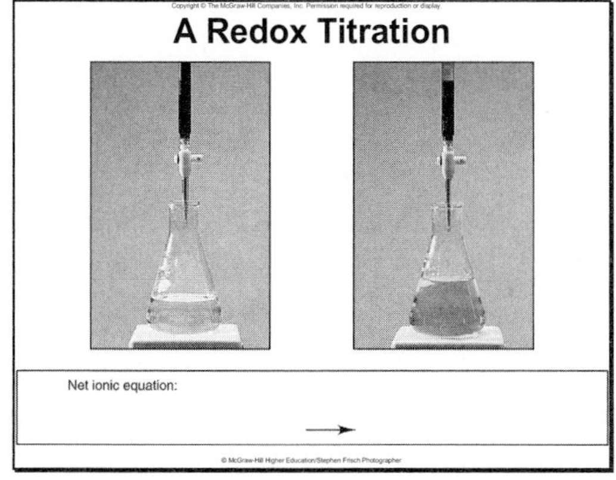
Copyright © The McGraw-Hill Companies, Inc. Permission required for reproduction or display.
A Redox Titration
Net ionic equation:
© McGraw-Hill Higher Education/Stephen Frisch Photographer

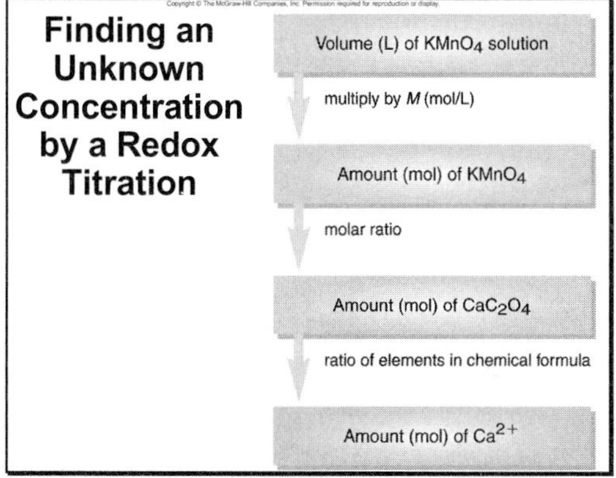
Copyright © The McGraw-Hill Companies, Inc. Permission required for reproduction or display.
Finding an Unknown Concentration by a Redox Titration
Volume (L) of KMnO4 solution
multiply by M (mol/L)
Amount (mol) of KMnO4
molar ratio
Amount (mol) of CaC2O4
ratio of elements in chemical formula
Amount (mol) of Ca2+

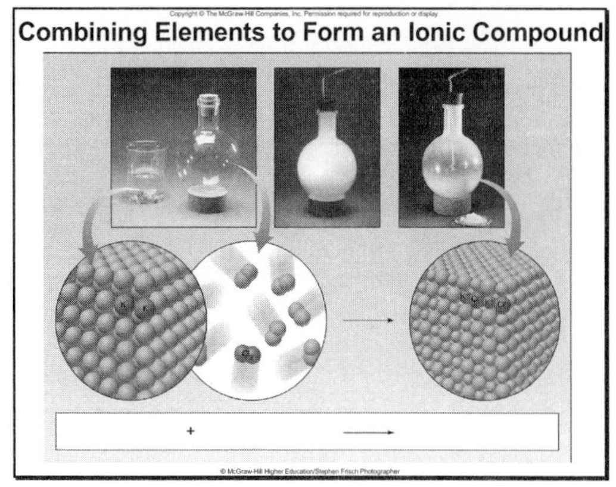
Copyright © The McGraw-Hill Companies, Inc. Permission required for reproduction or display.
Combining Elements to Form an Ionic Compound
© McGraw-Hill Higher Education/Stephen Frisch Photographer

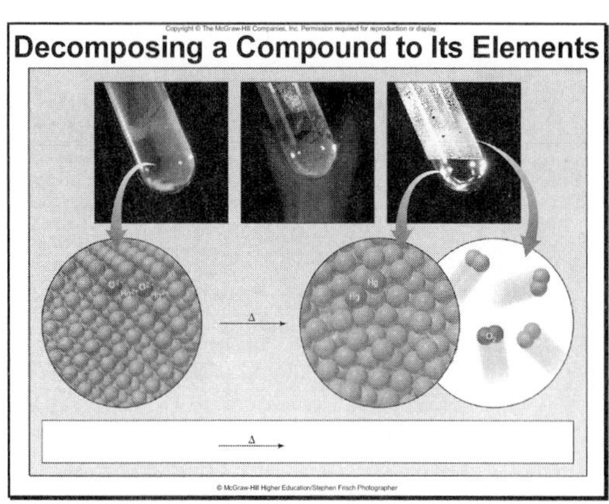
Copyright © The McGraw-Hill Companies, Inc. Permission required for reproduction or display.
Decomposing a Compound to Its Elements
© McGraw-Hill Higher Education/Stephen Frisch Photographer

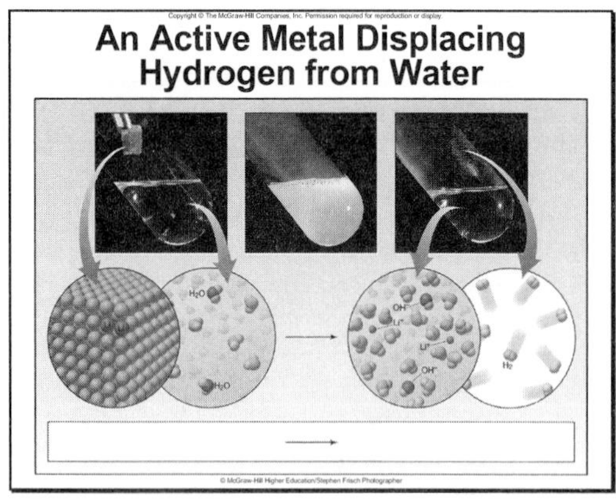
Copyright © The McGraw-Hill Companies, Inc. Permission required for reproduction or display.
An Active Metal Displacing Hydrogen from Water
© McGraw-Hill Higher Education/Stephen Frisch Photographer

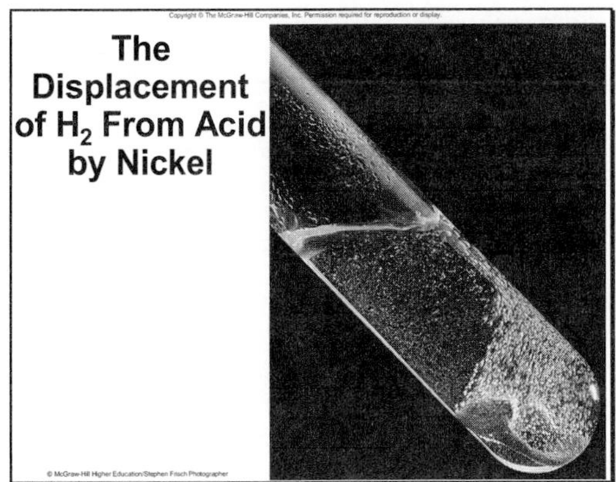
The Displacement of H_2 From Acid by Nickel

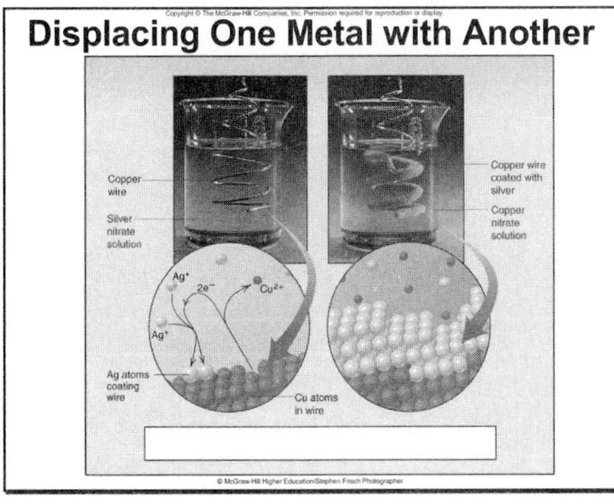
Displacing One Metal with Another
Copper wire
Silver nitrate solution
Copper wire coated with silver
Copper nitrate solution
Ag^+
$2e^-$
Cu^{2+}
Ag^+
Ag atoms coating wire
Cu atoms in wire

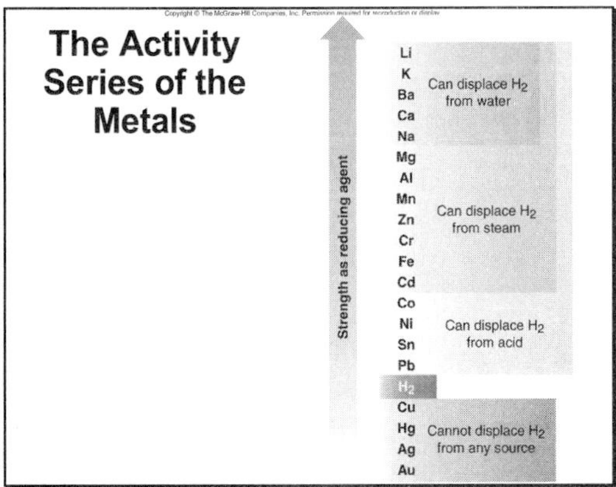
The Activity Series of the Metals
Strength as reducing agent
Li
K
Ba
Ca
Na
Mg
Al
Mn
Zn
Cr
Fe
Cd
Co
Ni
Sn
Pb
H_2
Cu
Hg
Ag
Au
Can displace H_2 from water
Can displace H_2 from steam
Can displace H_2 from acid
Cannot displace H_2 from any source

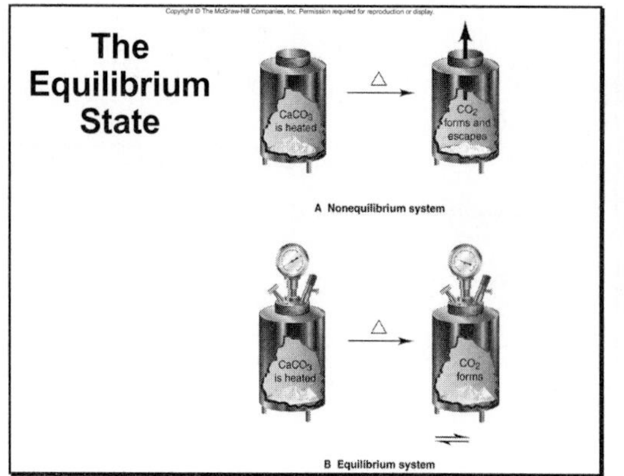
Copyright © The McGraw-Hill Companies, Inc. Permission required for reproduction or display.
The Equilibrium State
CaCO3 is heated
CO2 forms and escapes
A Nonequilibrium system
CaCO3 is heated
CO2 forms
B Equilibrium system

Chapter 5

Chemistry: The Molecular Nature of Matter and Change

Third Edition

Martin S. Silberberg

Atmosphere-Biosphere Redox Interconnections

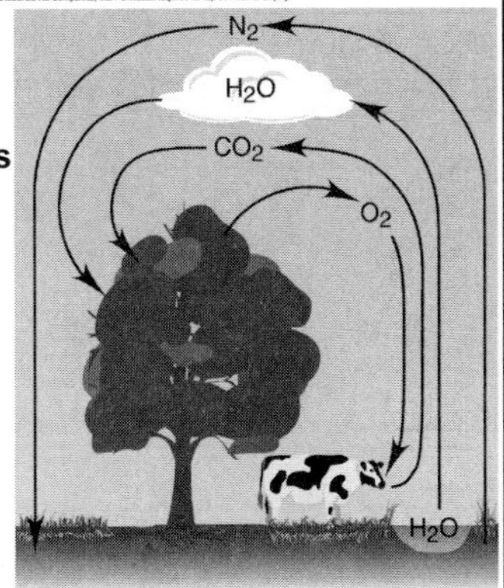

Table 5.1 Some Important Industrial Gases

Name (Formula)	Origin and Use
Methane (CH_4)	Natural deposits; domestic fuel
Ammonia (NH_3)	From N_2 + H_2; fertilizers, explosives
Chlorine (Cl_2)	Electrolysis of seawater; bleaching and disinfecting
Oxygen (O_2)	Liquefied air; steelmaking
Ethylene (C_2H_4)	High-temperature decomposition of natural gas; plastics

The Three States of Matter

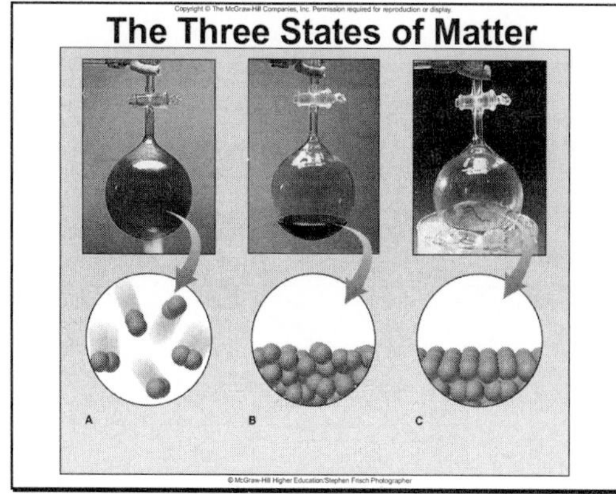

Effect of Atmospheric Pressure on Objects at the Earth's Surface

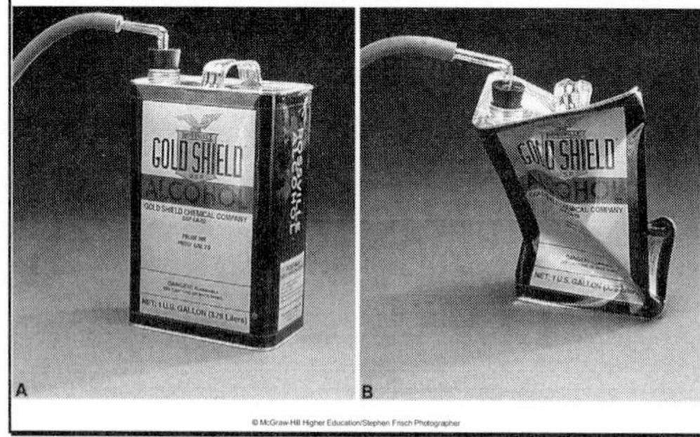

A Mercury Barometer

Δh = 760 mmHg

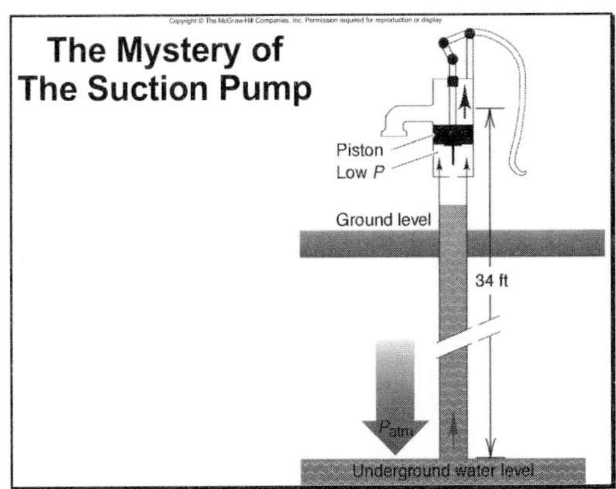

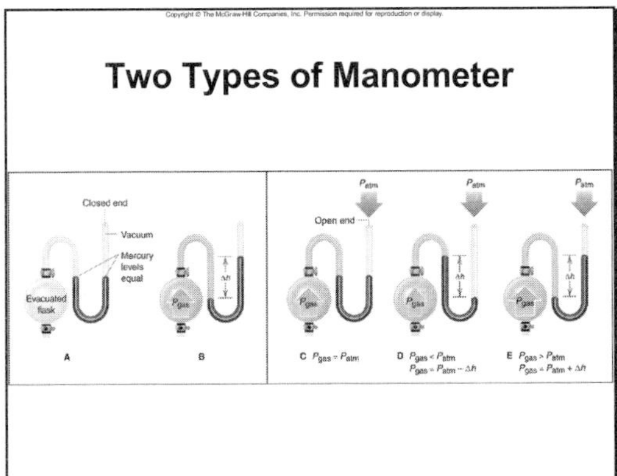

Table 5.2 Common Units of Pressure

Unit	Atmospheric Pressure	Scientific Field
pascal (Pa); kilopascal (kPa)	1.01325×10^5 Pa; 101.325 kPa	SI unit; physics, chemistry
atmosphere (atm)	1 atm*	Chemistry
millimeters of mercury (mmHg)	760 mmHg*	Chemistry, medicine, biology
torr	760 torr*	Chemistry
pounds per square inch (psi or lb/in^2)	14.7 lb/in^2	Engineering
bar	1.01325 bar	Meteorology, chemistry, physics

*This is an exact quantity; in calculations, we use as many significant figures as necessary.

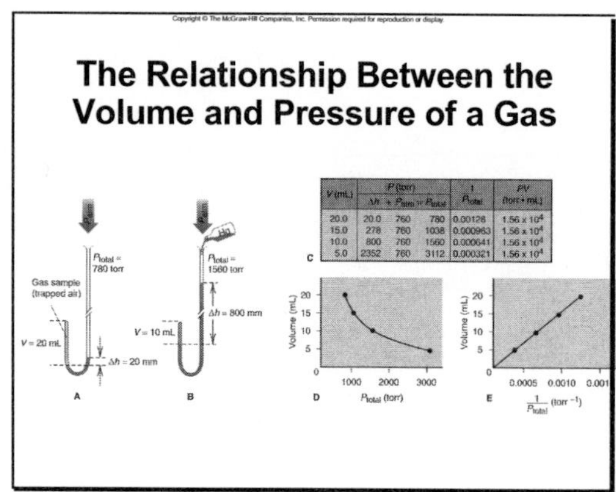

V (mL)	P (torr) Δh	+ P_{atm}	= P_{total}	$\frac{1}{P_{total}}$	PV (torr•mL)
20.0	20.0	760	780	0.00128	1.56×10^4
15.0	278	760	1038	0.000963	1.56×10^4
10.0	800	760	1560	0.000641	1.56×10^4
5.0	2352	760	3112	0.000321	1.56×10^4

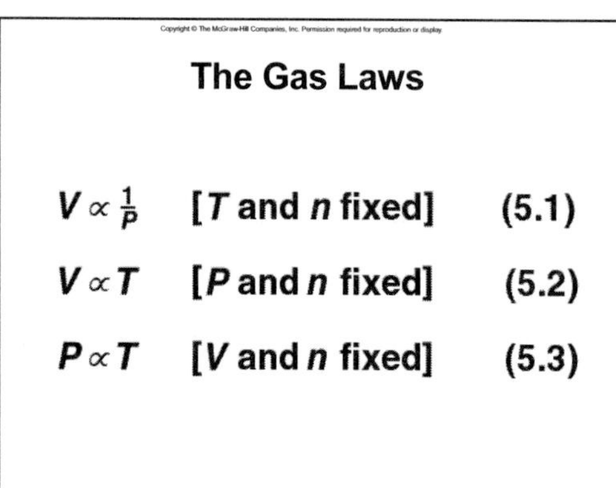

The Gas Laws
$V \propto \frac{1}{P}$ [T and n fixed] (5.1)
$V \propto T$ [P and n fixed] (5.2)
$P \propto T$ [V and n fixed] (5.3)

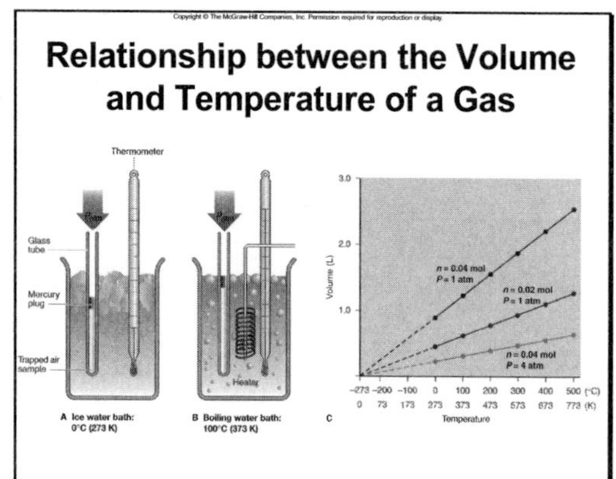

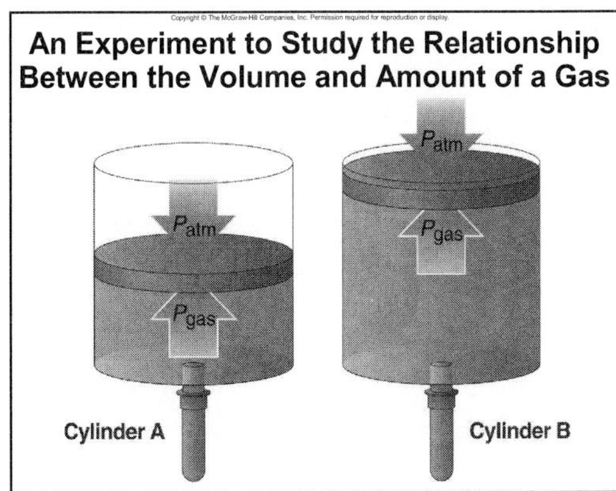

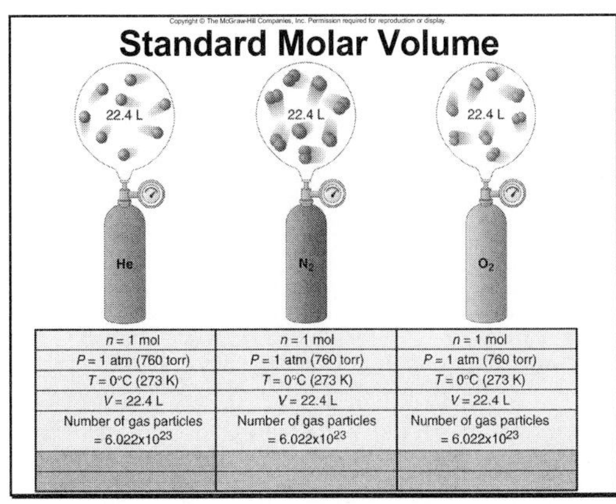

n = 1 mol	n = 1 mol	n = 1 mol
P = 1 atm (760 torr)	P = 1 atm (760 torr)	P = 1 atm (760 torr)
T = 0°C (273 K)	T = 0°C (273 K)	T = 0°C (273 K)
V = 22.4 L	V = 22.4 L	V = 22.4 L
Number of gas particles = 6.022×10^{23}	Number of gas particles = 6.022×10^{23}	Number of gas particles = 6.022×10^{23}

Relationship Between the Ideal Gas Law and the Individual Gas Laws

IDEAL GAS LAW

$PV = nRT$ or $V = \frac{nRT}{P}$

Boyle's law	Charles's law	Avogadro's law
$V = \frac{\text{constant}}{P}$	$V = \text{constant} \times T$	$V = \text{constant} \times n$

Determining the Molar Mass of an Unknown Volatile Liquid

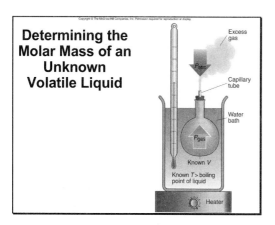

Table 5.3 Vapor Pressure of Water (P_{H_2O}) at Different T

T (°C)	P (torr)
0	4.6
5	6.5
10	9.2
11	9.8
12	10.5
13	11.2
14	12.0
15	12.8
16	13.6
18	15.5
20	17.5
22	19.8
24	22.4
26	25.2
28	28.3
30	31.8
35	42.2
40	55.3
45	71.9
50	92.5
55	118.0
60	149.4
65	187.5
70	233.7
75	289.1
80	355.1
85	433.6
90	525.8
95	633.9
100	760.0

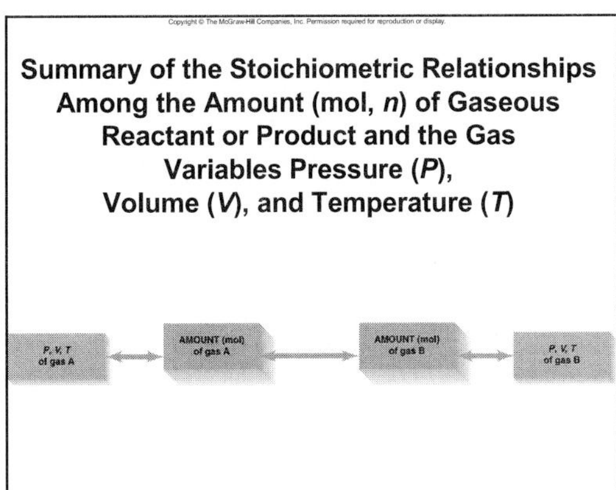
Copyright © The McGraw-Hill Companies, Inc. Permission required for reproduction or display.
Summary of the Stoichiometric Relationships Among the Amount (mol, n) of Gaseous Reactant or Product and the Gas Variables Pressure (P), Volume (V), and Temperature (T)
P, V, T of gas A
AMOUNT (mol) of gas A
AMOUNT (mol) of gas B
P, V, T of gas B

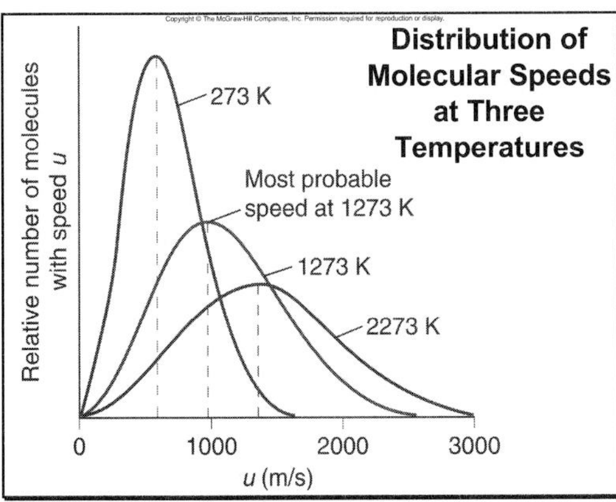
Copyright © The McGraw-Hill Companies, Inc. Permission required for reproduction or display.
Distribution of Molecular Speeds at Three Temperatures
Relative number of molecules with speed u
273 K
Most probable speed at 1273 K
1273 K
2273 K
0
1000
2000
3000
u (m/s)

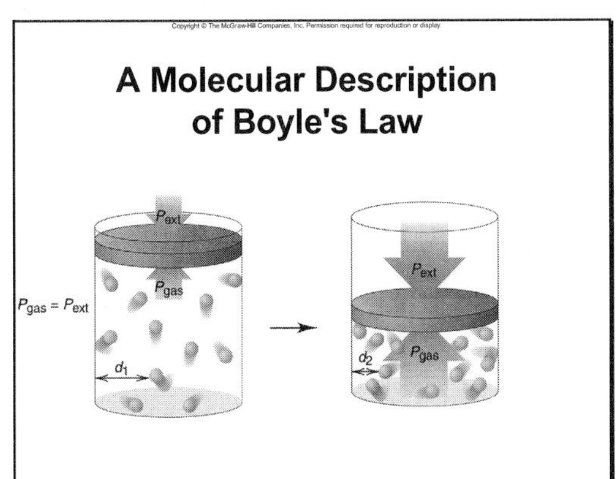
Copyright © The McGraw-Hill Companies, Inc. Permission required for reproduction or display.
A Molecular Description of Boyle's Law
Pext
Pgas
Pgas = Pext
d1
Pext
d2
Pgas

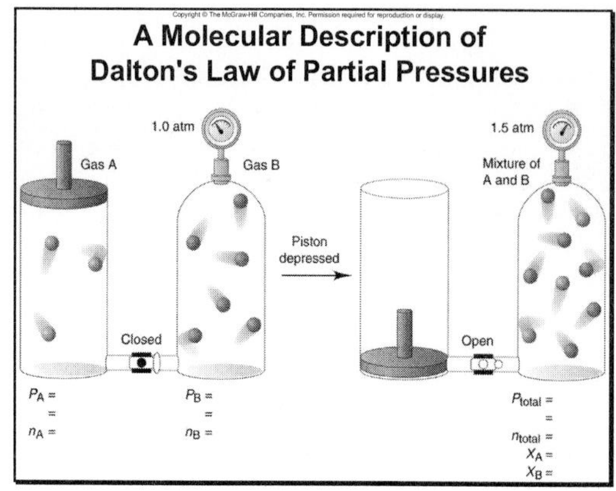
Copyright © The McGraw-Hill Companies, Inc. Permission required for reproduction or display.
A Molecular Description of Dalton's Law of Partial Pressures
1.0 atm
Gas A
Gas B
Closed
Piston depressed
1.5 atm
Mixture of A and B
Open
P_A =
=
n_A =
P_B =
=
n_B =
P_{total} =
=
n_{total} =
X_A =
X_B =

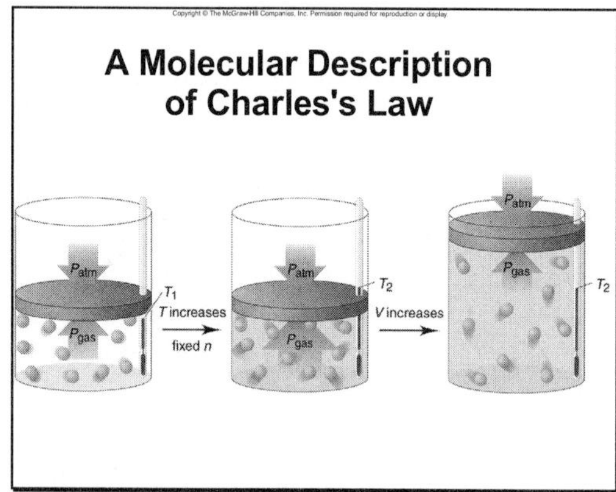
Copyright © The McGraw-Hill Companies, Inc. Permission required for reproduction or display.
A Molecular Description of Charles's Law
P_{atm}
P_{gas}
T_1
T increases
fixed n
T_2
V increases

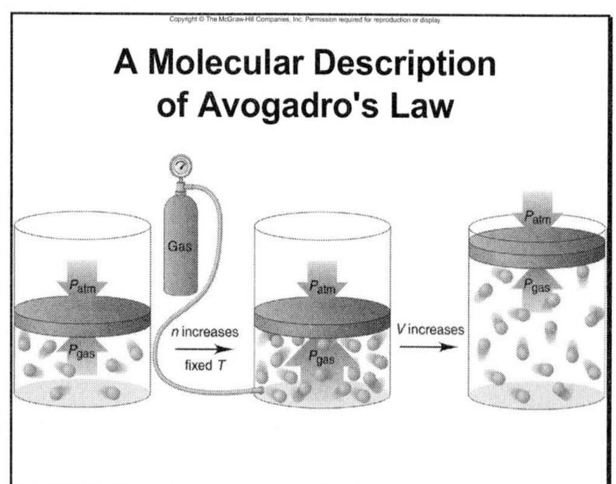
Copyright © The McGraw-Hill Companies, Inc. Permission required for reproduction or display.
A Molecular Description of Avogadro's Law
Gas
P_{atm}
P_{gas}
n increases
fixed T
V increases

Relationship Between Molar Mass and Molecular Speed

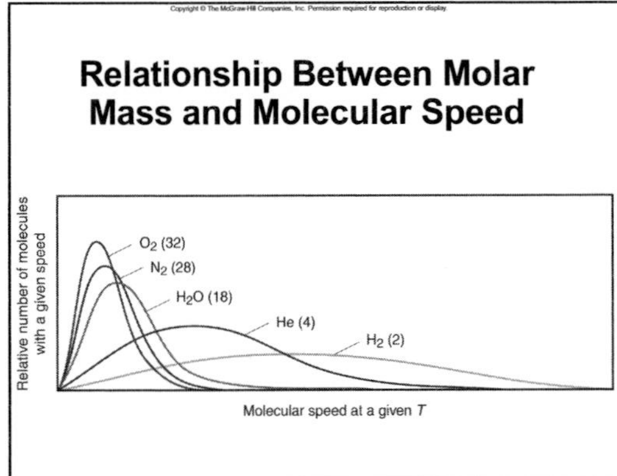

The Meaning of Temperature

$$\overline{E}_k = \frac{3}{2}\left(\frac{R}{N_A}\right)T$$

Diffusion of a Gas Particle Through a Space Filled with Other Particles

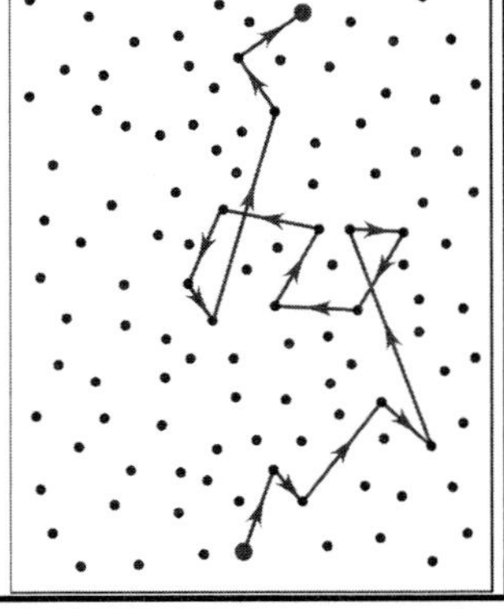

Variations in Pressure, Temperature, and Composition of the Earth's Atmosphere

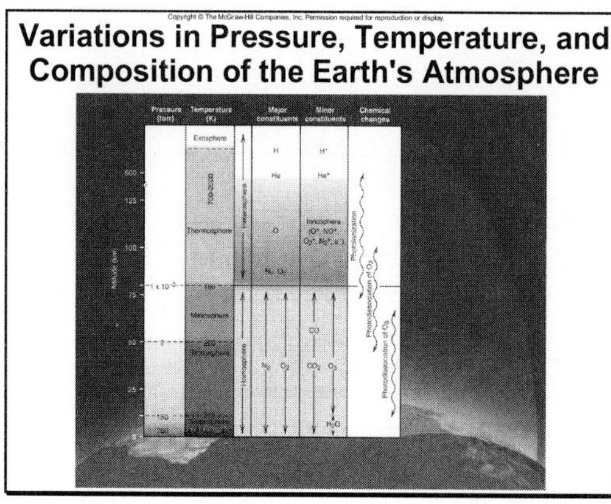

Table B5.1 Composition of Clean, Dry Air at Sea Level

Component	Mole Fraction
Nitrogen (N_2)	0.78084
Oxygen (O_2)	0.20946
Argon (Ar)	0.00934
Carbon dioxide (CO_2)	0.00033
Neon (Ne)	1.818×10^{-5}
Helium (He)	5.24×10^{-6}
Methane (CH_4)	2×10^{-6}
Krypton (Kr)	1.14×10^{-6}
Hydrogen (H_2)	5×10^{-7}
Dinitrogen monoxide (N_2O)	5×10^{-7}
Carbon monoxide (CO)	1×10^{-7}
Xenon (Xe)	8×10^{-8}
Ozone (O_3)	2×10^{-8}
Ammonia (NH_3)	6×10^{-9}
Nitrogen dioxide (NO_2)	6×10^{-9}
Nitrogen monoxide (NO)	6×10^{-10}
Sulfur dioxide (SO_2)	2×10^{-10}
Hydrogen sulfide (H_2S)	2×10^{-10}

Table B5.2 Planetary Atmospheres

Planet (Satellite)	Pressure* (atm)	Temperature† (K)	Composition (mol %)
Mercury	$<10^{-12}$	~700 (day) ~100 (night)	He, H_2, O_2, Ar, Ne (Na and K from solar wind)
Venus	~90	~730	CO_2 (96), N_2 (3), He, SO_2, H_2O, Ar, Ne
Earth	1.0	avg. range 250–310	N_2 (78), O_2 (21), Ar (0.9), H_2O, CO_2, Ne, He, CH_4, Kr
(Moon)	$\sim2\times10^{-14}$	370 (day) 120 (night)	Ne, Ar, He
Mars	7×10^{-3}	300 (summer day) 140 (pole in winter) 218 average	CO_2 (95), N_2(3), Ar (1.6), O_2, H_2O, Ne, CO, Kr
Jupiter	$(\sim4\times10^{6})$	(~140)	H_2 (89), He (11), CH_4, NH_3, C_2H_6, C_2H_2, PH_3
(Io)	$\sim10^{-10}$	~110	SO_2, S vapor
Saturn	$(\sim4\times10^{6})$	(~130)	H_2 (93), He (7), CH_4, NH_3, H_2O, C_2H_6, PH_3
(Titan)	1.6	~94	N_2 (90), Ar (<6), CH_4 (3?), C_2H_6, C_2H_2, C_2H_4, HCN, H_2
Uranus	$(>10^{6})$	(~60)	H_2 (83), He (15), CH_4 (2)
Neptune	$(>10^{6})$	(~60)	H_2 (<90), He (~10), CH_4
Pluto	$\sim10^{-6}$	~50	N_2, CO, CH_4

*Values in parentheses refer to interior pressures.
†Values in parentheses refer to cloud-top temperatures.

Table 5.4 Molar Volume of Some Common Gases at STP (0°C and 1 atm)

Gas	Molar Volume (L/mol)	Condensation Point (°C)
He	22.435	−268.9
H_2	22.432	−252.8
Ne	22.422	−246.1
Ideal gas	**22.414**	—
Ar	22.397	−185.9
N_2	22.396	−195.8
O_2	22.390	−183.0
CO	22.388	−191.5
Cl_2	22.184	−34.0
NH_3	22.079	−33.4

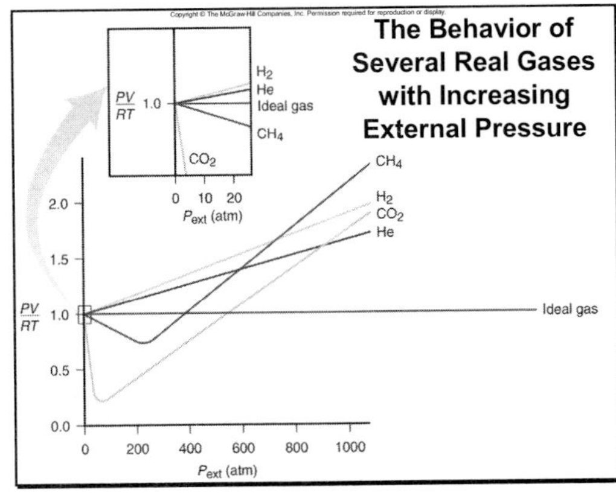

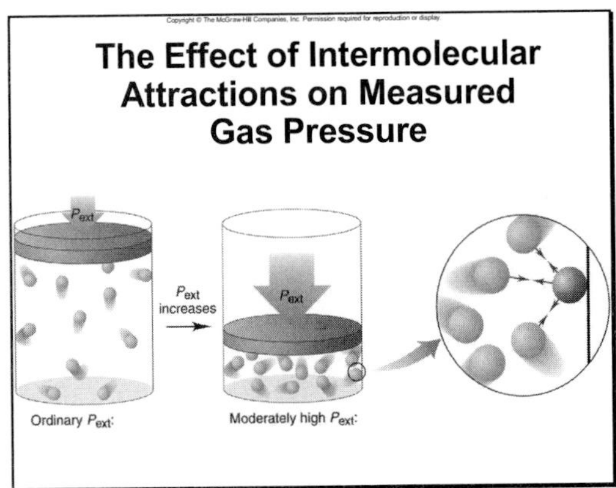

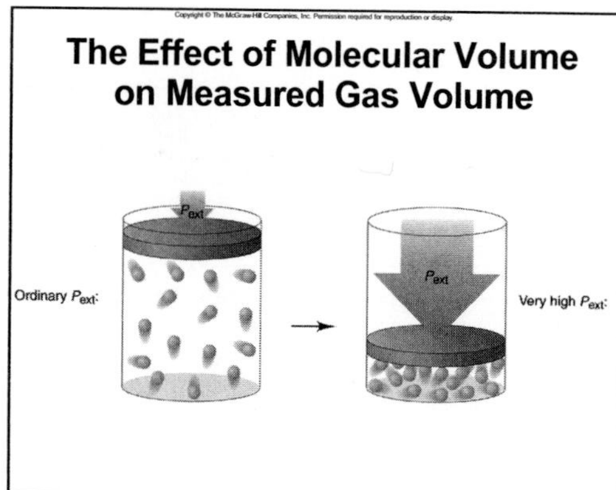

Table 5.5 Van der Waals Constants for Some Common Gases

Gas	$a \left(\frac{atm \cdot L^2}{mol^2}\right)$	$b \left(\frac{L}{mol}\right)$
He	0.034	0.0237
Ne	0.211	0.0171
Ar	1.35	0.0322
Kr	2.32	0.0398
Xe	4.19	0.0511
H_2	0.244	0.0266
N_2	1.39	0.0391
O_2	1.36	0.0318
Cl_2	6.49	0.0562
CO_2	3.59	0.0427
CH_4	2.25	0.0428
NH_3	4.17	0.0371
H_2O	5.46	0.0305

Chapter 6

Chemistry: The Molecular Nature of Matter and Change

Third Edition

Martin S. Silberberg

A Chemical System and Its Surroundings

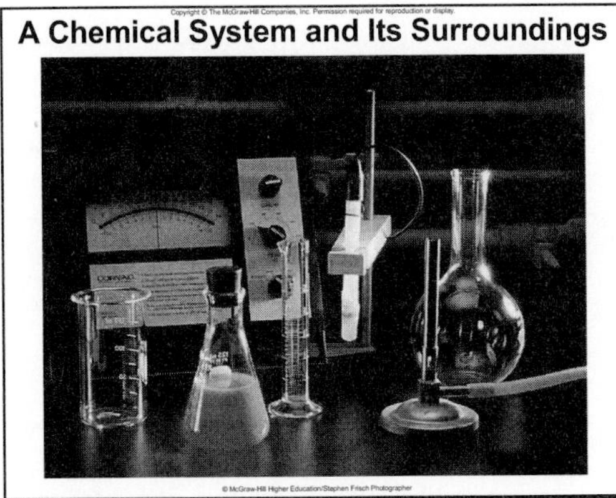

Energy Diagrams for the Transfer of Internal Energy (E) Between a System and Its Surroundings

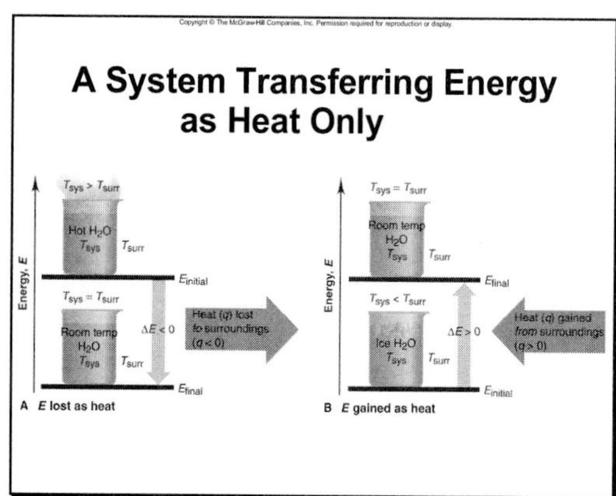

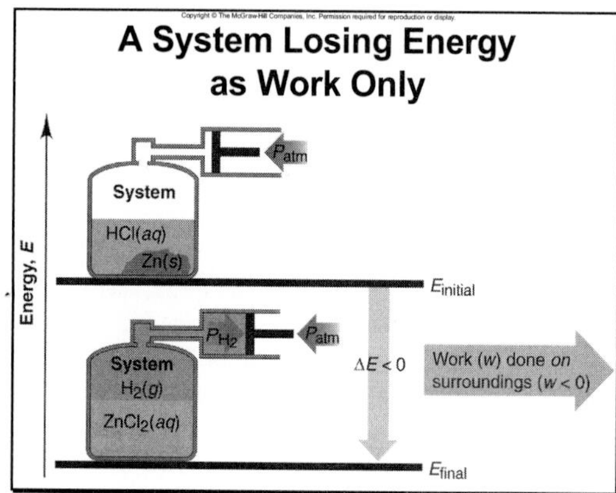

Table 6.1 The Sign Conventions* for q, w, and ΔE

q	+	w	=	ΔE
+		+		
+		−		
−		+		
−		−		

*For q: + means system *gains* heat; − means system *loses* heat.
For w: + means work done *on* system; − means work done *by* system.

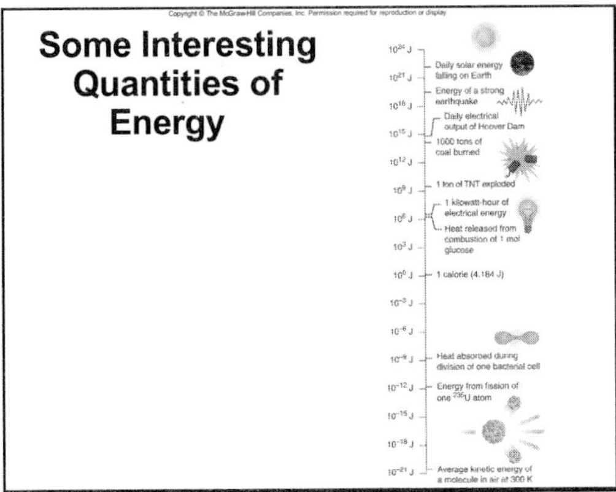
Copyright © The McGraw-Hill Companies, Inc. Permission required for reproduction or display.
Some Interesting Quantities of Energy
10^{24} J
10^{21} J
10^{18} J
10^{15} J
10^{12} J
10^{9} J
10^{6} J
10^{3} J
10^{0} J
10^{-3} J
10^{-6} J
10^{-9} J
10^{-12} J
10^{-15} J
10^{-18} J
10^{-21} J
Daily solar energy falling on Earth
Energy of a strong earthquake
Daily electrical output of Hoover Dam
1000 tons of coal burned
1 ton of TNT exploded
1 kilowatt-hour of electrical energy
Heat released from combustion of 1 mol glucose
1 calorie (4.184 J)
Heat absorbed during division of one bacterial cell
Energy from fission of one ^{235}U atom
Average kinetic energy of a molecule in air at 300 K

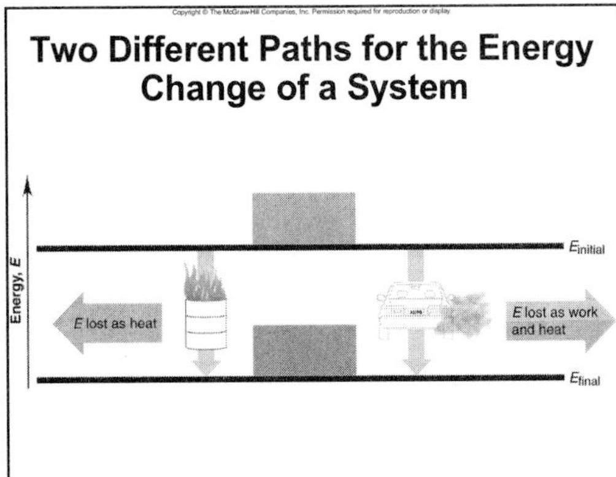
Copyright © The McGraw-Hill Companies, Inc. Permission required for reproduction or display.
Two Different Paths for the Energy Change of a System
Energy, E
$E_{initial}$
E lost as heat
E lost as work and heat
E_{final}

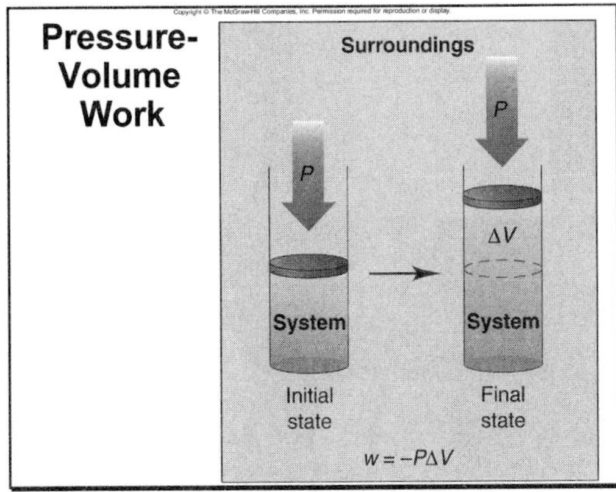
Copyright © The McGraw-Hill Companies, Inc. Permission required for reproduction or display.
Pressure-Volume Work
Surroundings
P
P
ΔV
System
System
Initial state
Final state
$w = -P\Delta V$

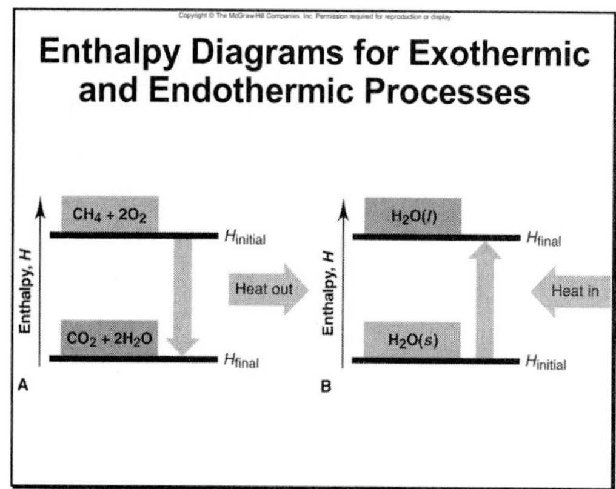
Copyright © The McGraw-Hill Companies, Inc. Permission required for reproduction or display.
Enthalpy Diagrams for Exothermic and Endothermic Processes
CH4 + 2O2
Hinitial
CO2 + 2H2O
Hfinal
Heat out
Enthalpy, H
A
H2O(l)
Hfinal
H2O(s)
Hinitial
Heat in
Enthalpy, H
B

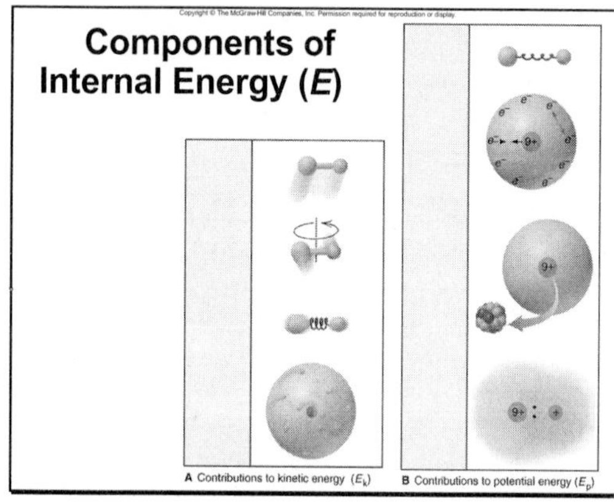
Components of Internal Energy (E)
A Contributions to kinetic energy (Ek)
B Contributions to potential energy (Ep)

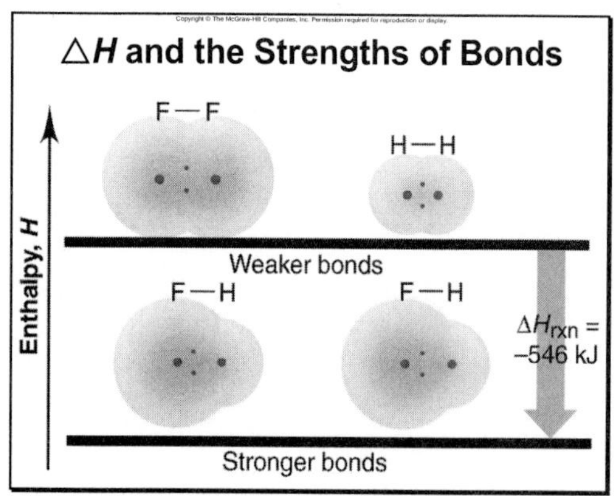
ΔH and the Strengths of Bonds
F—F
H—H
Enthalpy, H
Weaker bonds
F—H
F—H
ΔHrxn =
−546 kJ
Stronger bonds

Table 6.2 Heats of Combustion (ΔH_{comb}) of Some Carbon Compounds

	Two-Carbon Compounds		One-Carbon Compounds	
	Ethane (C_2H_6)	Ethanol (C_2H_5OH)	Methane (CH_4)	Methanol (CH_3OH)
Structural Formula	H H H—C—C—H H H	H H H—C—C—O—H H H	H H—C—H H	H H—C—O—H H
Sum of C—C and C—H bonds	7	6	4	3
Sum of C—O and O—H bonds	0	2	0	2
ΔH_{comb} (kJ/mol)	−1560	−1367	−890	−727
ΔH_{comb} (kJ/g)	−51.88	−29.67	−55.5	−22.7

Table 6.3 Heats of Combustion of Some Fats and Carbohydrates

Substance	ΔH_{comb} (kJ/g)
Fats	
Vegetable oil	−37.0
Margarine	−30.1
Butter	−30.0
Carbohydrates	
Table sugar (sucrose)	−16.2
Brown rice	−14.9
Maple syrup	−10.4

Molecular Drawings of Carbohydrate and Fat

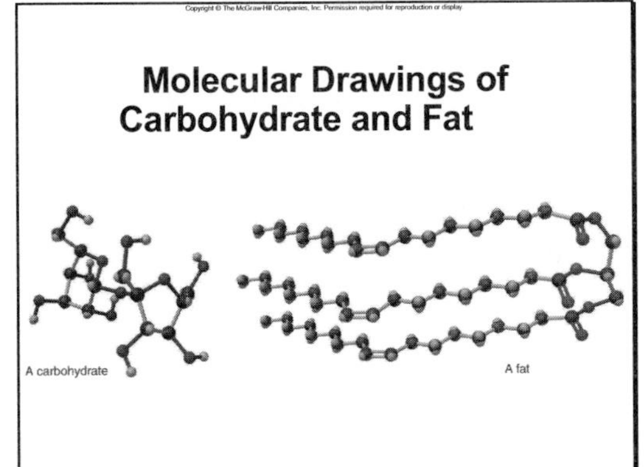

Table 6.4 Specific Heat Capacities of Some Elements, Compounds, and Materials

Substance	Specific Heat Capacity (J/g·K)*
Elements	
Aluminum, Al	0.900
Graphite, C	0.711
Iron, Fe	0.450
Copper, Cu	0.387
Gold, Au	0.129
Compounds	
Water, $H_2O(l)$	4.184
Ethyl alcohol, $C_2H_5OH(l)$	2.46
Ethylene glycol, $(CH_2OH)_2(l)$	2.42
Carbon tetrachloride, $CCl_4(l)$	0.862
Solid materials	
Wood	1.76
Cement	0.88
Glass	0.84
Granite	0.79
Steel	0.45

*At 298 K (25°C).

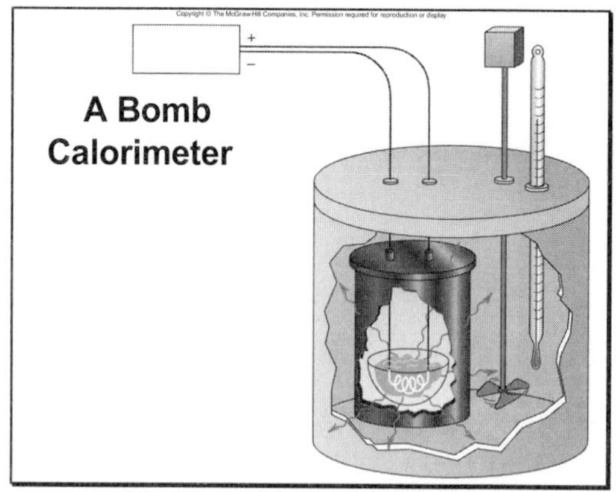

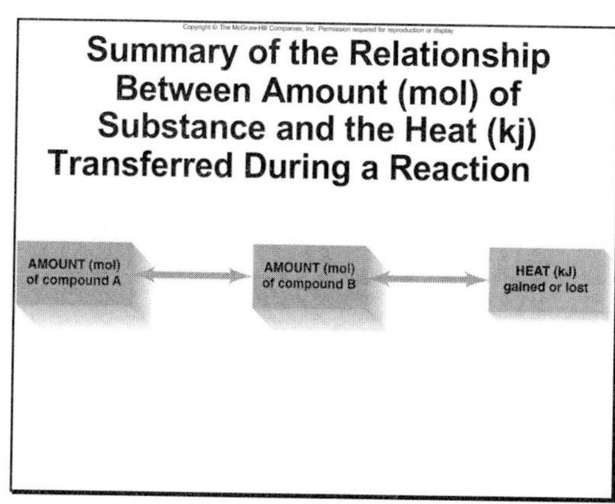

Table 6.5 Selected Standard Heats of Formation at 25°C (298 K)

Formula	ΔH^0_f (kJ/mol)	Formula	ΔH^0_f (kJ/mol)
Calcium		Nitrogen	
$Ca(s)$	0	$N_2(g)$	0
$CaO(s)$	−635.1	$NH_3(g)$	−45.9
$CaCO_3(s)$	−1206.9	$NO(g)$	90.3
Carbon		Oxygen	
C(graphite)	0	$O_2(g)$	0
C(diamond)	1.9	$O_3(g)$	143
$CO(g)$	−110.5	$H_2O(g)$	−241.8
$CO_2(g)$	−393.5	$H_2O(l)$	−285.8
$CH_4(g)$	−74.9	Silver	
$CH_3OH(l)$	−238.6	$Ag(s)$	0
$HCN(g)$	135	$AgCl(s)$	−127.0
$CS_2(l)$	87.9	Sodium	
Chlorine		$Na(s)$	0
$Cl(g)$	121.0	$Na(g)$	107.8
$Cl_2(g)$	0	$NaCl(s)$	−411.1
$HCl(g)$	−92.3	Sulfur	
Hydrogen		S_8(rhombic)	0
$H(g)$	218.0	S_8(monoclinic)	2
$H_2(g)$	0	$SO_2(g)$	−296.8
		$SO_3(g)$	−396.0

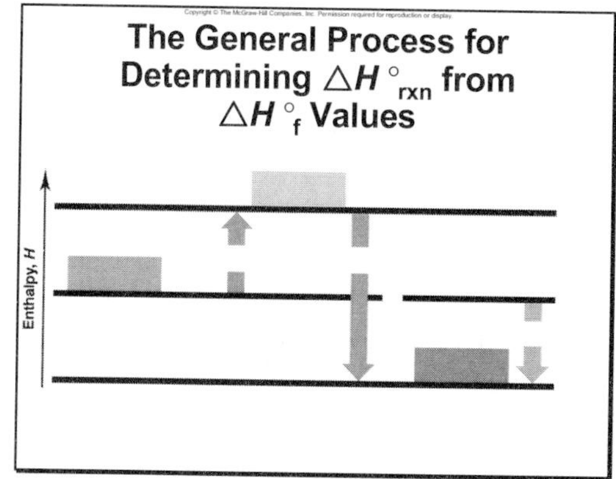

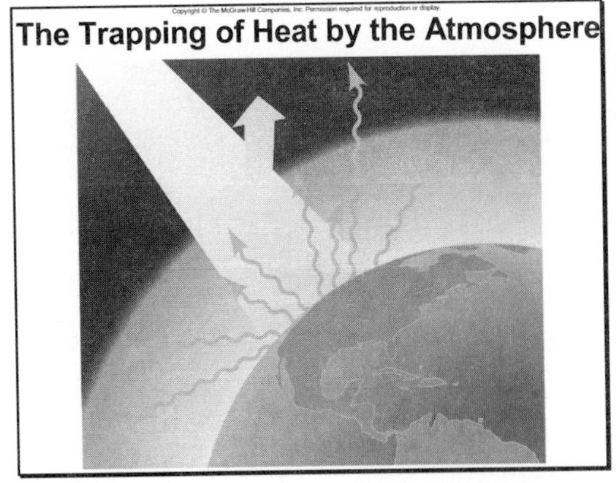
The Trapping of Heat by the Atmosphere

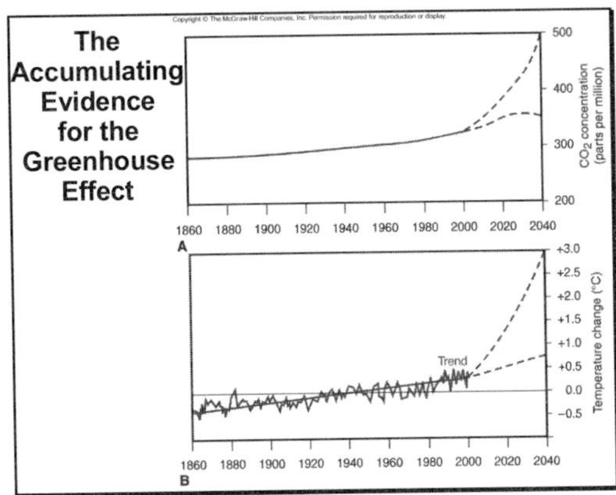
The Accumulating Evidence for the Greenhouse Effect
CO2 concentration (parts per million)
500
400
300
200
1860 1880 1900 1920 1940 1960 1980 2000 2020 2040
A
Temperature change (°C)
+3.0
+2.5
+2.0
+1.5
+1.0
+0.5
0.0
−0.5
Trend
1860 1880 1900 1920 1940 1960 1980 2000 2020 2040
B

Chapter 7

Chemistry: The Molecular Nature of Matter and Change

Third Edition

Martin S. Silberberg

Frequency and Wavelength

Wavelength = distance per cycle

Wavelength

A

B

C

Frequency = cycles per second

Amplitude (Intensity) of a Wave

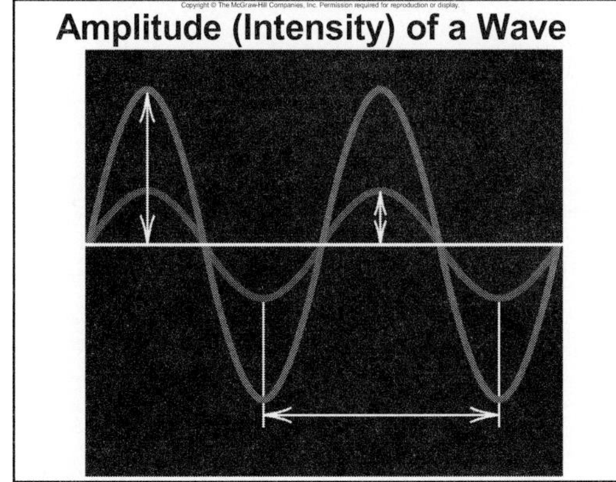

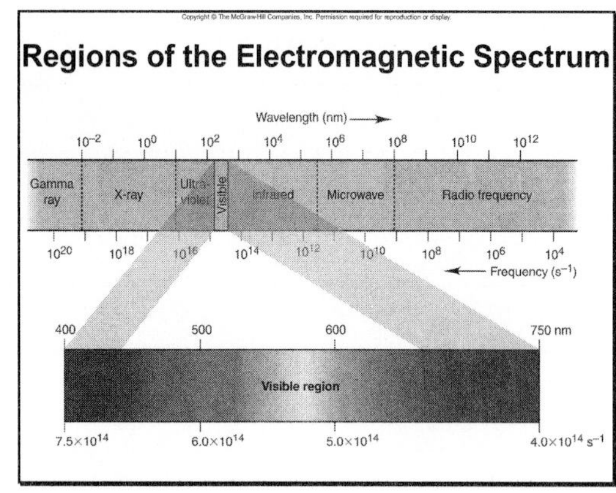
Copyright © The McGraw-Hill Companies, Inc. Permission required for reproduction or display.
Regions of the Electromagnetic Spectrum
Wavelength (nm)
Gamma ray
X-ray
Ultraviolet
Visible
Infrared
Microwave
Radio frequency
Frequency (s⁻¹)
400
500
600
750 nm
Visible region

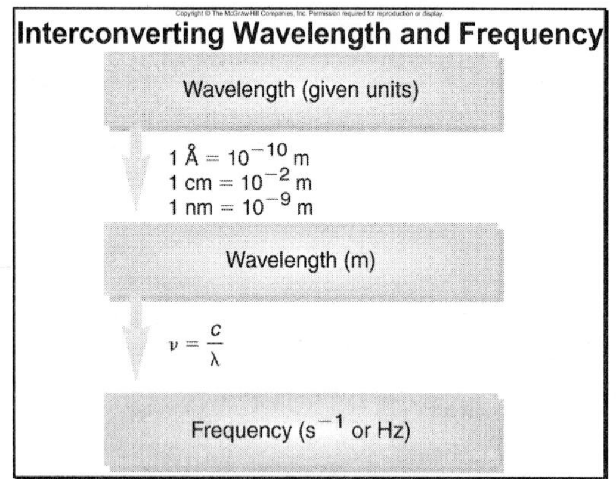
Copyright © The McGraw-Hill Companies, Inc. Permission required for reproduction or display.
Interconverting Wavelength and Frequency
Wavelength (given units)
1 Å = 10⁻¹⁰ m
1 cm = 10⁻² m
1 nm = 10⁻⁹ m
Wavelength (m)
ν = c/λ
Frequency (s⁻¹ or Hz)

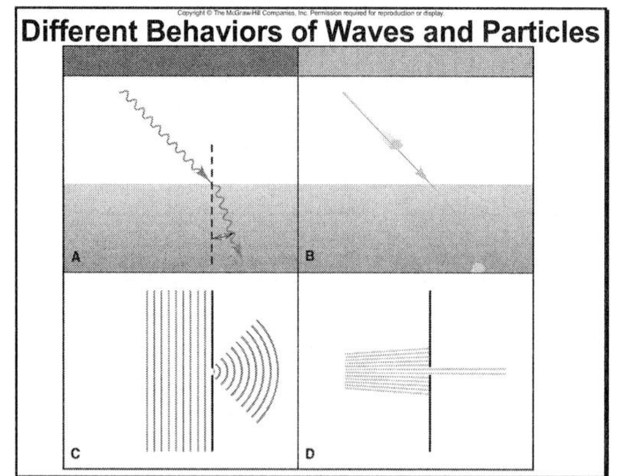
Copyright © The McGraw-Hill Companies, Inc. Permission required for reproduction or display.
Different Behaviors of Waves and Particles
A
B
C
D

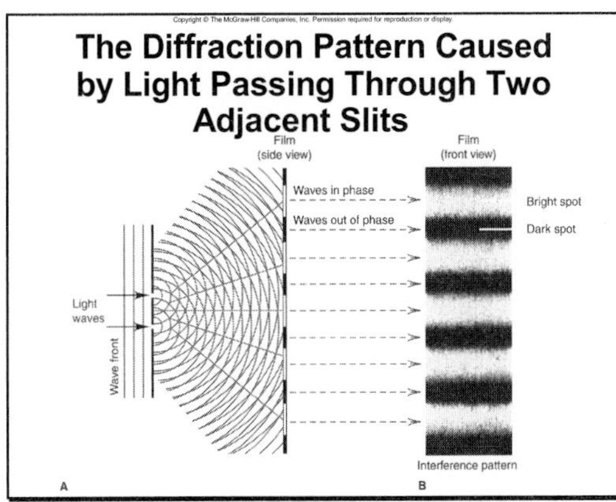
Copyright © The McGraw-Hill Companies, Inc. Permission required for reproduction or display
The Diffraction Pattern Caused by Light Passing Through Two Adjacent Slits
Film (side view)
Film (front view)
Waves in phase
Waves out of phase
Bright spot
Dark spot
Light waves
Wave front
Interference pattern
A
B

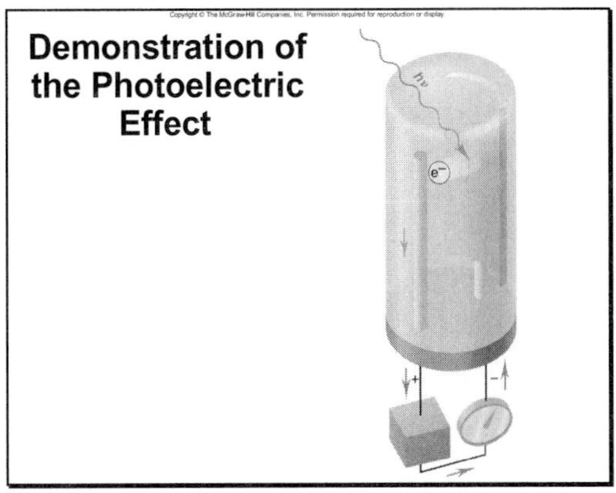
Copyright © The McGraw-Hill Companies, Inc. Permission required for reproduction or display
Demonstration of the Photoelectric Effect
hν
e⁻
+
−

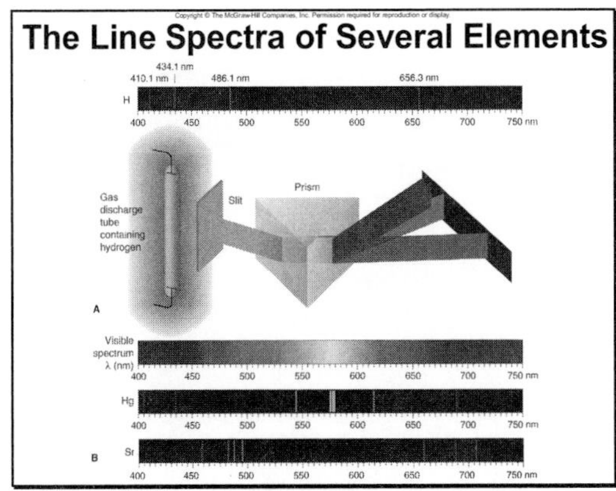
Copyright © The McGraw-Hill Companies, Inc. Permission required for reproduction or display
The Line Spectra of Several Elements
434.1 nm
410.1 nm
486.1 nm
656.3 nm
H
400 450 500 550 600 650 700 750 nm
Gas discharge tube containing hydrogen
Slit
Prism
A
Visible spectrum λ (nm)
400 450 500 550 600 650 700 750 nm
Hg
400 450 500 550 600 650 700 750 nm
Sr
400 450 500 550 600 650 700 750 nm
B

Determination of Line Spectra

$$\frac{1}{\lambda} = R\left(\frac{1}{n_1^2} - \frac{1}{n_2^2}\right) \qquad (7.3)$$

Three Series of Spectral Lines of Atomic Hydrogen

Quantum Staircase

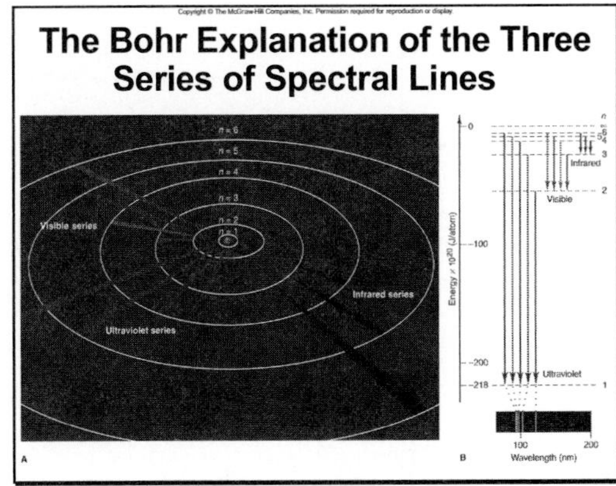
The Bohr Explanation of the Three Series of Spectral Lines
Visible series
Infrared series
Ultraviolet series
Infrared
Visible
Ultraviolet
Energy × 10^20 (J/atom)
Wavelength (nm)

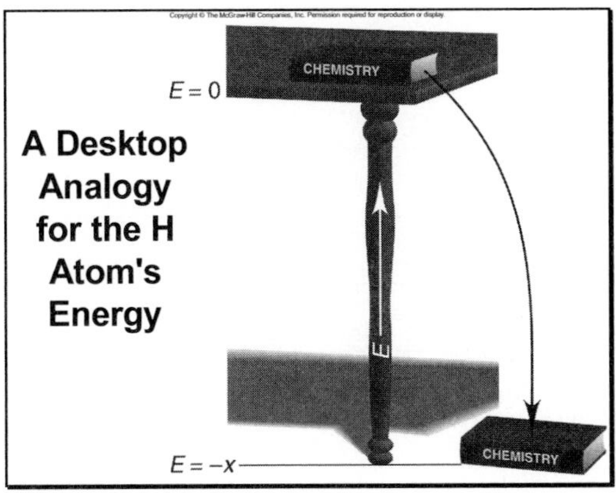
A Desktop Analogy for the H Atom's Energy
CHEMISTRY
E = 0
E
E = −x
CHEMISTRY

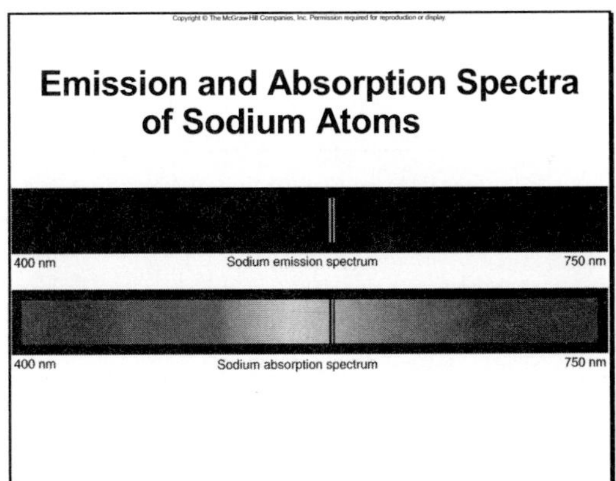
Emission and Absorption Spectra of Sodium Atoms
400 nm
Sodium emission spectrum
750 nm
400 nm
Sodium absorption spectrum
750 nm

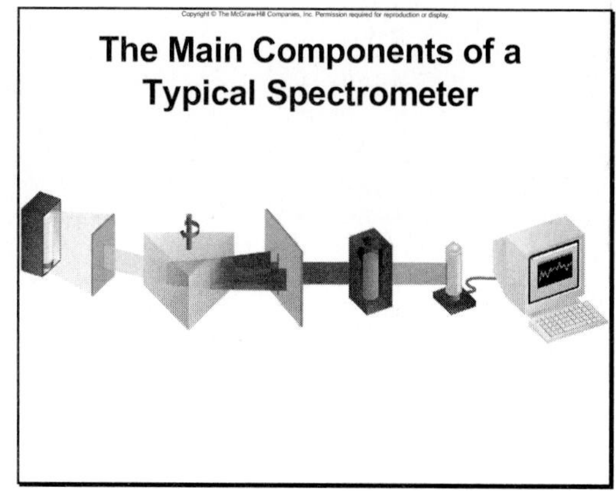

Copyright © The McGraw-Hill Companies, Inc. Permission required for reproduction or display
The Main Components of a Typical Spectrometer

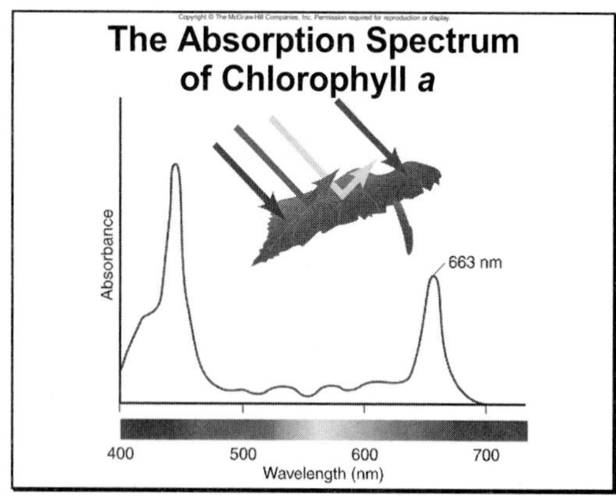

Copyright © The McGraw-Hill Companies, Inc. Permission required for reproduction or display
The Absorption Spectrum of Chlorophyll a
Absorbance
663 nm
400
500
600
700
Wavelength (nm)

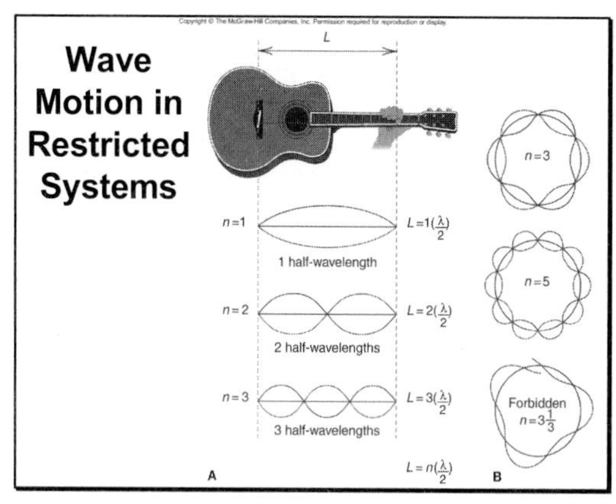

Copyright © The McGraw-Hill Companies, Inc. Permission required for reproduction or display
Wave Motion in Restricted Systems
L
n=1
L=1(λ/2)
1 half-wavelength
n=2
L=2(λ/2)
2 half-wavelengths
n=3
L=3(λ/2)
3 half-wavelengths
L=n(λ/2)
A
n=3
n=5
Forbidden
n=3 1/3
B

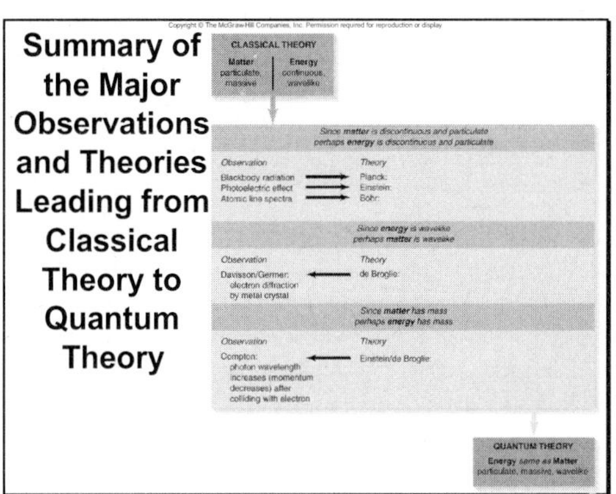
Copyright © The McGraw-Hill Companies, Inc. Permission required for reproduction or display.
Summary of the Major Observations and Theories Leading from Classical Theory to Quantum Theory
CLASSICAL THEORY
Matter particulate, massive
Energy continuous, wavelike
Since matter is discontinuous and particulate perhaps energy is discontinuous and particulate
Observation
Theory
Blackbody radiation
Photoelectric effect
Atomic line spectra
Planck:
Einstein:
Bohr:
Since energy is wavelike perhaps matter is wavelike
Observation
Theory
Davisson/Germer: electron diffraction by metal crystal
de Broglie:
Since matter has mass perhaps energy has mass
Observation
Theory
Compton: photon wavelength increases (momentum decreases) after colliding with electron
Einstein/de Broglie:
QUANTUM THEORY
Energy same as Matter
particulate, massive, wavelike

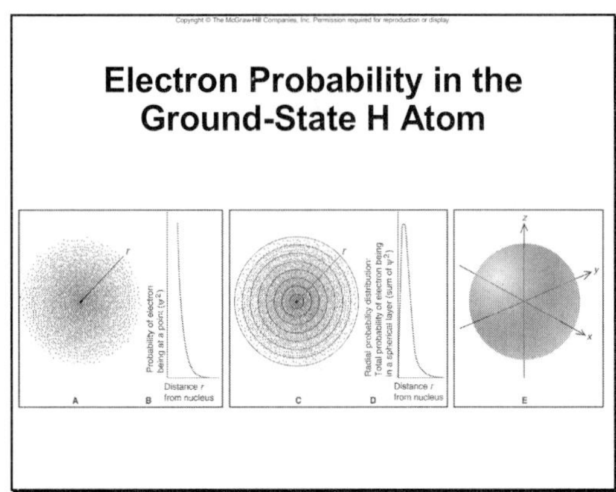
Copyright © The McGraw-Hill Companies, Inc. Permission required for reproduction or display.
Electron Probability in the Ground-State H Atom
r
Probability of electron being at a point (ψ^2)
Distance r from nucleus
A
B
r
Radial probability distribution: Total probability of electron being in a spherical layer (sum of ψ^2)
Distance r from nucleus
C
D
z
y
x
E

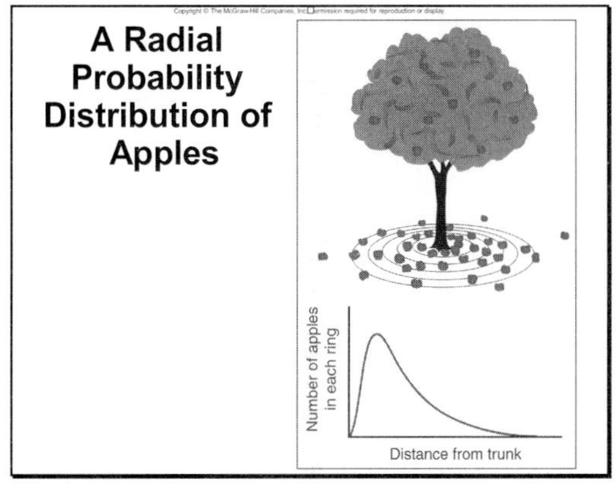
Copyright © The McGraw-Hill Companies, Inc. Permission required for reproduction or display.
A Radial Probability Distribution of Apples
Number of apples in each ring
Distance from trunk

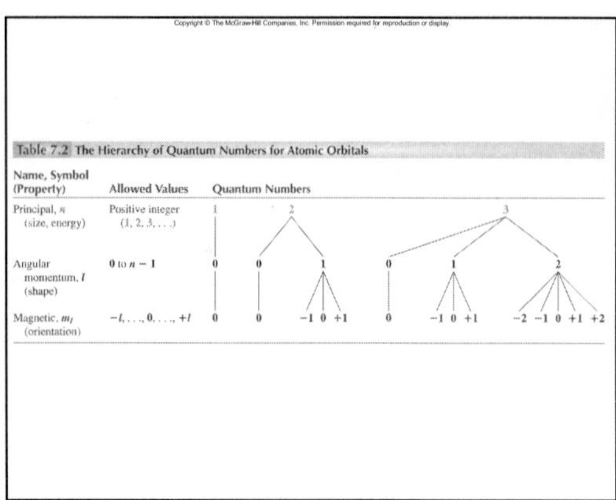

Table 7.2 The Hierarchy of Quantum Numbers for Atomic Orbitals

Name, Symbol (Property)	Allowed Values	Quantum Numbers												
Principal, n (size, energy)	Positive integer (1, 2, 3, . . .)	1	2				3							
Angular momentum, l (shape)	0 to $n - 1$	0	0	1			0	1			2			
Magnetic, m_l (orientation)	$-l, \ldots, 0, \ldots, +l$	0	0	−1	0	+1	0	−1	0	+1	−2	−1	0	+1 +2

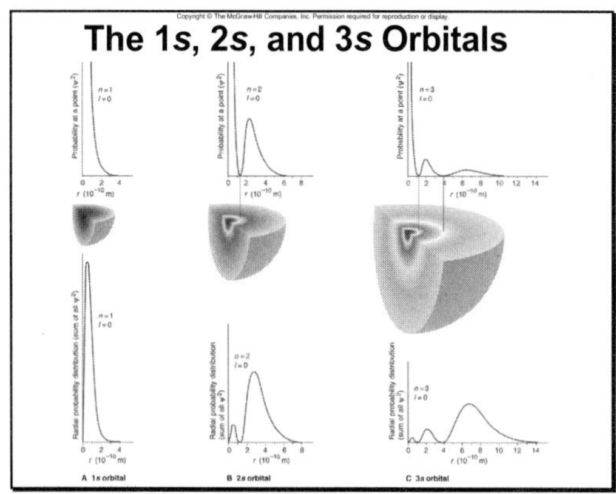

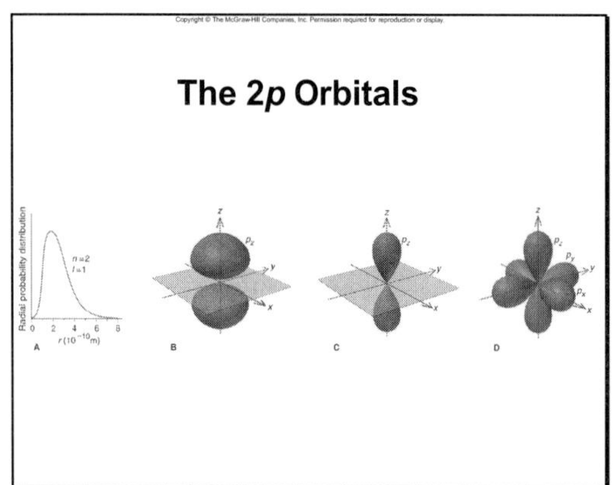

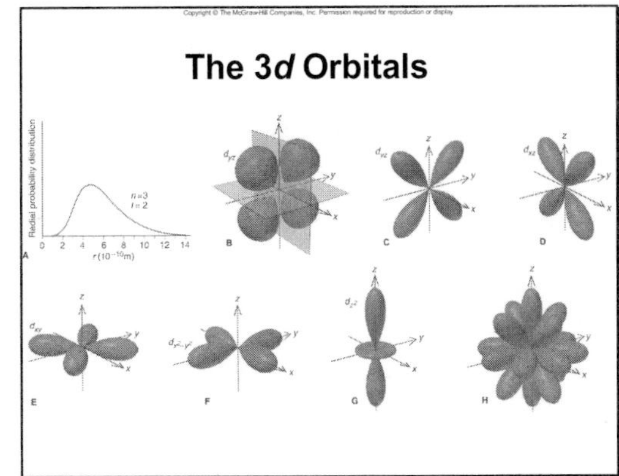

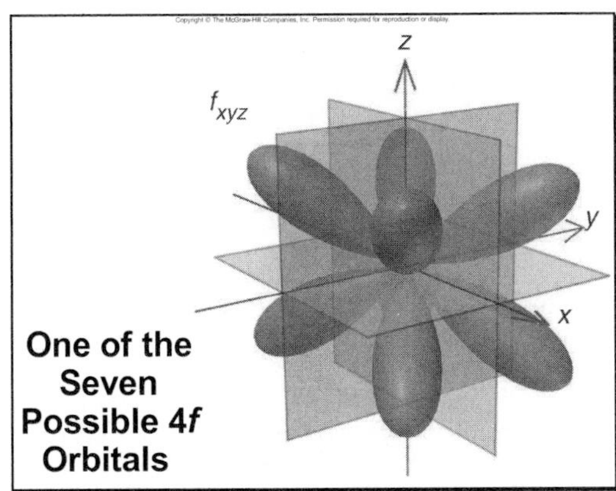

The Energy Levels in the H Atom

Energy

3s — 3p — — — 3d — — — — —

2s — 2p — — —

1s —

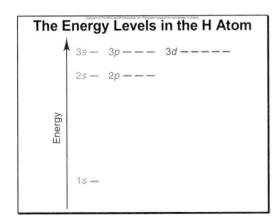

Chapter 8

Chemistry: The Molecular Nature of Matter and Change

Third Edition

Martin S. Silberberg

Table 8.1 Mendeleev's Predicted Properties of Germanium ("eka Silicon") and Its Actual Properties

Property	Predicted Properties of eka Silicon (E)	Actual Properties of Germanium (Ge)
Atomic mass	72 amu	72.61 amu
Appearance	Gray metal	Gray metal
Density	5.5 g/cm^3	5.32 g/cm^3
Molar volume	13 cm^3/mol	13.65 cm^3/mol
Specific heat capacity	0.31 J/g·K	0.32 J/g·K
Oxide formula	EO_2	GeO_2
Oxide density	4.7 g/cm^3	4.23 g/cm^3
Sulfide formula and solubility	ES_2; insoluble in H_2O; soluble in aqueous $(NH_4)_2S$	GeS_2; insoluble in H_2O; soluble in aqueous $(NH_4)_2S$
Chloride formula (boiling point)	ECl_4 (<100°C)	$GeCl_4$ (84°C)
Chloride density	1.9 g/cm^3	1.844 g/cm^3
Element preparation	Reduction of K_2EF_6 with sodium	Reduction of K_2GeF_6 with sodium

Observing the Effect of Electron Spin

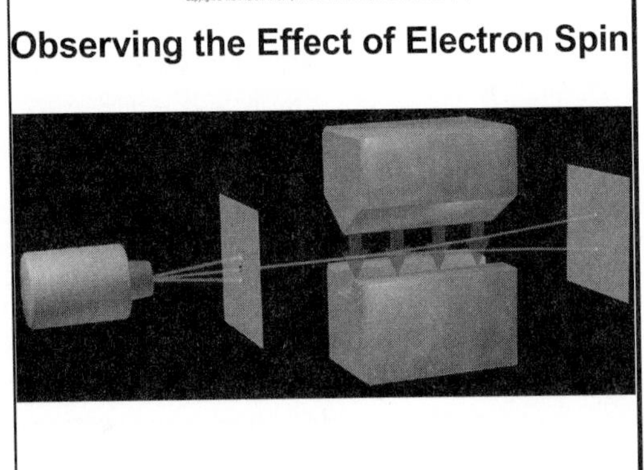

Table 8.2 Summary of Quantum Numbers of Electrons in Atoms

Name	Symbol	Permitted Values	Property
Principal	n	Positive integers (1, 2, 3, etc.)	Orbital energy (size)
Angular momentum	l	Integers from 0 to $n-1$	Orbital shape (The l values 0, 1, 2, and 3 correspond to s, p, d, and f orbitals, respectively.)
Magnetic	m_l	Integers from $-l$ to 0 to $+l$	Orbital orientation
Spin	m_s	$+\frac{1}{2}$ or $-\frac{1}{2}$	Direction of e^- spin

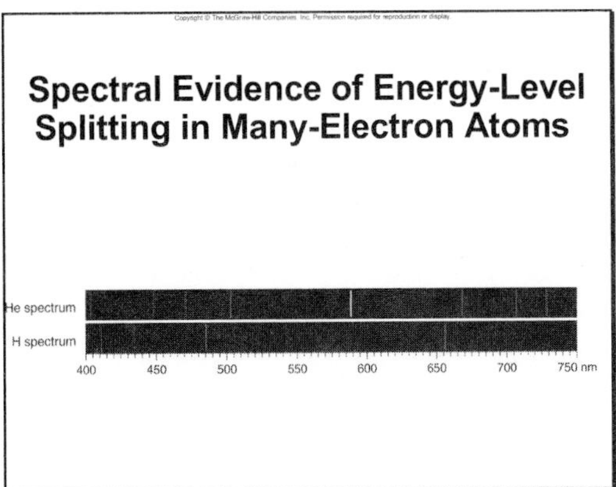

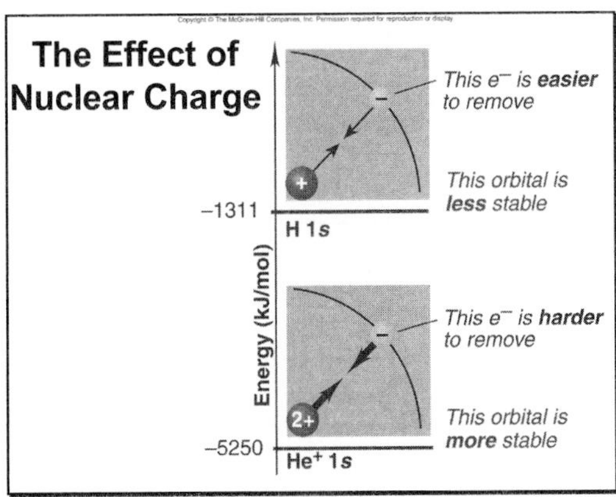

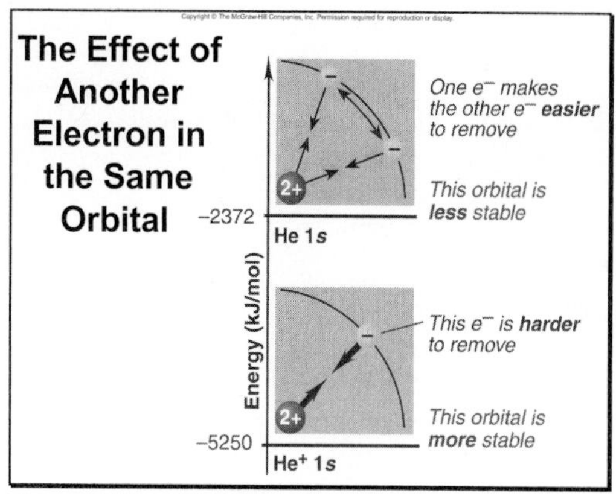
The Effect of Another Electron in the Same Orbital
One e⁻ makes the other e⁻ easier to remove
This orbital is less stable
−2372
He 1s
Energy (kJ/mol)
This e⁻ is harder to remove
This orbital is more stable
−5250
He⁺ 1s
2+

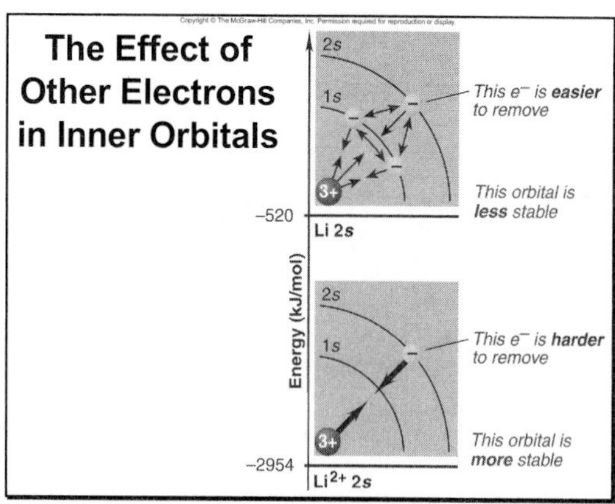
The Effect of Other Electrons in Inner Orbitals
2s
1s
This e⁻ is easier to remove
This orbital is less stable
−520
Li 2s
Energy (kJ/mol)
This e⁻ is harder to remove
This orbital is more stable
−2954
Li2+ 2s
3+

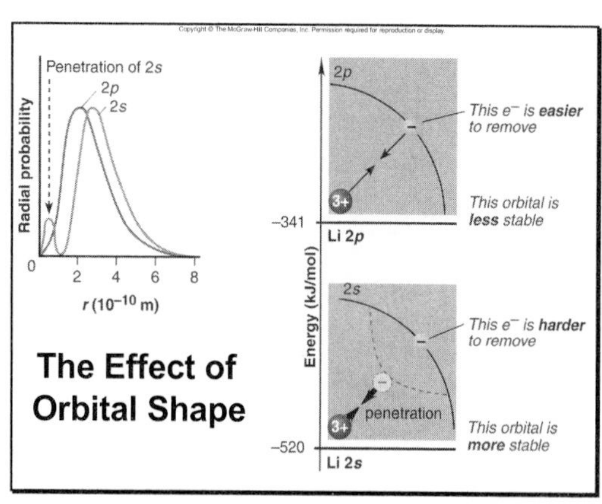
Penetration of 2s
2p
2s
Radial probability
0 2 4 6 8
r (10−10 m)
The Effect of Orbital Shape
This e⁻ is easier to remove
This orbital is less stable
−341
Li 2p
Energy (kJ/mol)
This e⁻ is harder to remove
penetration
This orbital is more stable
−520
Li 2s
3+

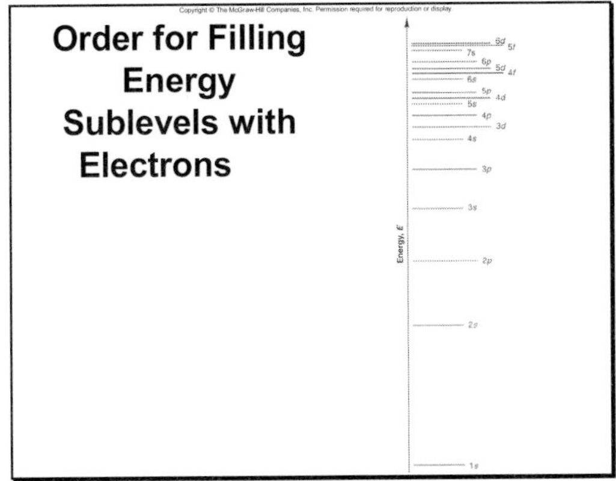
Copyright © The McGraw-Hill Companies, Inc. Permission required for reproduction or display.
Order for Filling Energy Sublevels with Electrons
Energy, E
6d
5f
7s
6p
5d
4f
6s
5p
4d
5s
4p
3d
4s
3p
3s
2p
2s
1s

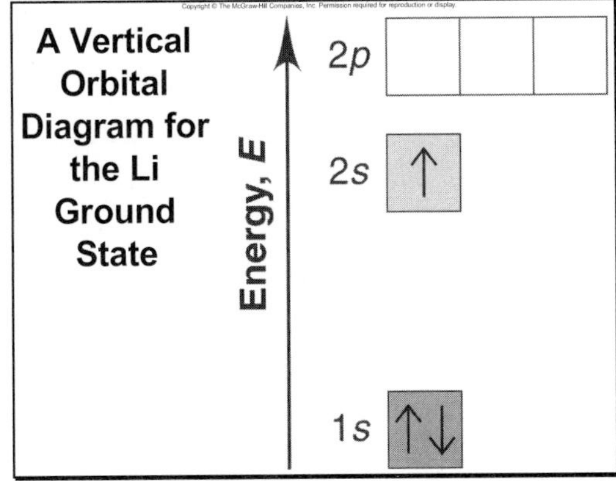
Copyright © The McGraw-Hill Companies, Inc. Permission required for reproduction or display.
A Vertical Orbital Diagram for the Li Ground State
Energy, E
2p
2s
1s

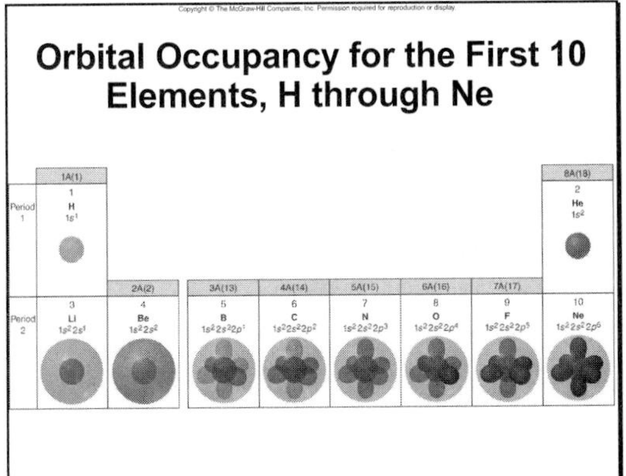
Copyright © The McGraw-Hill Companies, Inc. Permission required for reproduction or display.
Orbital Occupancy for the First 10 Elements, H through Ne
1A(1)
8A(18)
Period 1
1
H
1s1
2
He
1s2
2A(2)
3A(13)
4A(14)
5A(15)
6A(16)
7A(17)
Period 2
3
Li
1s2 2s1
4
Be
1s2 2s2
5
B
1s2 2s2 2p1
6
C
1s2 2s2 2p2
7
N
1s2 2s2 2p3
8
O
1s2 2s2 2p4
9
F
1s2 2s2 2p5
10
Ne
1s2 2s2 2p6

Table 8.3 Partial Orbital Diagrams and Electron Configurations* for the Elements in Period 3

Atomic Number/Element	Partial Orbital Diagram (3s and 3p Sublevels Only): 3s	3p	Full Electron Configuration	Condensed Electron Configuration
11/Na	↑	☐ ☐ ☐	$[1s^22s^22p^6]\,3s^1$	$[Ne]\,3s^1$
12/Mg	↑↓	☐ ☐ ☐	$[1s^22s^22p^6]\,3s^2$	$[Ne]\,3s^2$
13/Al	↑↓	↑ ☐ ☐	$[1s^22s^22p^6]\,3s^23p^1$	$[Ne]\,3s^23p^1$
14/Si	↑↓	↑ ↑ ☐	$[1s^22s^22p^6]\,3s^23p^2$	$[Ne]\,3s^23p^2$
15/P	↑↓	↑ ↑ ↑	$[1s^22s^22p^6]\,3s^23p^3$	$[Ne]\,3s^23p^3$
16/S	↑↓	↑↓ ↑ ↑	$[1s^22s^22p^6]\,3s^23p^4$	$[Ne]\,3s^23p^4$
17/Cl	↑↓	↑↓ ↑↓ ↑	$[1s^22s^22p^6]\,3s^23p^5$	$[Ne]\,3s^23p^5$
18/Ar	↑↓	↑↓ ↑↓ ↑↓	$[1s^22s^22p^6]\,3s^23p^6$	$[Ne]\,3s^23p^6$

*Colored type indicates sublevel to which last electron is added.

Condensed Ground-State Electron Configurations in the First Three Periods

Period	1A (1)	2A (2)	3A (13)	4A (14)	5A (15)	6A (16)	7A (17)	8A (18)
1	1 H $1s^1$							2 He $1s^2$
2	3 Li [He] $2s^1$	4 Be [He] $2s^2$	5 B [He] $2s^22p^1$	6 C [He] $2s^22p^2$	7 N [He] $2s^22p^3$	8 O [He] $2s^22p^4$	9 F [He] $2s^22p^5$	10 Ne [He] $2s^22p^6$
3	11 Na [Ne] $3s^1$	12 Mg [Ne] $3s^2$	13 Al [Ne] $3s^23p^1$	14 Si [Ne] $3s^23p^2$	15 P [Ne] $3s^23p^3$	16 S [Ne] $3s^23p^4$	17 Cl [Ne] $3s^23p^5$	18 Ar [Ne] $3s^23p^6$

Table 8.4 Partial Orbital Diagrams and Electron Configurations* for the Elements in Period 4

Atomic Number	Element	Partial Orbital Diagram (4s, 3d, and 4p Sublevels Only): 4s	3d	4p	Full Electron Configuration	Condensed Electron Configuration
19	K	↑	☐ ☐ ☐ ☐ ☐	☐ ☐ ☐	$[1s^22s^22p^63s^23p^6]\,4s^1$	$[Ar]\,4s^1$
20	Ca	↑↓	☐ ☐ ☐ ☐ ☐	☐ ☐ ☐	$[1s^22s^22p^63s^23p^6]\,4s^2$	$[Ar]\,4s^2$
21	Sc	↑↓	↑ ☐ ☐ ☐ ☐	☐ ☐ ☐	$[1s^22s^22p^63s^23p^6]\,4s^23d^1$	$[Ar]\,4s^23d^1$
22	Ti	↑↓	↑ ↑ ☐ ☐ ☐	☐ ☐ ☐	$[1s^22s^22p^63s^23p^6]\,4s^23d^2$	$[Ar]\,4s^23d^2$
23	V	↑↓	↑ ↑ ↑ ☐ ☐	☐ ☐ ☐	$[1s^22s^22p^63s^23p^6]\,4s^23d^3$	$[Ar]\,4s^23d^3$
24	Cr	↑	↑ ↑ ↑ ↑ ↑	☐ ☐ ☐	$[1s^22s^22p^63s^23p^6]\,4s^13d^5$	$[Ar]\,4s^13d^5$
25	Mn	↑↓	↑ ↑ ↑ ↑ ↑	☐ ☐ ☐	$[1s^22s^22p^63s^23p^6]\,4s^23d^5$	$[Ar]\,4s^23d^5$
26	Fe	↑↓	↑↓ ↑ ↑ ↑ ↑	☐ ☐ ☐	$[1s^22s^22p^63s^23p^6]\,4s^23d^6$	$[Ar]\,4s^23d^6$
27	Co	↑↓	↑↓ ↑↓ ↑ ↑ ↑	☐ ☐ ☐	$[1s^22s^22p^63s^23p^6]\,4s^23d^7$	$[Ar]\,4s^23d^7$
28	Ni	↑↓	↑↓ ↑↓ ↑↓ ↑ ↑	☐ ☐ ☐	$[1s^22s^22p^63s^23p^6]\,4s^23d^8$	$[Ar]\,4s^23d^8$
29	Cu	↑	↑↓ ↑↓ ↑↓ ↑↓ ↑↓	☐ ☐ ☐	$[1s^22s^22p^63s^23p^6]\,4s^13d^{10}$	$[Ar]\,4s^13d^{10}$
30	Zn	↑↓	↑↓ ↑↓ ↑↓ ↑↓ ↑↓	☐ ☐ ☐	$[1s^22s^22p^63s^23p^6]\,4s^23d^{10}$	$[Ar]\,4s^23d^{10}$
31	Ga	↑↓	↑↓ ↑↓ ↑↓ ↑↓ ↑↓	↑ ☐ ☐	$[1s^22s^22p^63s^23p^6]\,4s^23d^{10}4p^1$	$[Ar]\,4s^23d^{10}4p^1$
32	Ge	↑↓	↑↓ ↑↓ ↑↓ ↑↓ ↑↓	↑ ↑ ☐	$[1s^22s^22p^63s^23p^6]\,4s^23d^{10}4p^2$	$[Ar]\,4s^23d^{10}4p^2$
33	As	↑↓	↑↓ ↑↓ ↑↓ ↑↓ ↑↓	↑ ↑ ↑	$[1s^22s^22p^63s^23p^6]\,4s^23d^{10}4p^3$	$[Ar]\,4s^23d^{10}4p^3$
34	Se	↑↓	↑↓ ↑↓ ↑↓ ↑↓ ↑↓	↑↓ ↑ ↑	$[1s^22s^22p^63s^23p^6]\,4s^23d^{10}4p^4$	$[Ar]\,4s^23d^{10}4p^4$
35	Br	↑↓	↑↓ ↑↓ ↑↓ ↑↓ ↑↓	↑↓ ↑↓ ↑	$[1s^22s^22p^63s^23p^6]\,4s^23d^{10}4p^5$	$[Ar]\,4s^23d^{10}4p^5$
36	Kr	↑↓	↑↓ ↑↓ ↑↓ ↑↓ ↑↓	↑↓ ↑↓ ↑↓	$[1s^22s^22p^63s^23p^6]\,4s^23d^{10}4p^6$	$[Ar]\,4s^23d^{10}4p^6$

*Colored type indicates sublevel(s) whose occupancy changes when last electron is added.

A Periodic Table of Partial Ground-State Electron Configurations

Main-Group Elements (s block) — Transition Elements (d block) — Main-Group Elements (p block)

Period number: highest occupied energy level

Period	1A (1) ns^1	2A (2) ns^2	3B (3)	4B (4)	5B (5)	6B (6)	7B (7)	8B (8)	8B (9)	8B (10)	1B (11)	2B (12)	3A (13) ns^2np^1	4A (14) ns^2np^2	5A (15) ns^2np^3	6A (16) ns^2np^4	7A (17) ns^2np^5	8A (18) ns^2np^6
1	1 H																	2 He
2	3 Li	4 Be											5 B	6 C	7 N	8 O	9 F	10 Ne
3	11 Na	12 Mg											13 Al	14 Si	15 P	16 S	17 Cl	18 Ar
4	19 K	20 Ca	21 Sc	22 Ti	23 V	24 Cr	25 Mn	26 Fe	27 Co	28 Ni	29 Cu	30 Zn	31 Ga	32 Ge	33 As	34 Se	35 Br	36 Kr
5	37 Rb	38 Sr	39 Y	40 Zr	41 Nb	42 Mo	43 Tc	44 Ru	45 Rh	46 Pd	47 Ag	48 Cd	49 In	50 Sn	51 Sb	52 Te	53 I	54 Xe
6	55 Cs	56 Ba	57 La*	72 Hf	73 Ta	74 W	75 Re	76 Os	77 Ir	78 Pt	79 Au	80 Hg	81 Tl	82 Pb	83 Bi	84 Po	85 At	86 Rn
7	87 Fr	88 Ra	89 Ac**	104 Rf	105 Db	106 Sg	107 Bh	108 Hs	109 Mt	110	111	112		114				

Inner Transition Elements (f block)

Period															
6	*Lanthanides	58 Ce	59 Pr	60 Nd	61 Pm	62 Sm	63 Eu	64 Gd	65 Tb	66 Dy	67 Ho	68 Er	69 Tm	70 Yb	71 Lu
7	**Actinides	90 Th	91 Pa	92 U	93 Np	94 Pu	95 Am	96 Cm	97 Bk	98 Cf	99 Es	100 Fm	101 Md	102 No	103 Lr

The Relation Between Orbital Filling and the Periodic Table

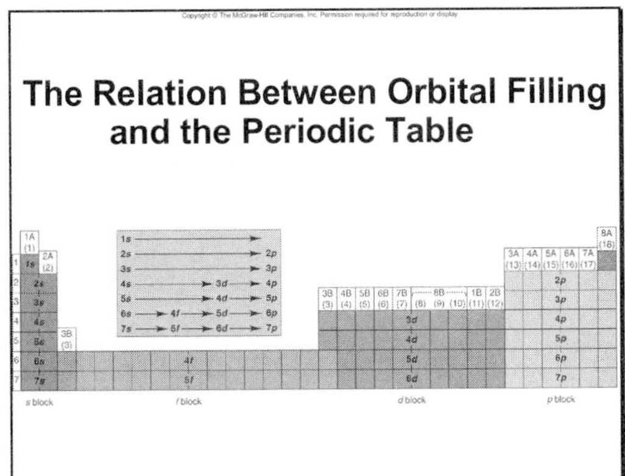

Periodic Memory Aids

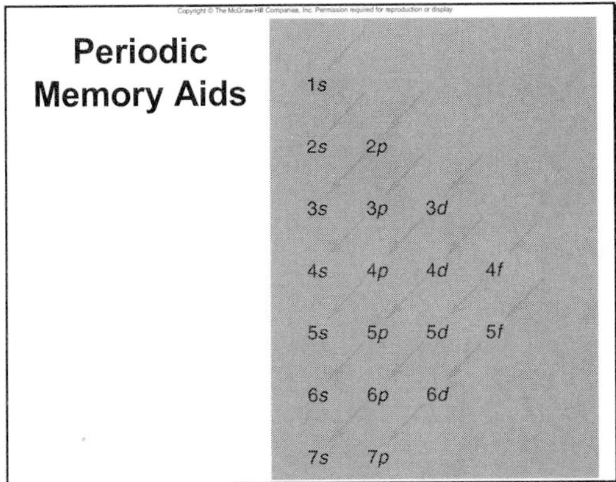

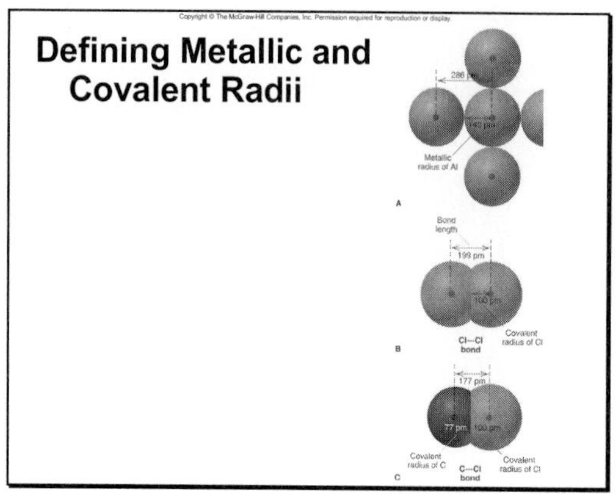

Defining Metallic and Covalent Radii
286 pm
143 pm
Metallic radius of Al
Bond length
199 pm
100 pm
Cl—Cl bond
Covalent radius of Cl
177 pm
77 pm
100 pm
Covalent radius of C
C—Cl bond
Covalent radius of Cl

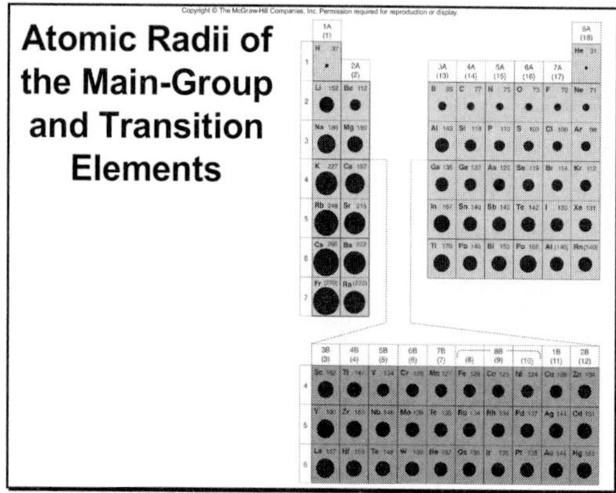

Atomic Radii of the Main-Group and Transition Elements

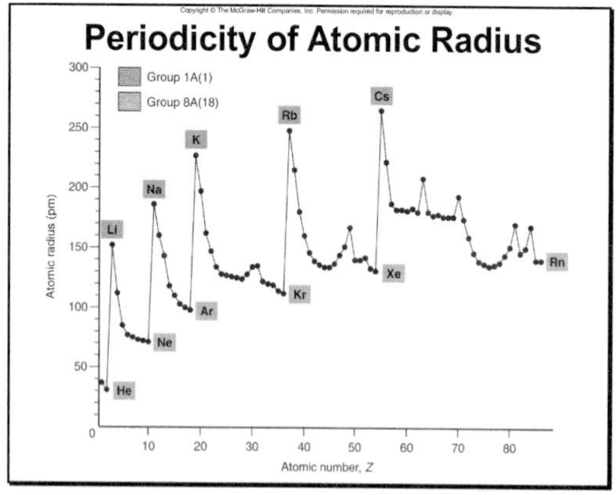

Periodicity of Atomic Radius
Group 1A(1)
Group 8A(18)
Atomic radius (pm)
Atomic number, Z
Li
Na
K
Rb
Cs
He
Ne
Ar
Kr
Xe
Rn

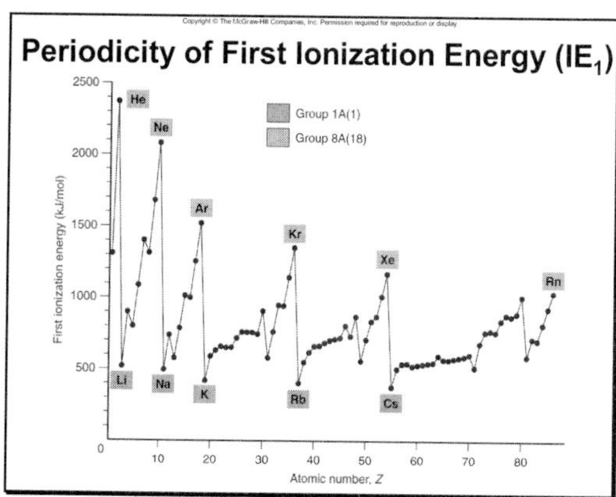
Periodicity of First Ionization Energy (IE_1)
Group 1A(1)
Group 8A(18)
First ionization energy (kJ/mol)
Atomic number, Z
He
Ne
Ar
Kr
Xe
Rn
Li
Na
K
Rb
Cs

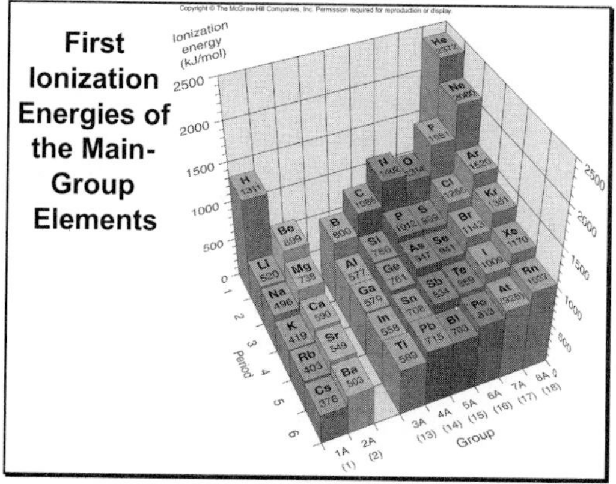
First Ionization Energies of the Main-Group Elements
Ionization energy (kJ/mol)
Period
Group

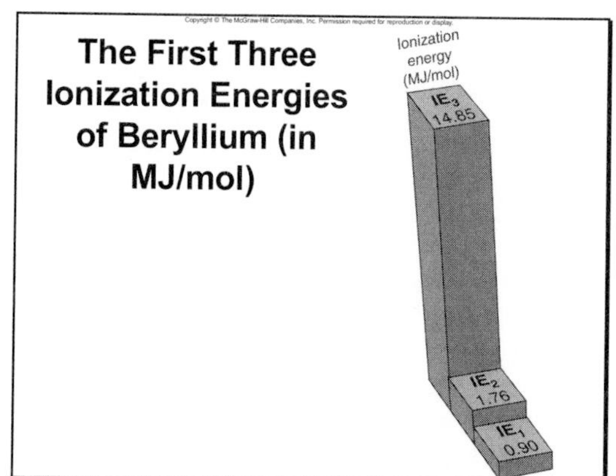
The First Three Ionization Energies of Beryllium (in MJ/mol)
Ionization energy (MJ/mol)
IE_3 14.85
IE_2 1.76
IE_1 0.90

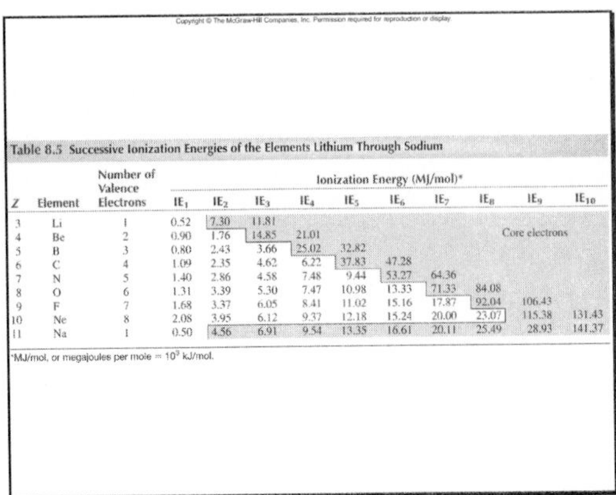

Table 8.5 Successive Ionization Energies of the Elements Lithium Through Sodium

Z	Element	Number of Valence Electrons	Ionization Energy (MJ/mol)*									
			IE_1	IE_2	IE_3	IE_4	IE_5	IE_6	IE_7	IE_8	IE_9	IE_{10}
3	Li	1	0.52	7.30	11.81							
4	Be	2	0.90	1.76	14.85	21.01				Core electrons		
5	B	3	0.80	2.43	3.66	25.02	32.82					
6	C	4	1.09	2.35	4.62	6.22	37.83	47.28				
7	N	5	1.40	2.86	4.58	7.48	9.44	53.27	64.36			
8	O	6	1.31	3.39	5.30	7.47	10.98	13.33	71.33	84.08		
9	F	7	1.68	3.37	6.05	8.41	11.02	15.16	17.87	92.04	106.43	
10	Ne	8	2.08	3.95	6.12	9.37	12.18	15.24	20.00	23.07	115.38	131.43
11	Na	1	0.50	4.56	6.91	9.54	13.35	16.61	20.11	25.49	28.93	141.37

*MJ/mol, or megajoules per mole = 10^3 kJ/mol.

Electron Affinities of the Main-Group Elements

1A (1)	2A (2)	3A (13)	4A (14)	5A (15)	6A (16)	7A (17)	8A (18)
H −72.8							He (0.0)
Li −59.6	Be (+18)	B −26.7	C −122	N +7	O −141	F −328	Ne (+29)
Na −52.9	Mg (+21)	Al −42.5	Si −134	P −72.0	S −200	Cl −349	Ar (+35)
K −48.4	Ca (+186)	Ga −28.9	Ge −119	As −78.2	Se −195	Br −325	Kr (+39)
Rb −46.9	Sr (+146)	In −28.9	Sn −107	Sb −103	Te −190	I −295	Xe (+41)
Cs −45.5	Ba (+46)	Tl −19.3	Pb −35.1	Bi −91.3	Po −183	At −270	Rn (+41)

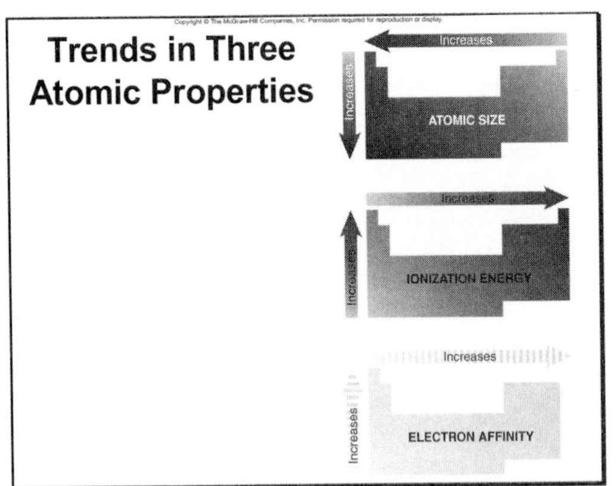

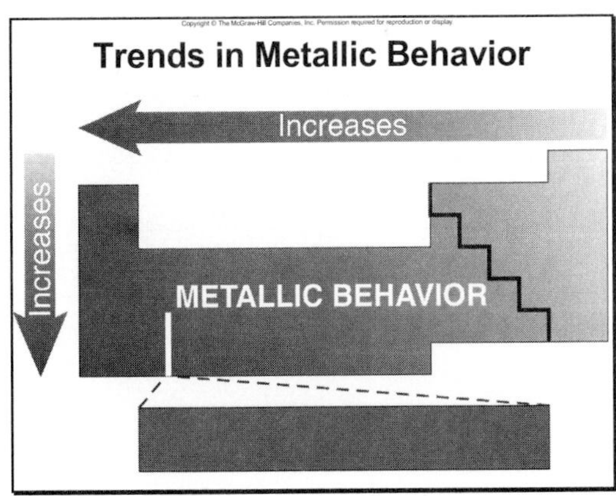
Copyright © The McGraw-Hill Companies, Inc. Permission required for reproduction or display.
Trends in Metallic Behavior
Increases
Increases
METALLIC BEHAVIOR

Copyright © The McGraw-Hill Companies, Inc. Permission required for reproduction or display.
The Change in Metallic Behavior in Group 5A(15) and Period 3
Group 5A (15)
7 N 1402
Period 3
11 Na 496
12 Mg 738
13 Al 577
14 Si 786
15 P 1012
16 S 999
17 Cl 1256
33 As 947
51 Sb 834
83 Bi 703

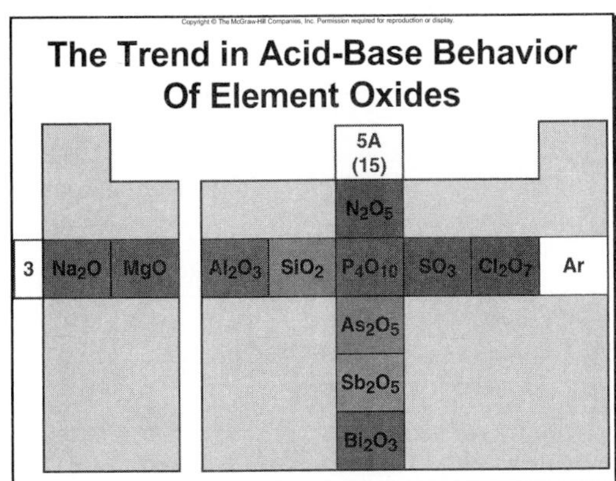
Copyright © The McGraw-Hill Companies, Inc. Permission required for reproduction or display.
The Trend in Acid-Base Behavior Of Element Oxides
5A (15)
N2O5
3
Na2O
MgO
Al2O3
SiO2
P4O10
SO3
Cl2O7
Ar
As2O5
Sb2O5
Bi2O3

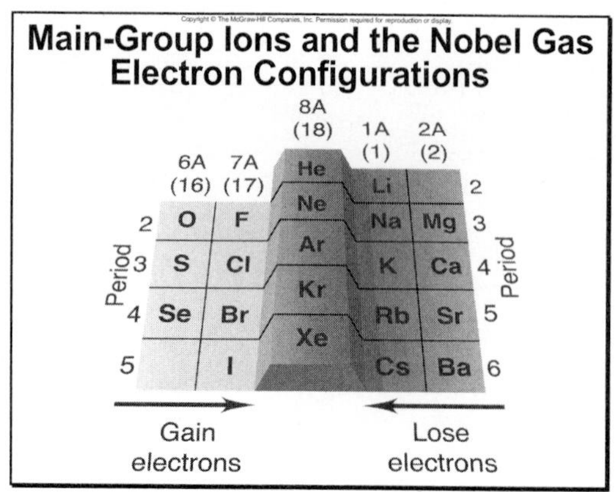
Main-Group Ions and the Nobel Gas Electron Configurations
8A (18)
1A (1)
2A (2)
6A (16)
7A (17)
He
Ne
Ar
Kr
Xe
O
F
S
Cl
Se
Br
I
Li
Na
Mg
K
Ca
Rb
Sr
Cs
Ba
Period
Gain electrons
Lose electrons

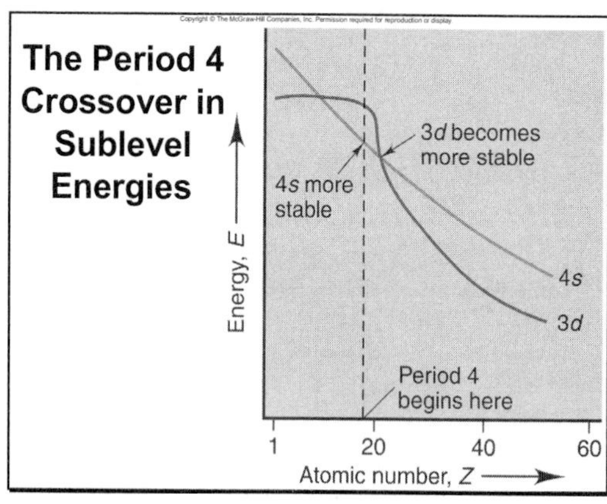
The Period 4 Crossover in Sublevel Energies
3d becomes more stable
4s more stable
4s
3d
Period 4 begins here
Energy, E
Atomic number, Z
1
20
40
60

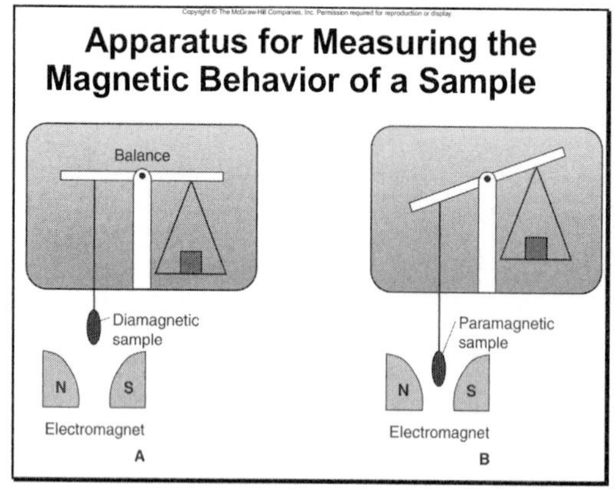
Apparatus for Measuring the Magnetic Behavior of a Sample
Balance
Diamagnetic sample
N
S
Electromagnet
A
Paramagnetic sample
Electromagnet
B

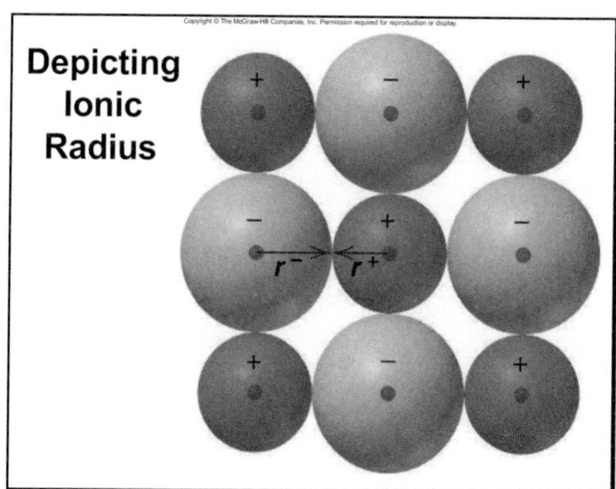

Copyright © The McGraw-Hill Companies, Inc. Permission required for reproduction or display.
Depicting Ionic Radius
+
−
+
−
+
−
r^-
r^+
+
−
+

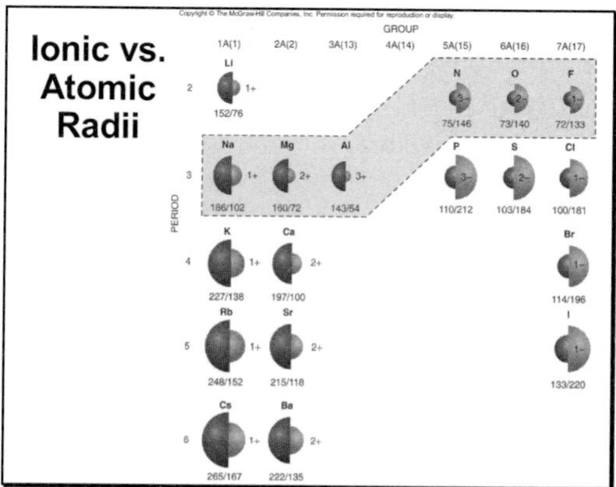

Copyright © The McGraw-Hill Companies, Inc. Permission required for reproduction or display.
Ionic vs. Atomic Radii
GROUP
1A(1)
2A(2)
3A(13)
4A(14)
5A(15)
6A(16)
7A(17)
PERIOD
2
3
4
5
6
Li 1+ 152/76
N 3− 75/146
O 2− 73/140
F 1− 72/133
Na 1+ 186/102
Mg 2+ 160/72
Al 3+ 143/54
P 3− 110/212
S 2− 103/184
Cl 1− 100/181
K 1+ 227/138
Ca 2+ 197/100
Br 1− 114/196
Rb 1+ 248/152
Sr 2+ 215/118
I 1− 133/220
Cs 1+ 265/167
Ba 2+ 222/135

Chapter 9

Chemistry: The Molecular Nature of Matter and Change

Third Edition

Martin S. Silberberg

A General Comparison of Metals and Nonmetals

Key:
Metals
Nonmetals
Metalloids

A

PROPERTY	METAL ATOM	NONMETAL ATOM
Atomic size	Larger	Smaller
Z_{eff}	Lower	Higher
IE	Lower	Higher
EA	Less negative	More negative

B Relative magnitudes of atomic properties within a period

The Three Models of Chemical Bonding

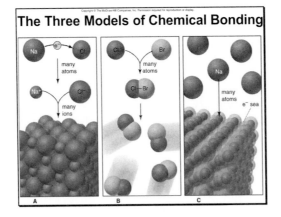

Na
e^-
Cl
many atoms
Na^+
Cl^-
many ions

A

Cl
Br
many atoms
Cl—Br

B

Na
many atoms
e^- sea

C

Lewis Electron-Dot Symbols for Elements in Periods 2 and 3

Period	1A(1)	2A(2)	3A(13)	4A(14)	5A(15)	6A(16)	7A(17)	8A(18)
	ns^1	ns^2	ns^2np^1	ns^2np^2	ns^2np^3	ns^2np^4	ns^2np^5	ns^2np^6
2	· Li	· Be ·	· B ·	· C ·	· N ·	: O ·	: F :	: Ne :
3	· Na	· Mg ·	· Al ·	· Si ·	· P ·	: S ·	: Cl :	: Ar :

Three Ways to Represent the Formation of Li^+ and F^- Through Electron Transfer

Electron configurations

Li $1s^22s^1$ + F $1s^22s^22p^5$ →

Orbital diagrams

Li [↑↓] [↑] [ ][ ][ ] + F [↑↓] [↑↓] [↑↓][↑↓][↑] →

1s 2s 2p 1s 2s 2p

Lewis electron-dot symbols

Li· + ·F: →

The Reaction Between Sodium and Bromine

A

B

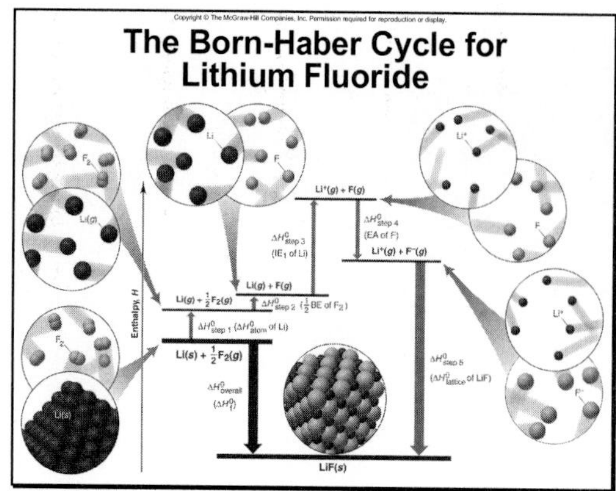

Coulomb's Law Used to Predict Lattice energy

$$\text{Electrostatic energy} \propto \frac{\text{charge A} \times \text{charge B}}{\text{distance}} \qquad (9.1)$$

$$\text{Electrostatic energy} \propto \frac{\text{cation charge} \times \text{anion charge}}{\text{cation radius} + \text{anion radius}} \propto \Delta H^0_{\text{lattice}} \qquad (9.2)$$

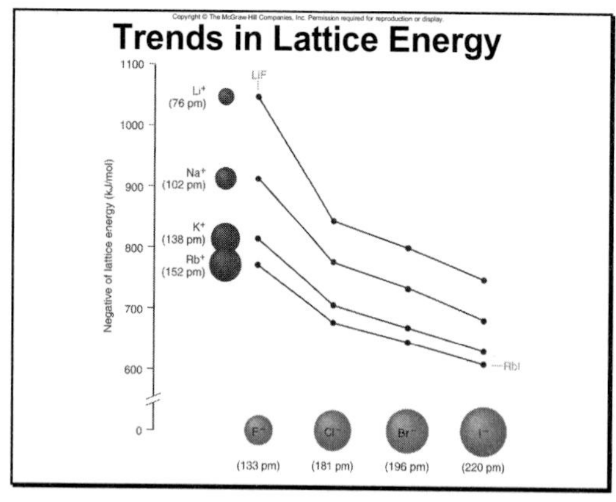

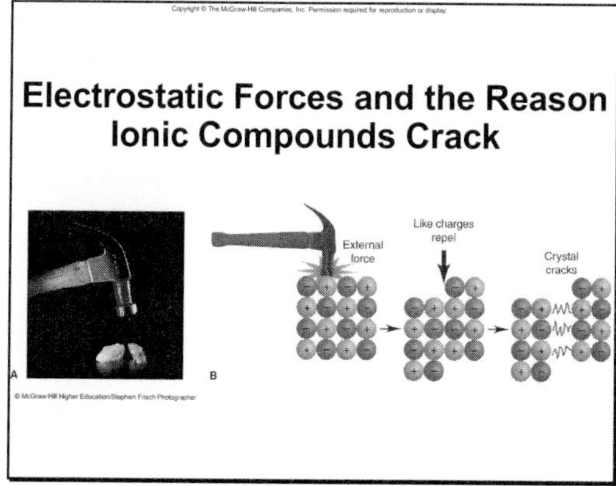

Table 9.1 Melting and Boiling Points of Some Ionic Compounds

Compound	mp (°C)	bp (°C)
CsBr	636	1300
NaI	661	1304
$MgCl_2$	714	1412
KBr	734	1435
$CaCl_2$	782	>1600
NaCl	801	1413
LiF	845	1676
KF	858	1505
MgO	2852	3600

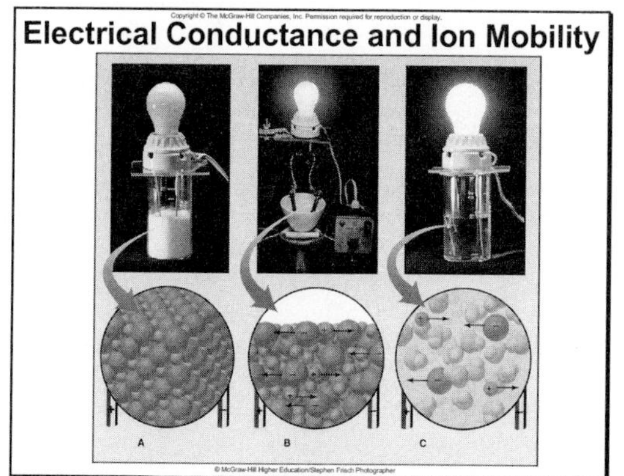

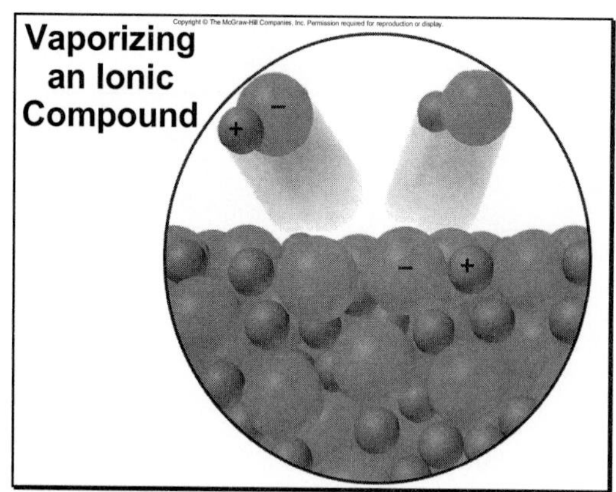
Vaporizing an Ionic Compound
Copyright © The McGraw-Hill Companies, Inc. Permission required for reproduction or display.

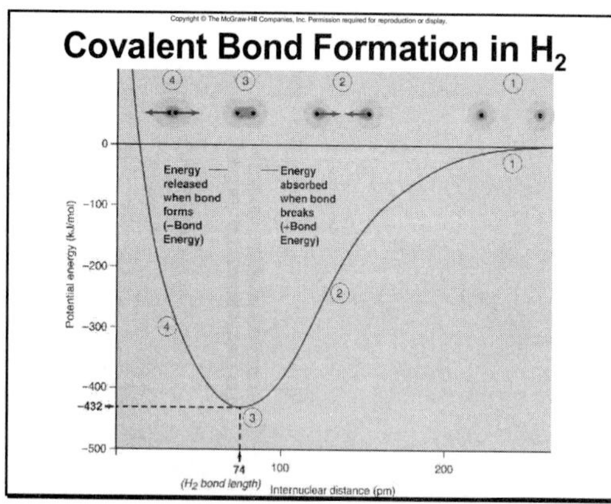
Copyright © The McGraw-Hill Companies, Inc. Permission required for reproduction or display.
Covalent Bond Formation in H2
Energy released when bond forms (−Bond Energy)
Energy absorbed when bond breaks (+Bond Energy)
Potential energy (kJ/mol)
0
-100
-200
-300
-400
-432
-500
74
(H2 bond length)
100
200
Internuclear distance (pm)

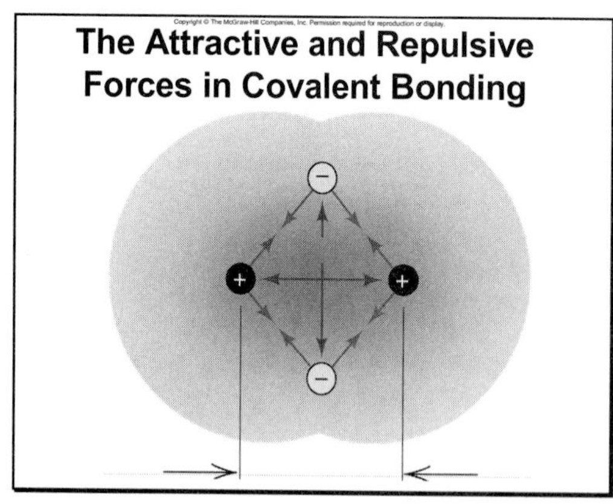
Copyright © The McGraw-Hill Companies, Inc. Permission required for reproduction or display.
The Attractive and Repulsive Forces in Covalent Bonding

Table 9.2 Average Bond Energies (kJ/mol)

Bond	Energy	Bond	Energy	Bond	Energy	Bond	Energy
Single Bonds							
H—H	432	N—H	391	Si—H	323	S—H	347
H—F	565	N—N	160	Si—Si	226	S—S	266
H—Cl	427	N—P	209	Si—O	368	S—F	327
H—Br	363	N—O	201	Si—S	226	S—Cl	271
H—I	295	N—F	272	Si—F	565	S—Br	218
		N—Cl	200	Si—Cl	381	S—I	~170
C—H	413	N—Br	243	Si—Br	310		
C—C	347	N—I	159	Si—I	234	F—F	159
C—Si	301					F—Cl	193
C—N	305	O—H	467	P—H	320	F—Br	212
C—O	358	O—P	351	P—Si	213	F—I	263
C—P	264	O—O	204	P—P	200	Cl—Cl	243
C—S	259	O—S	265	P—F	490	Cl—Br	215
C—F	453	O—F	190	P—Cl	331	Cl—I	208
C—Cl	339	O—Cl	203	P—Br	272	Br—Br	193
C—Br	276	O—Br	234	P—I	184	Br—I	175
C—I	216	O—I	234			I—I	151
Multiple Bonds							
C=C	614	N=N	418	C≡C	839	N≡N	945
C=N	615	N=O	607	C≡N	891		
C=O	745 (799 in CO_2)	O_2	498	C≡O	1070		

Table 9.3 Average Bond Lengths (pm)

Bond	Length	Bond	Length	Bond	Length	Bond	Length
Single Bonds							
H—H	74	N—H	101	Si—H	148	S—H	134
H—F	92	N—N	146	Si—Si	234	S—P	210
H—Cl	127	N—P	177	Si—O	161	S—S	204
H—Br	141	N—O	144	Si—S	210	S—F	158
H—I	161	N—S	168	Si—N	172	S—Cl	201
		N—F	139	Si—F	156	S—Br	225
		N—Cl	191	Si—Cl	204	S—I	234
C—H	109	N—Br	214	Si—Br	216		
C—C	154	N—I	222	Si—I	240	F—F	143
C—Si	186					F—Cl	166
C—N	147	O—H	96	P—H	142	F—Br	178
C—O	143	O—P	160	P—Si	227	F—I	187
C—P	187	O—O	148	P—P	221	Cl—Cl	199
C—S	181	O—S	151	P—F	156	Cl—Br	214
C—F	133	O—F	142	P—Cl	204	Cl—I	243
C—Cl	177	O—Cl	164	P—Br	222	Br—Br	228
C—Br	194	O—Br	172	P—I	243	Br—I	248
C—I	213	O—I	194			I—I	266
Multiple Bonds							
C=C	134	N=N	122	C≡C	121	N≡N	110
C=N	127	N=O	120	C≡N	115	N≡O	106
C=O	123	O_2	121	C≡O	113		

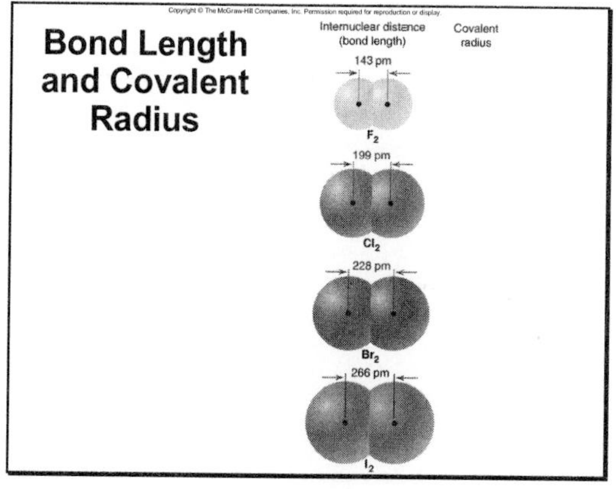

Table 9.4 The Relation of Bond Order, Bond Length, and Bond Energy

Bond	Bond Order	Average Bond Length (pm)	Average Bond Energy (kJ/mol)
C—O	1	143	358
C=O	2	123	745
C≡O	3	113	1070
C—C	1	154	347
C=C	2	134	614
C≡C	3	121	839
N—N	1	146	160
N=N	2	122	418
N≡N	3	110	945

Strong Forces Within Molecules and Weak Forces Between Them

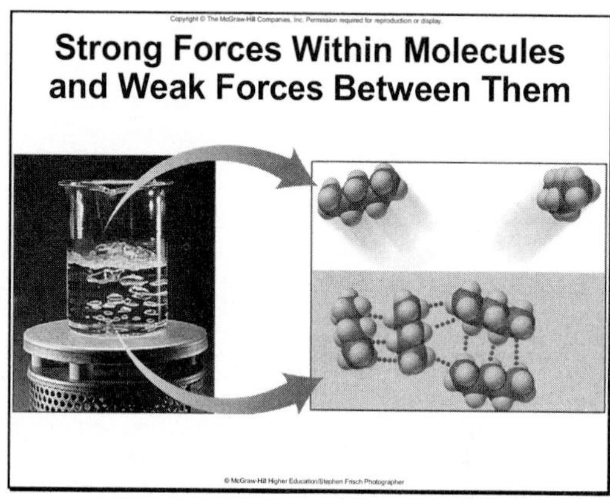

Covalent Bonds of Network Covalent Solids

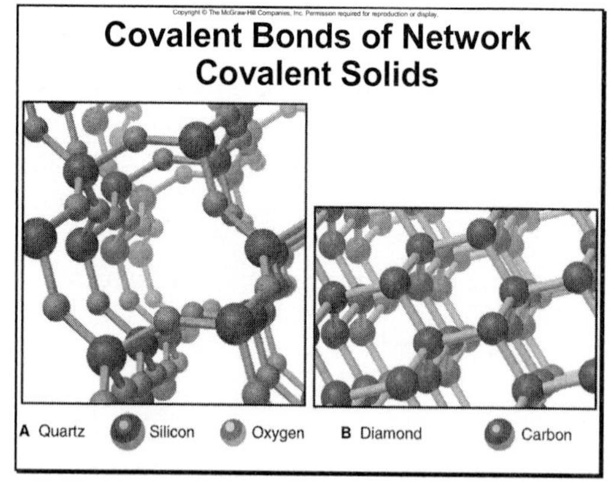

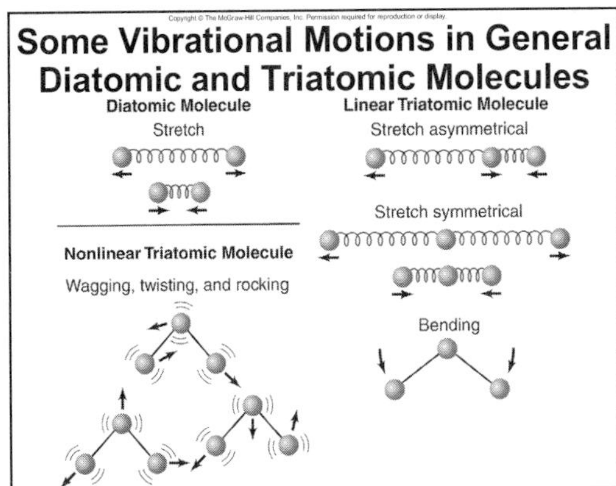
Copyright © The McGraw-Hill Companies, Inc. Permission required for reproduction or display.
Some Vibrational Motions in General Diatomic and Triatomic Molecules
Diatomic Molecule
Stretch
Linear Triatomic Molecule
Stretch asymmetrical
Stretch symmetrical
Nonlinear Triatomic Molecule
Wagging, twisting, and rocking
Bending

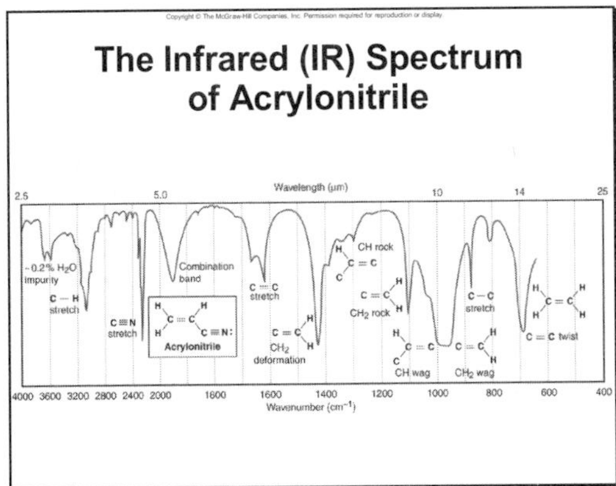
Copyright © The McGraw-Hill Companies, Inc. Permission required for reproduction or display.
The Infrared (IR) Spectrum of Acrylonitrile
Wavelength (μm)
Wavenumber (cm⁻¹)
~0.2% H₂O impurity
C–H stretch
C≡N stretch
Combination band
Acrylonitrile
C=C stretch
CH₂ deformation
CH rock
CH₂ rock
CH wag
CH₂ wag
C–C stretch
C=C twist

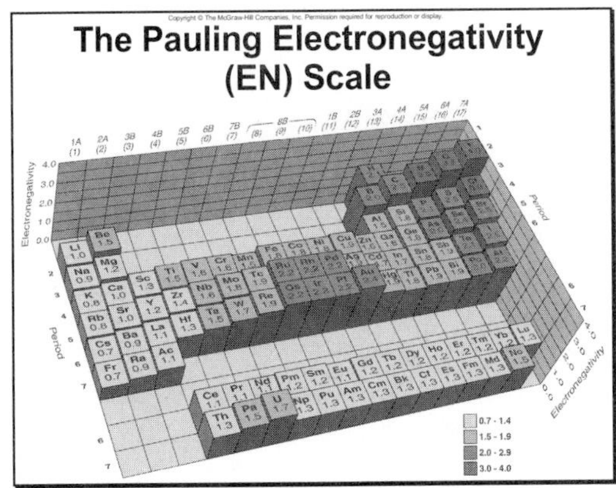
Copyright © The McGraw-Hill Companies, Inc. Permission required for reproduction or display.
The Pauling Electronegativity (EN) Scale
Electronegativity
Period
0.7 - 1.4
1.5 - 1.9
2.0 - 2.9
3.0 - 4.0

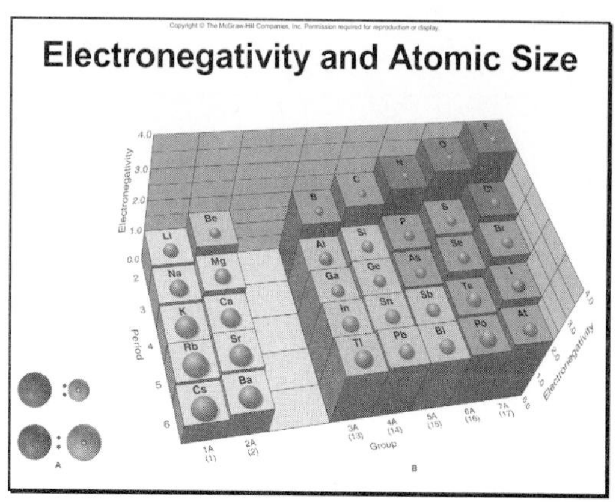

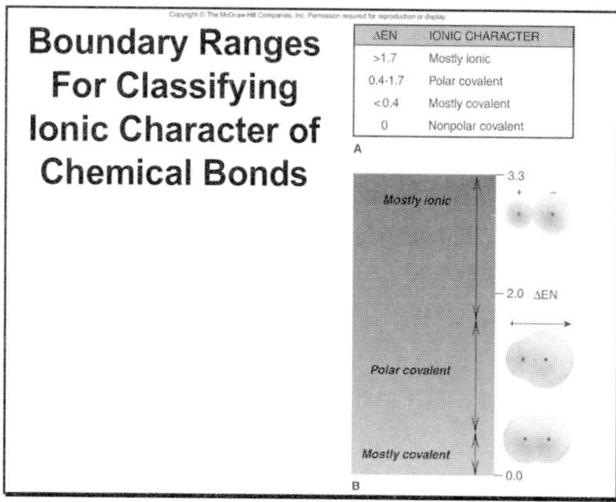

ΔEN	IONIC CHARACTER
>1.7	Mostly ionic
0.4-1.7	Polar covalent
<0.4	Mostly covalent
0	Nonpolar covalent

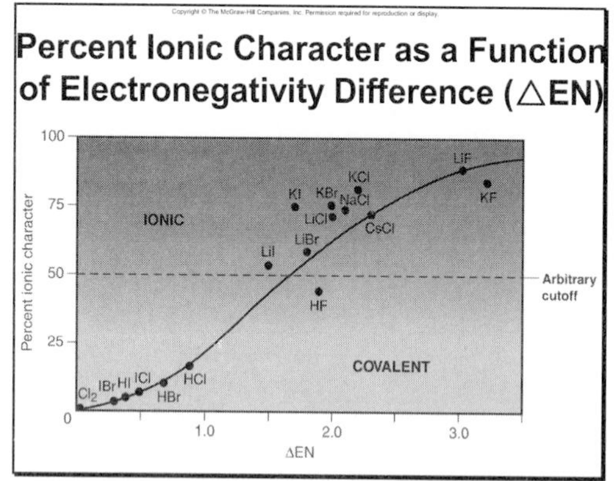

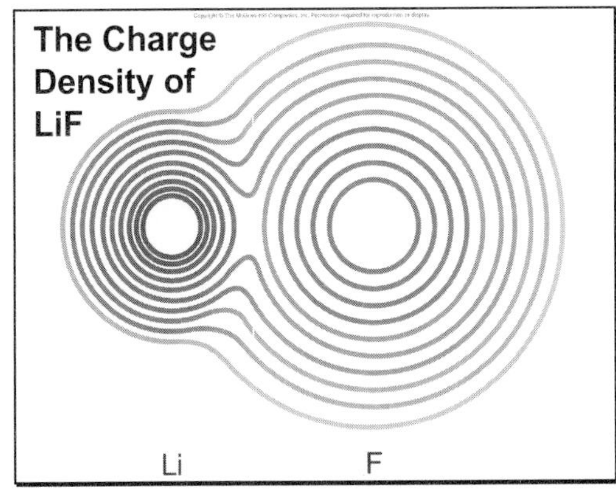

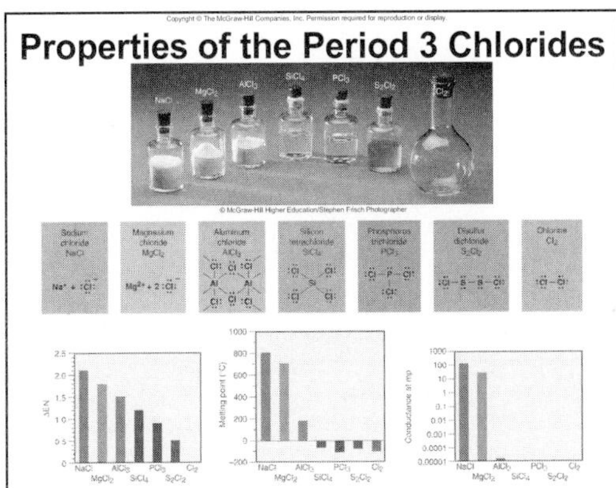

Table 9.5 Melting and Boiling Points of Some Metals

Element	mp (°C)	bp (°C)
Lithium (Li)	180	1347
Tin (Sn)	232	2623
Aluminum (Al)	660	2467
Barium (Ba)	727	1850
Silver (Ag)	961	2155
Copper (Cu)	1083	2570
Uranium (U)	1130	3930

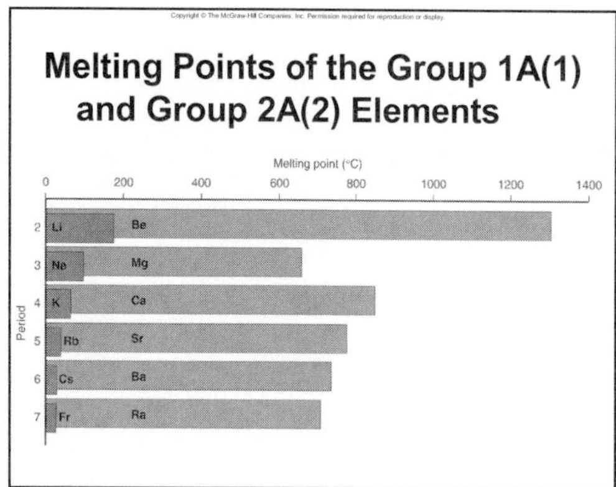
Copyright © The McGraw-Hill Companies, Inc. Permission required for reproduction or display.
Melting Points of the Group 1A(1) and Group 2A(2) Elements
Melting point (°C)
0
200
400
600
800
1000
1200
1400
Period
2
3
4
5
6
7
Li
Be
Na
Mg
K
Ca
Rb
Sr
Cs
Ba
Fr
Ra

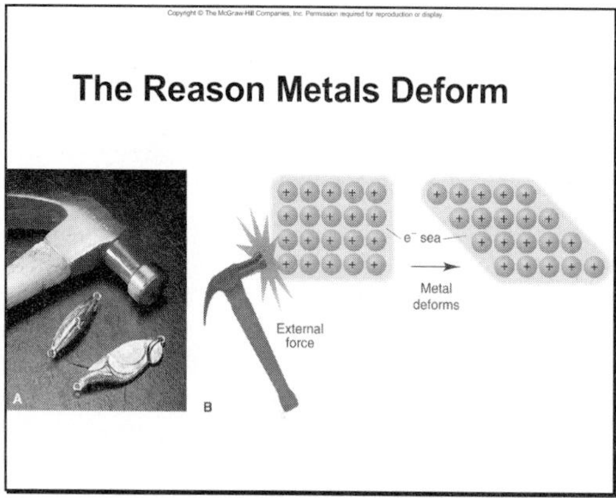
Copyright © The McGraw-Hill Companies, Inc. Permission required for reproduction or display.
The Reason Metals Deform
e⁻ sea
Metal deforms
External force
A
B

Chapter 10

Chemistry: The Molecular Nature of Matter and Change

Third Edition

Martin S. Silberberg

The Steps in Converting a Molecular Formula into a Lewis Structure

Molecular formula → Step 1 → Atom placement → Step 2 → Sum of valence e^- → Step 3 → Remaining valence e^- → Step 4 → Lewis structure

A Purple Mule, Not a Blue Horse and a Red Donkey

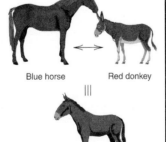

Blue horse ⟷ Red donkey

|||

Purple mule

Copyright © The McGraw-Hill Companies, Inc. Permission required for reproduction or display.

Resonance Structures

resonance forms

Copyright © The McGraw-Hill Companies, Inc. Permission required for reproduction or display.

Formal Charge: Selecting the Best Resonance Structure

Formal charge of atom = no. of valence e^- − (no. of unshared valence e^- + $\frac{1}{2}$ no. of shared valence e^-) (10.1)

$O_A[6 - 4 - \frac{1}{2}(4)] = 0$ $O_A[6 - 6 - \frac{1}{2}(2)] = -1$

$O_B[6 - 2 - \frac{1}{2}(6)] = +1$ $O_B[6 - 2 - \frac{1}{2}(6)] = +1$

$O_C[6 - 6 - \frac{1}{2}(2)] = -1$ $O_C[6 - 4 - \frac{1}{2}(4)] = 0$

Formal charges: (−2) (0) (+1) (−1) (0) (0) (0) (0) (−1)

Resonance forms: A B C

Copyright © The McGraw-Hill Companies, Inc. Permission required for reproduction or display.

Exceptions to the Octet Rule

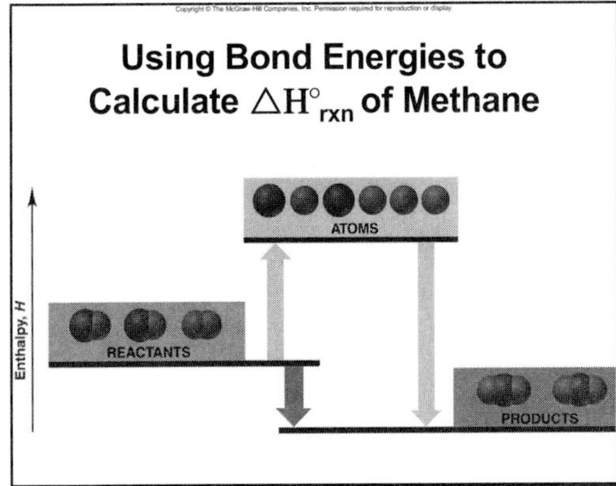
Copyright © The McGraw-Hill Companies, Inc. Permission required for reproduction or display
Using Bond Energies to Calculate △H°rxn of Methane
ATOMS
Enthalpy, H
REACTANTS
PRODUCTS

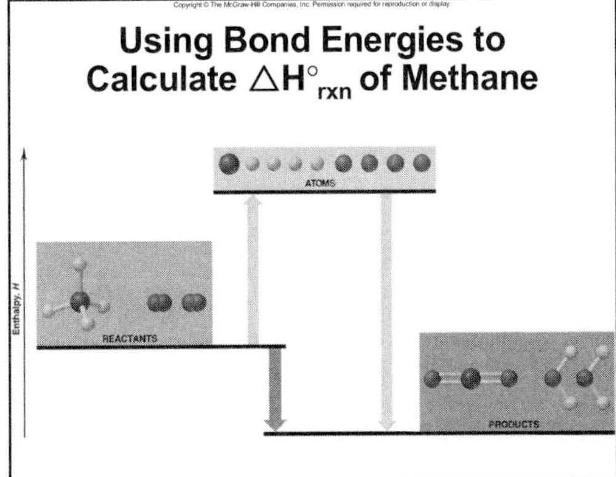
Copyright © The McGraw-Hill Companies, Inc. Permission required for reproduction or display
Using Bond Energies to Calculate △H°rxn of Methane
ATOMS
Enthalpy, H
REACTANTS
PRODUCTS

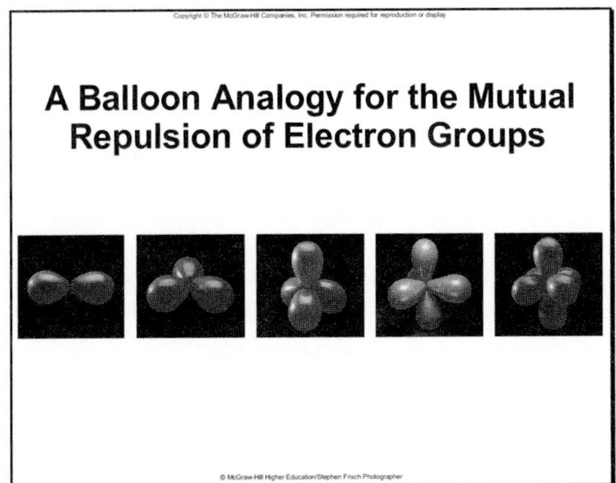
Copyright © The McGraw-Hill Companies, Inc. Permission required for reproduction or display
A Balloon Analogy for the Mutual Repulsion of Electron Groups
© McGraw-Hill Higher Education/Stephen Frisch Photographer

Electron-Group Repulsions and the Five Basic Molecular Shapes

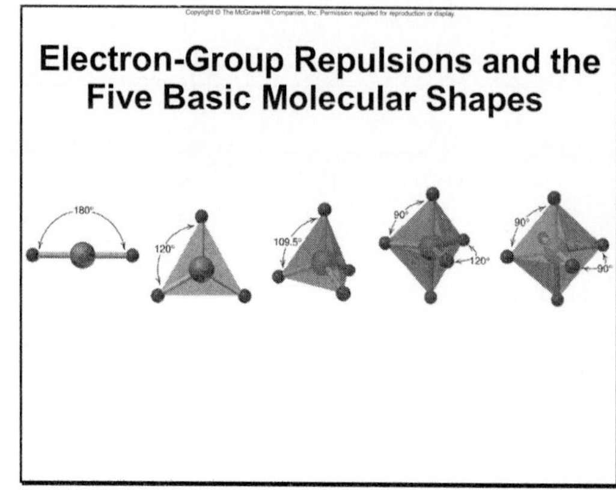

The Single Molecular Shape of the Linear Electron-Group Arrangement

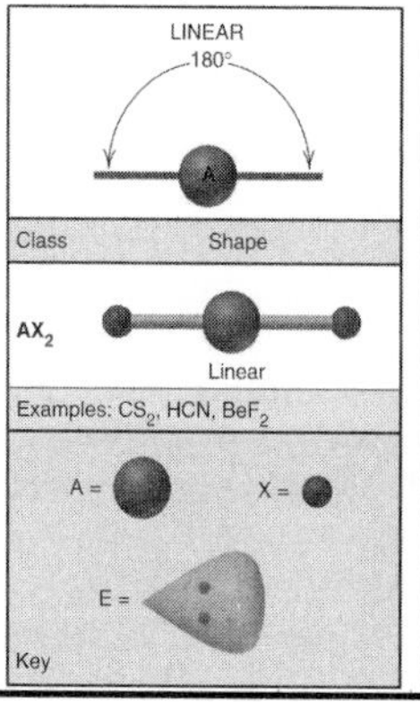

The Two Molecular Shapes of the Trigonal Planar Electron-Group Arrangement

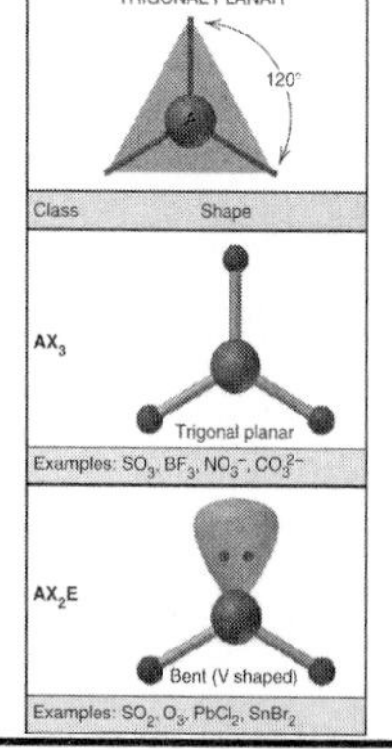

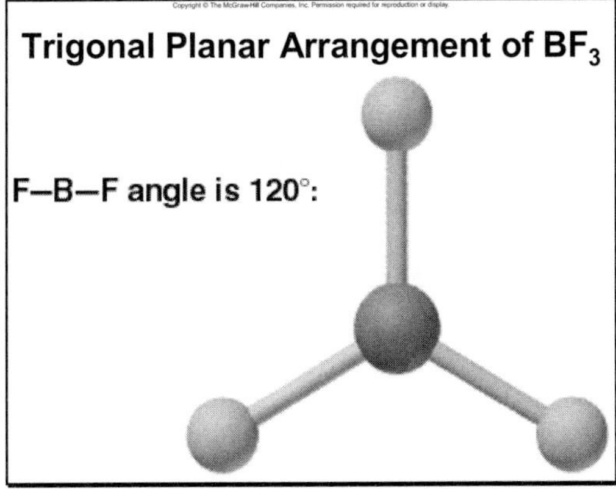
Copyright © The McGraw-Hill Companies, Inc. Permission required for reproduction or display.
Trigonal Planar Arrangement of BF3
F—B—F angle is 120°:

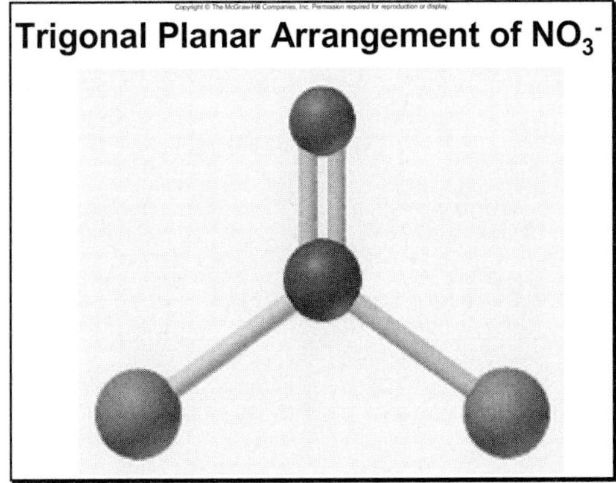
Copyright © The McGraw-Hill Companies, Inc. Permission required for reproduction or display.
Trigonal Planar Arrangement of NO3-

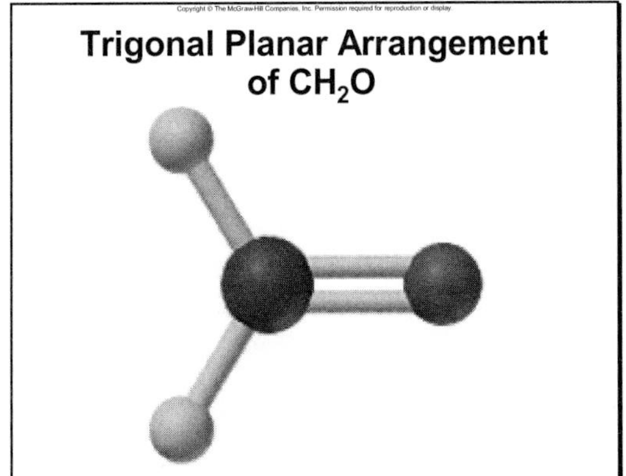
Copyright © The McGraw-Hill Companies, Inc. Permission required for reproduction or display.
Trigonal Planar Arrangement of CH2O

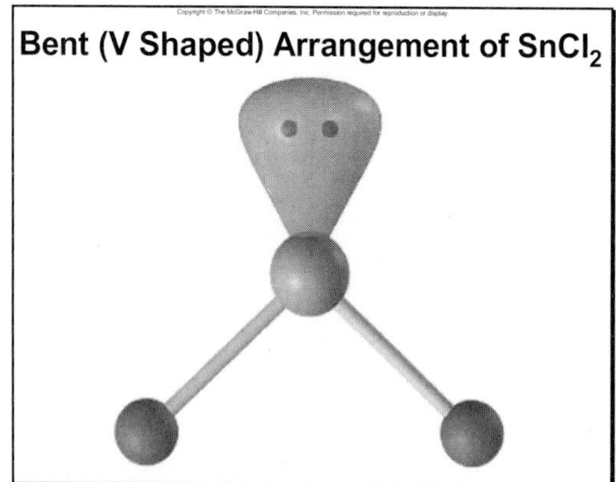
Copyright © The McGraw-Hill Companies, Inc. Permission required for reproduction or display.
Bent (V Shaped) Arrangement of $SnCl_2$

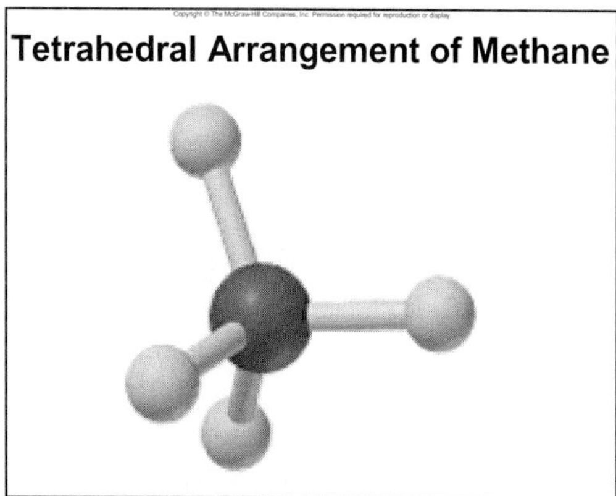
Copyright © The McGraw-Hill Companies, Inc. Permission required for reproduction or display.
Tetrahedral Arrangement of Methane

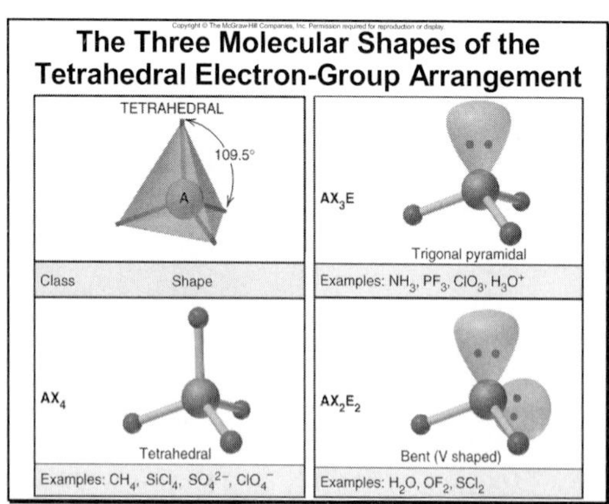
Copyright © The McGraw-Hill Companies, Inc. Permission required for reproduction or display.
The Three Molecular Shapes of the Tetrahedral Electron-Group Arrangement
TETRAHEDRAL
109.5°
A
Class
Shape
AX_3E
Trigonal pyramidal
Examples: NH_3, PF_3, ClO_3, H_3O^+
AX_4
Tetrahedral
Examples: CH_4, $SiCl_4$, SO_4^{2-}, ClO_4^-
AX_2E_2
Bent (V shaped)
Examples: H_2O, OF_2, SCl_2

Lewis Structures and Molecular Shapes

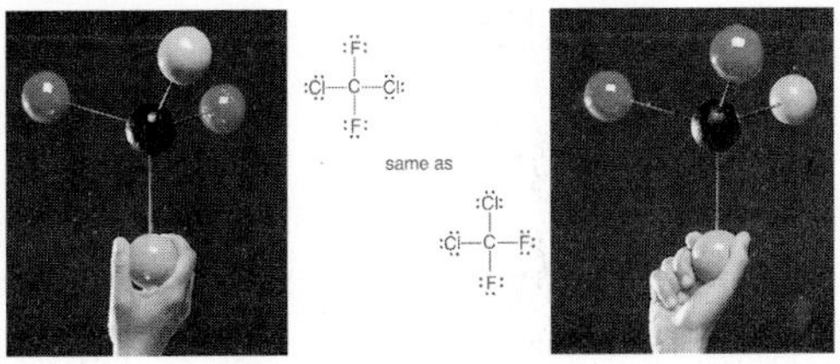

same as

Trigonal Pyramidal Shape of Tetrahedral Arrangement

$+ H^+ \longrightarrow$

Bent or V Shaped Tetrahedral Arrangement

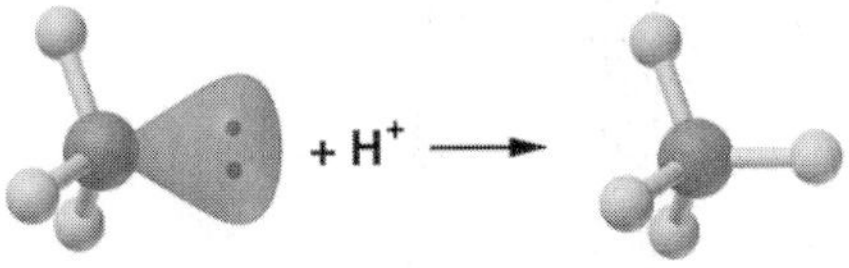

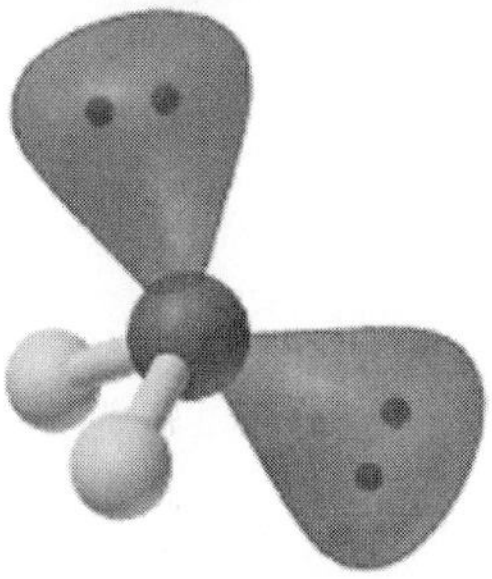

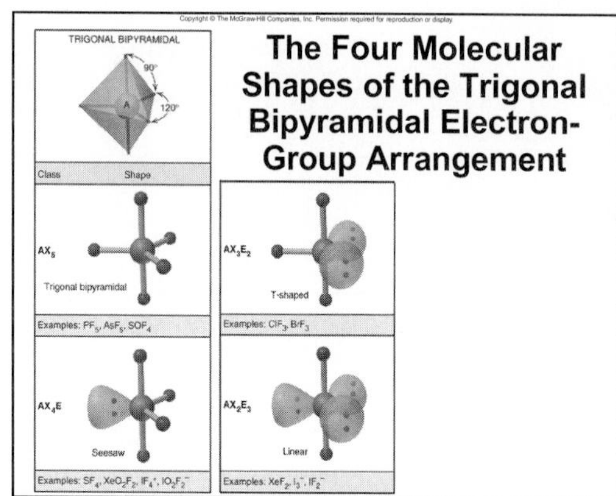

Copyright © The McGraw-Hill Companies, Inc. Permission required for reproduction or display.
The Four Molecular Shapes of the Trigonal Bipyramidal Electron-Group Arrangement
TRIGONAL BIPYRAMIDAL
90°
A
120°
Class
Shape
AX_5
Trigonal bipyramidal
Examples: PF_5, AsF_5, SOF_4
AX_3E_2
T-shaped
Examples: ClF_3, BrF_3
AX_4E
Seesaw
Examples: SF_4, XeO_2F_2, IF_4^+, $IO_2F_2^-$
AX_2E_3
Linear
Examples: XeF_2, I_3^-, IF_2^-

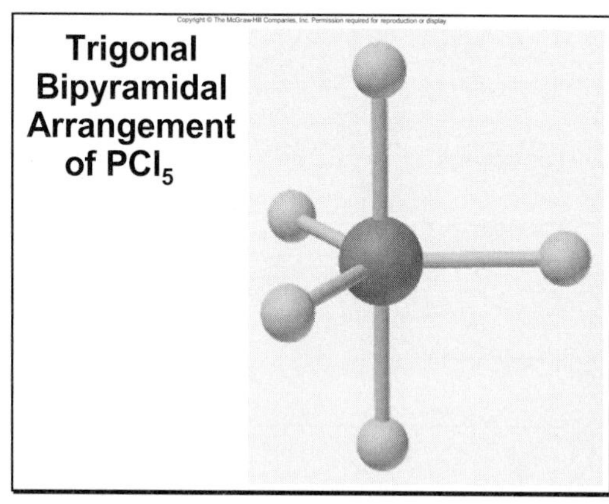

Trigonal Bipyramidal Arrangement of PCl_5

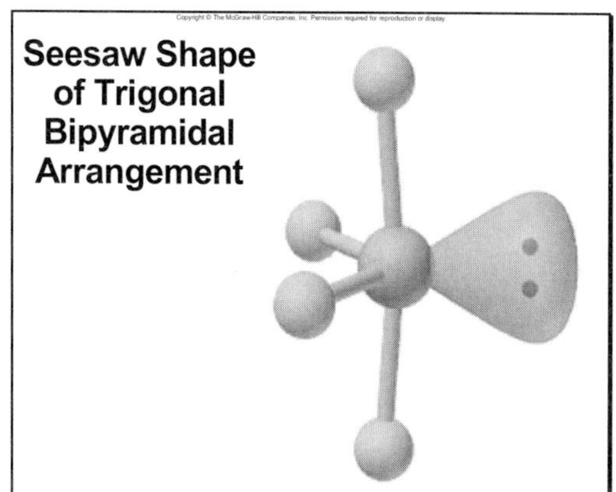

Seesaw Shape of Trigonal Bipyramidal Arrangement

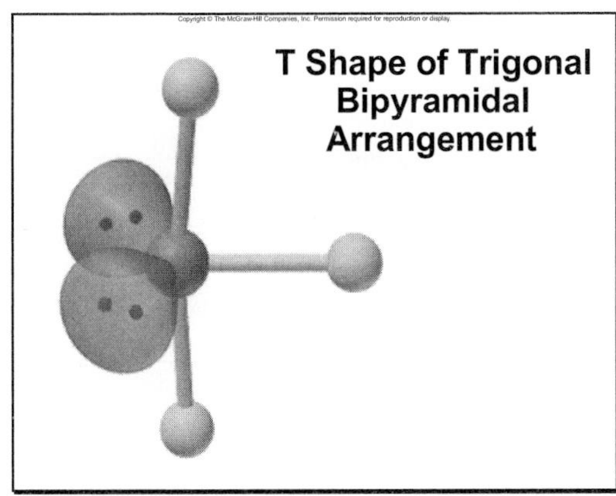

Copyright © The McGraw-Hill Companies, Inc. Permission required for reproduction or display.
T Shape of Trigonal Bipyramidal Arrangement

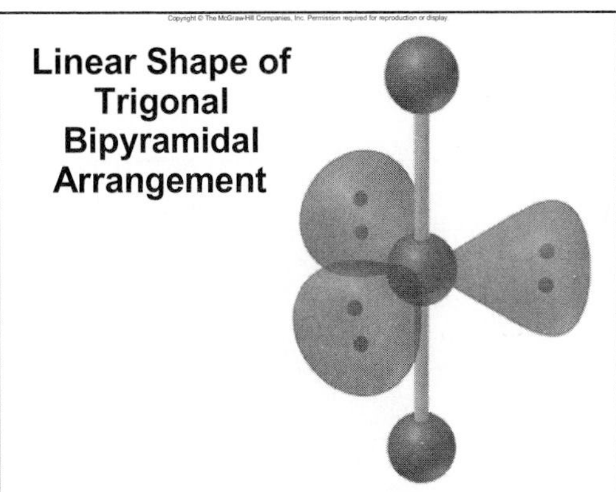

Copyright © The McGraw-Hill Companies, Inc. Permission required for reproduction or display.
Linear Shape of Trigonal Bipyramidal Arrangement

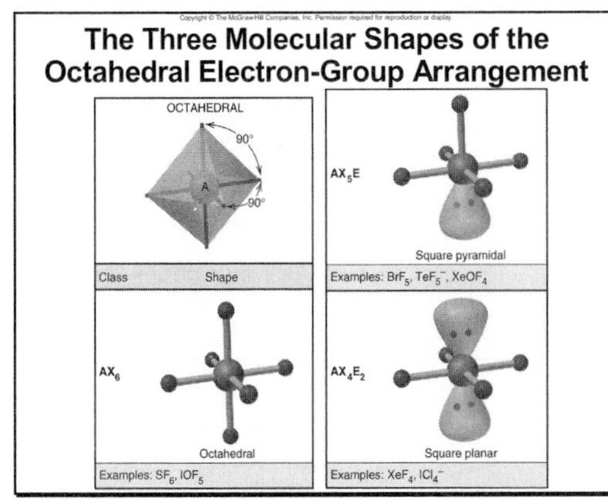

Copyright © The McGraw-Hill Companies, Inc. Permission required for reproduction or display.
The Three Molecular Shapes of the Octahedral Electron-Group Arrangement
OCTAHEDRAL
90°
A
90°
Class
Shape
AX$_5$E
Square pyramidal
Examples: BrF_5, TeF_5^-, $XeOF_4$
AX$_6$
Octahedral
Examples: SF_6, IOF_5
AX$_4$E$_2$
Square planar
Examples: XeF_4, ICl_4^-

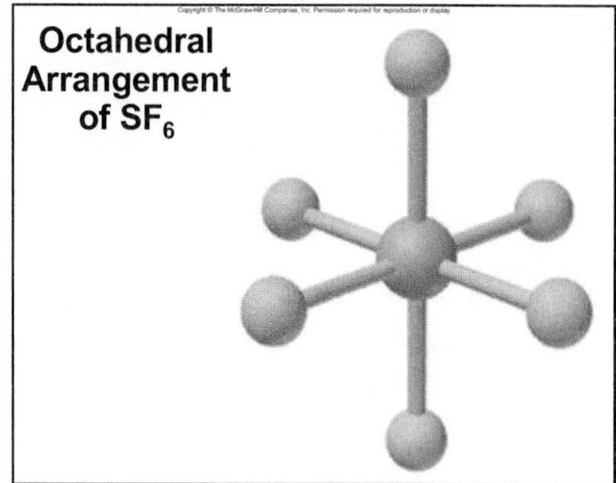
Copyright © The McGraw-Hill Companies, Inc. Permission required for reproduction or display.
Octahedral Arrangement of SF_6

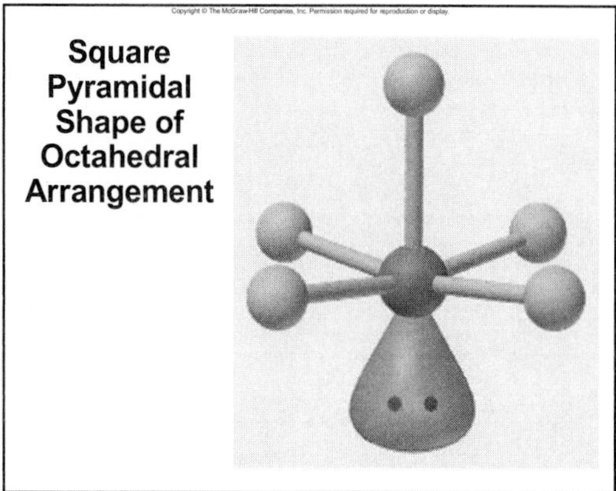
Copyright © The McGraw-Hill Companies, Inc. Permission required for reproduction or display.
Square Pyramidal Shape of Octahedral Arrangement

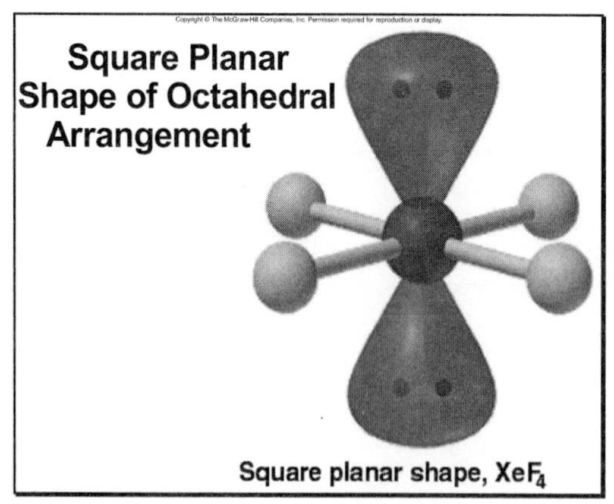
Copyright © The McGraw-Hill Companies, Inc. Permission required for reproduction or display.
Square Planar Shape of Octahedral Arrangement
Square planar shape, XeF_4

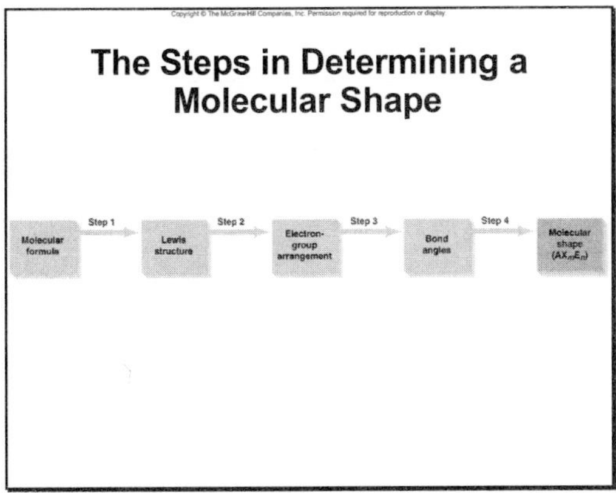
Copyright © The McGraw-Hill Companies, Inc. Permission required for reproduction or display.
The Steps in Determining a Molecular Shape
Molecular formula
Step 1
Lewis structure
Step 2
Electron-group arrangement
Step 3
Bond angles
Step 4
Molecular shape (AX_mE_n)

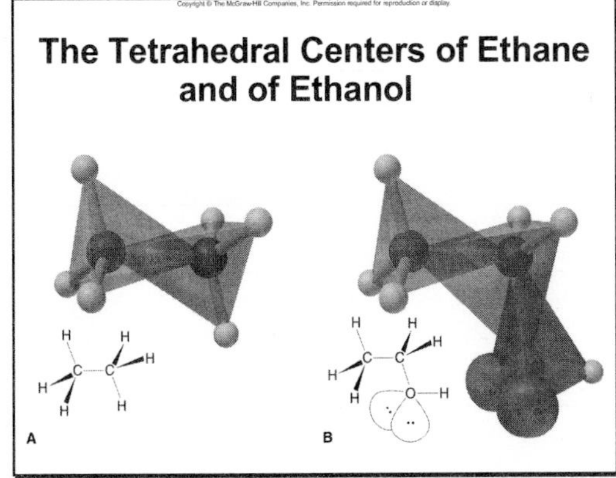
Copyright © The McGraw-Hill Companies, Inc. Permission required for reproduction or display.
The Tetrahedral Centers of Ethane and of Ethanol
A
B

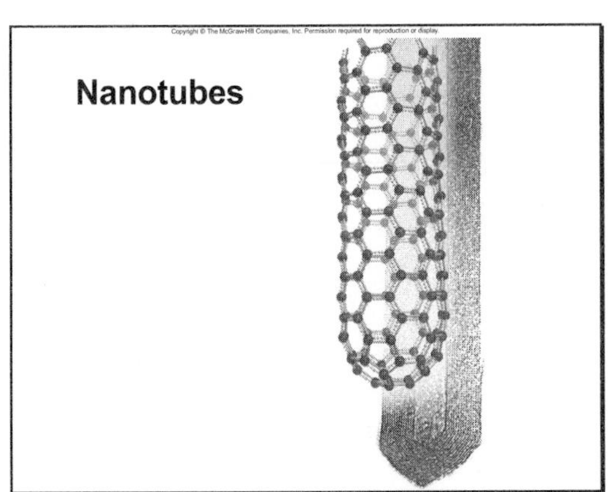
Copyright © The McGraw-Hill Companies, Inc. Permission required for reproduction or display.
Nanotubes

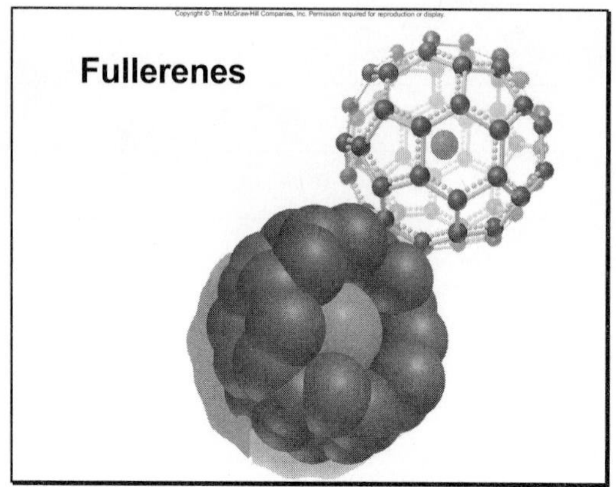
Fullerenes

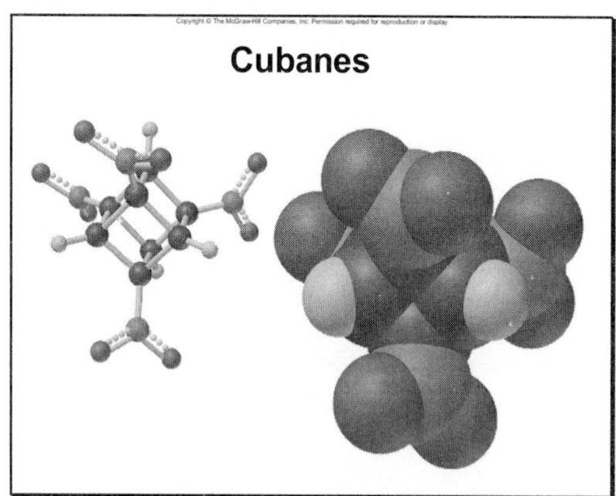
Cubanes

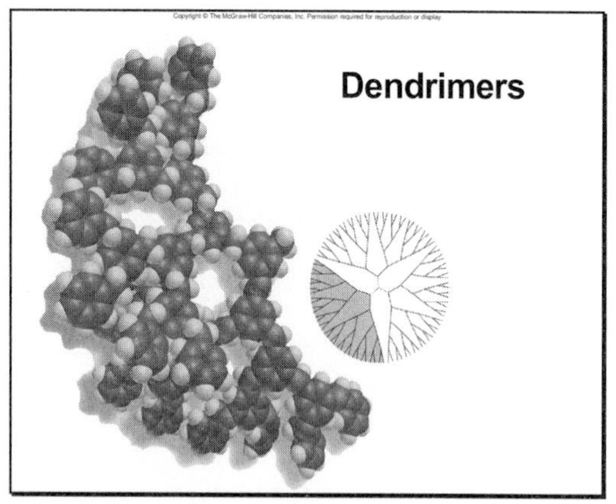
Dendrimers

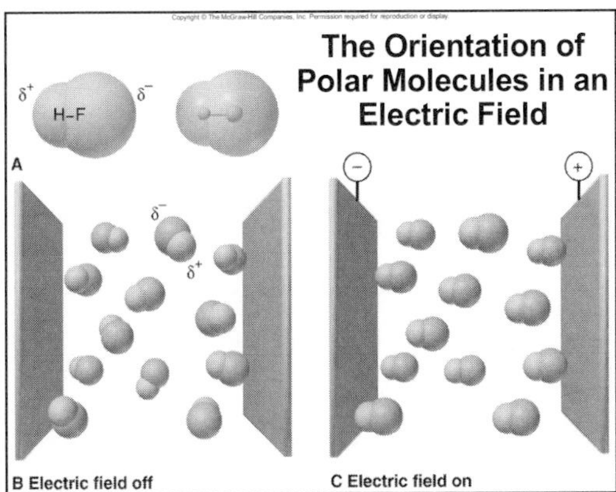
Copyright © The McGraw-Hill Companies, Inc. Permission required for reproduction or display.
The Orientation of Polar Molecules in an Electric Field
δ+
H–F
δ−
A
δ−
δ+
B Electric field off
C Electric field on

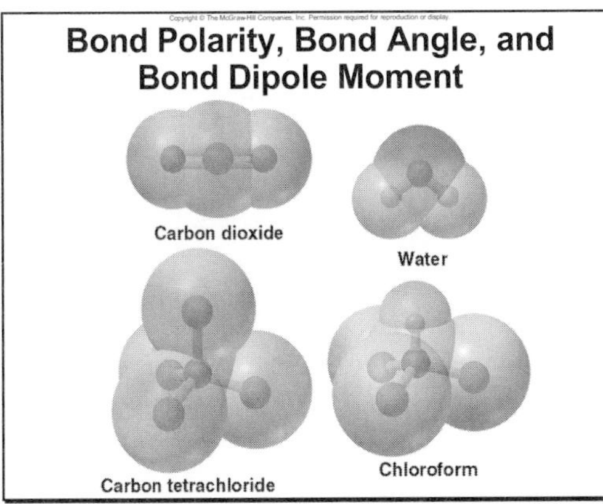
Copyright © The McGraw-Hill Companies, Inc. Permission required for reproduction or display.
Bond Polarity, Bond Angle, and Bond Dipole Moment
Carbon dioxide
Water
Carbon tetrachloride
Chloroform

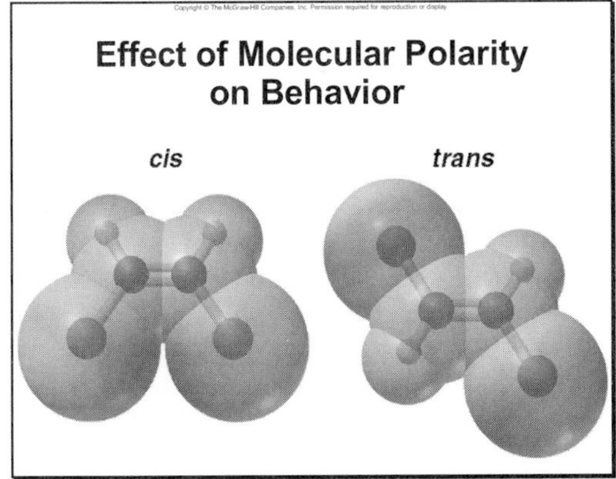
Copyright © The McGraw-Hill Companies, Inc. Permission required for reproduction or display.
Effect of Molecular Polarity on Behavior
cis
trans

The Location of Olfactory Receptors Within the Nose

Brain
Air flow
Lining of olfactory bulb in nasal passage
A
Olfactory bulb
Olfactory nerve cell
Mucus
Nasal passage
Olfactory hairs
B
Odorous molecule
Receptor on olfactory hair
C

Shapes of Some Olfactory Receptor Sites

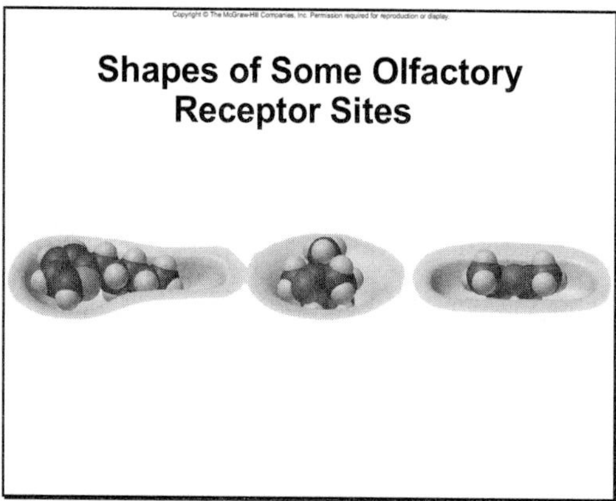

Different Molecules With the Same Odor

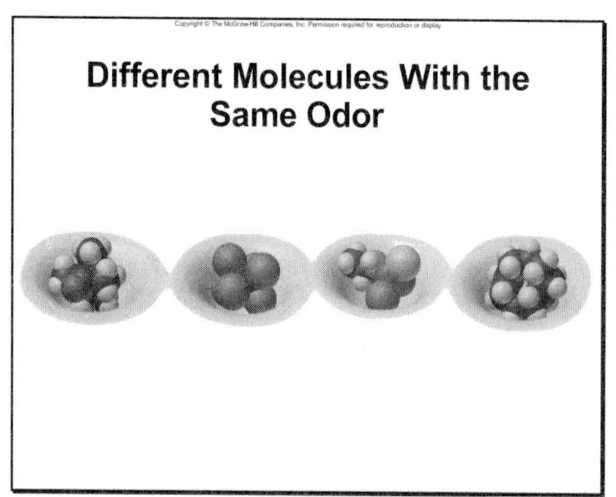

Chapter 11

Chemistry: The Molecular Nature of Matter and Change

Third Edition

Martin S. Silberberg

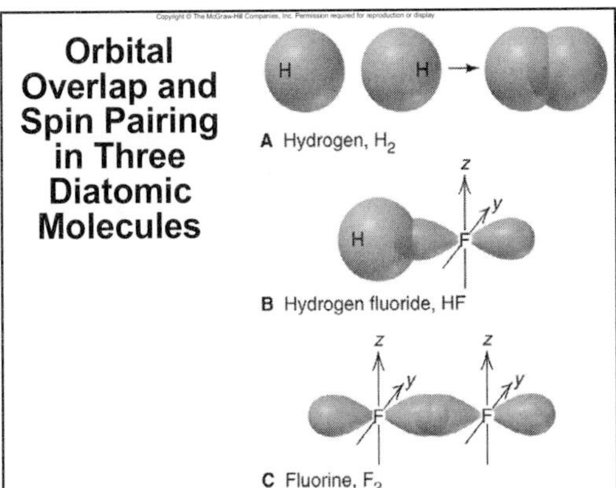

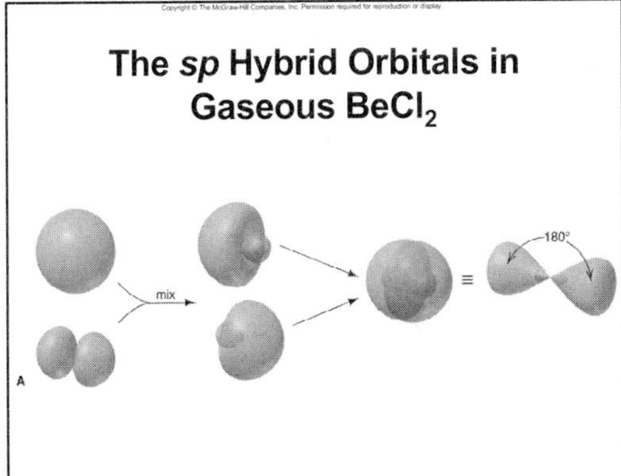

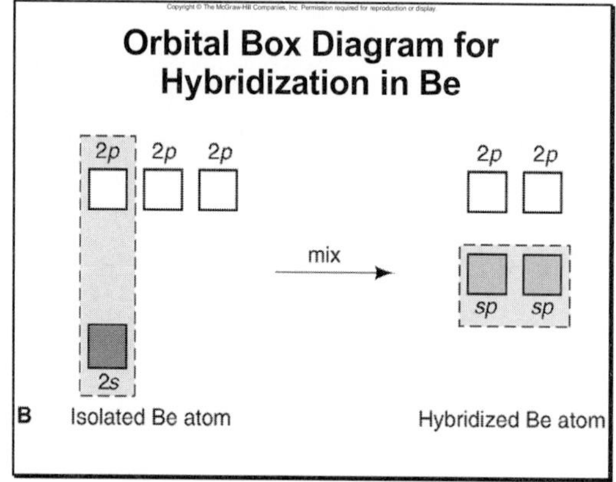
Copyright © The McGraw-Hill Companies, Inc. Permission required for reproduction or display
Orbital Box Diagram for Hybridization in Be
2p
2p
2p
2s
mix
2p
2p
sp
sp
B
Isolated Be atom
Hybridized Be atom

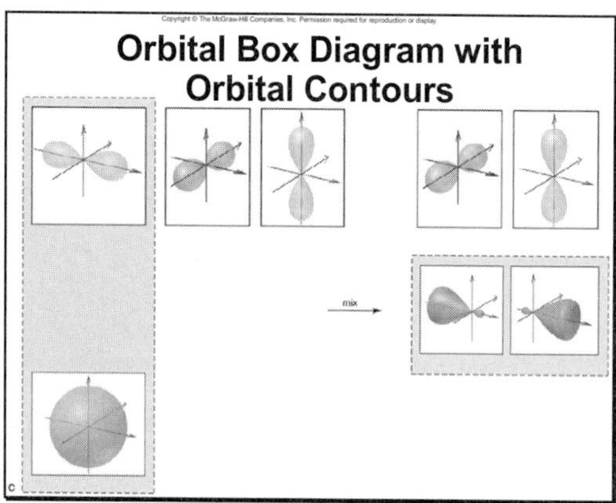
Copyright © The McGraw-Hill Companies, Inc. Permission required for reproduction or display
Orbital Box Diagram with Orbital Contours
mix
C

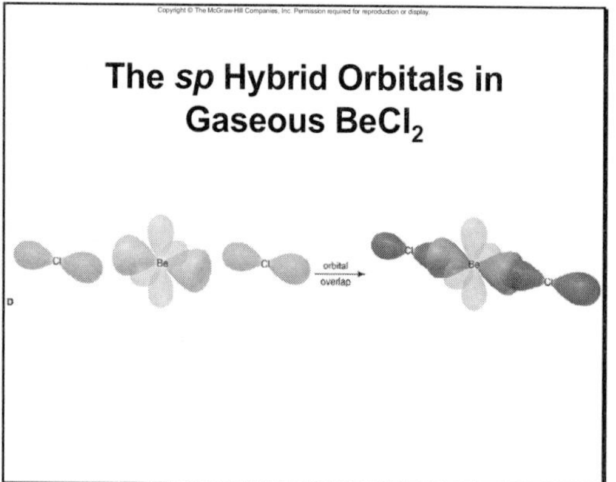
Copyright © The McGraw-Hill Companies, Inc. Permission required for reproduction or display
The sp Hybrid Orbitals in Gaseous BeCl2
Cl
Be
Cl
orbital overlap
D

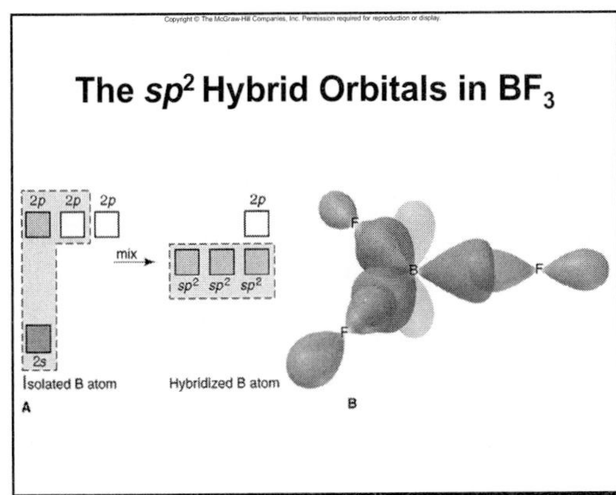
Copyright © The McGraw-Hill Companies, Inc. Permission required for reproduction or display.
The sp² Hybrid Orbitals in BF₃
2p
2p
2p
mix
sp² sp² sp²
2s
Isolated B atom
Hybridized B atom
A
B
F
B
F
F

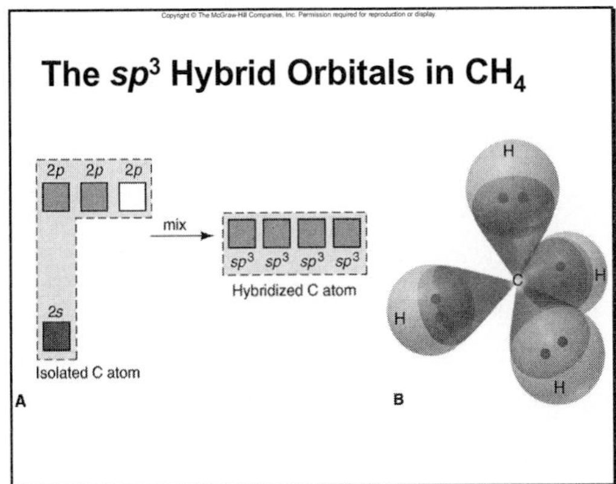
Copyright © The McGraw-Hill Companies, Inc. Permission required for reproduction or display.
The sp³ Hybrid Orbitals in CH₄
2p 2p 2p
mix
sp³ sp³ sp³ sp³
Hybridized C atom
2s
Isolated C atom
A
B
H
C
H
H
H

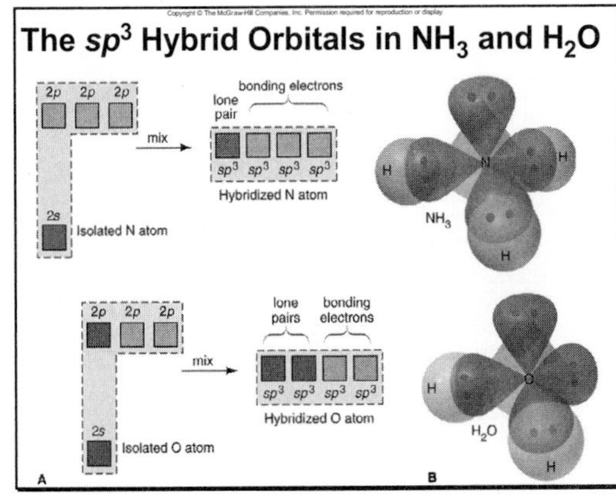
Copyright © The McGraw-Hill Companies, Inc. Permission required for reproduction or display.
The sp³ Hybrid Orbitals in NH₃ and H₂O
2p 2p 2p
bonding electrons
lone pair
mix
sp³ sp³ sp³ sp³
Hybridized N atom
2s
Isolated N atom
NH₃
2p 2p 2p
lone pairs
bonding electrons
mix
sp³ sp³ sp³ sp³
Hybridized O atom
2s
Isolated O atom
H₂O
A
B

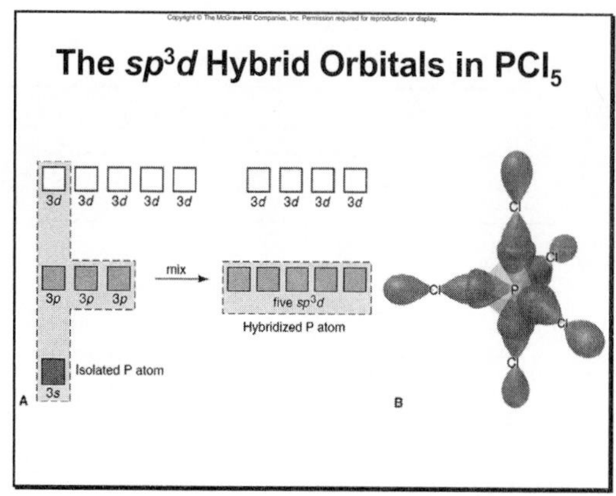

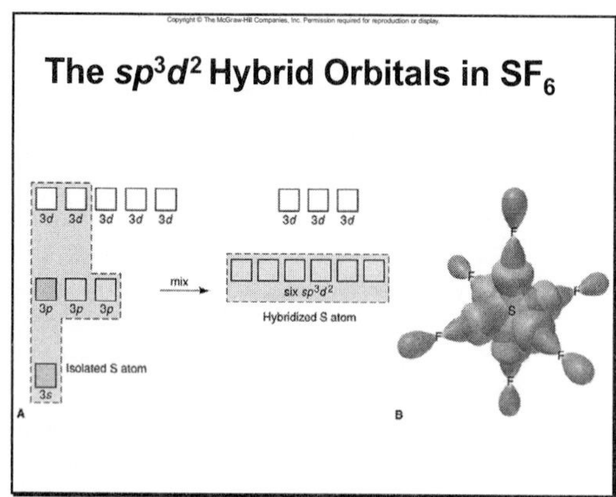

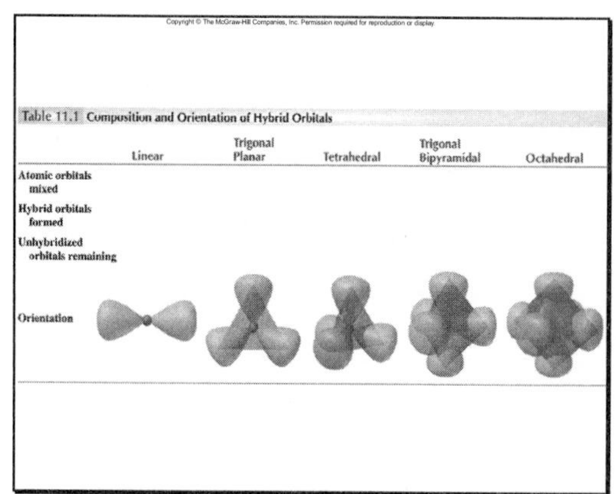
Table 11.1 Composition and Orientation of Hybrid Orbitals

	Linear	Trigonal Planar	Tetrahedral	Trigonal Bipyramidal	Octahedral
Atomic orbitals mixed					
Hybrid orbitals formed					
Unhybridized orbitals remaining					
Orientation					

The Conceptual Steps From Molecular Formula to the Hybrid Orbitals Used in Bonding

Molecular formula → Step 1 → Lewis structure → Step 2 → Molecular shape and e^--group arrangement → Step 3 → Hybrid orbitals

When the Concept of Hybridization May Not Apply

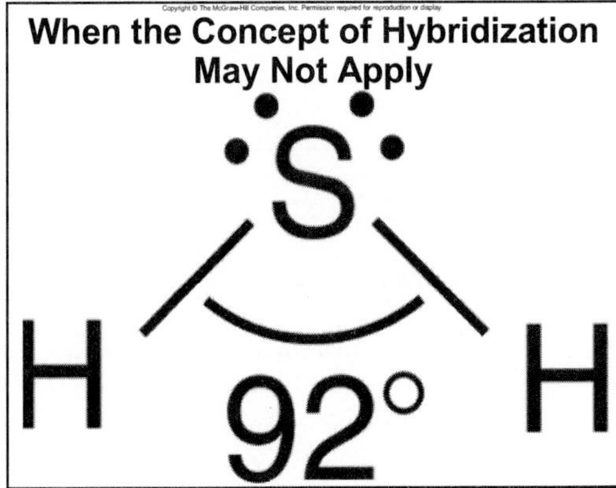

VB Treatment of Single and Multiple Bonds

~109.5°

ethane

~120°

ethylene

180°

H—C≡C—H

acetylene

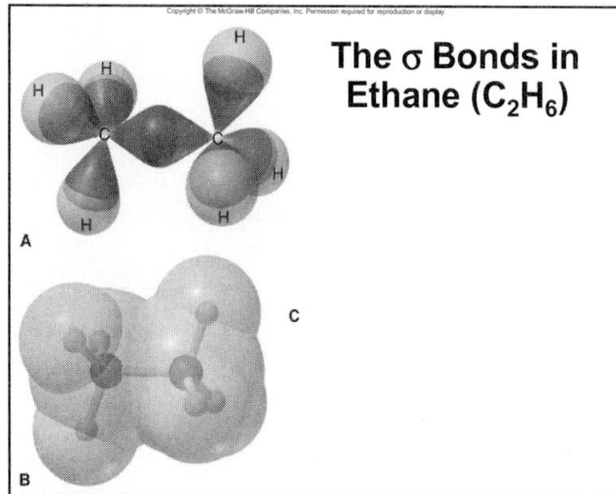
Copyright © The McGraw-Hill Companies, Inc. Permission required for reproduction or display.
The σ Bonds in Ethane (C_2H_6)
H
H
H
C
C
H
H
H
A
B
C

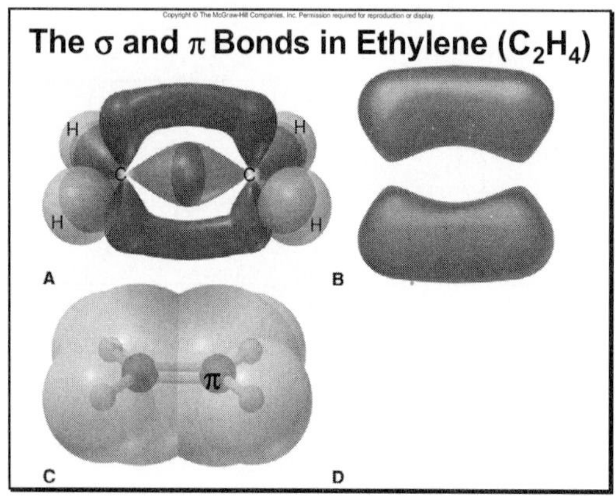
Copyright © The McGraw-Hill Companies, Inc. Permission required for reproduction or display.
The σ and π Bonds in Ethylene (C_2H_4)
H
H
C
C
H
H
A
B
π
C
D

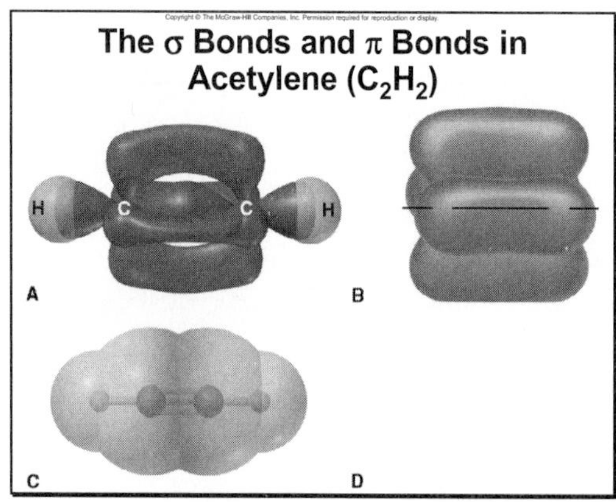
Copyright © The McGraw-Hill Companies, Inc. Permission required for reproduction or display.
The σ Bonds and π Bonds in Acetylene (C_2H_2)
H
C
C
H
A
B
C
D

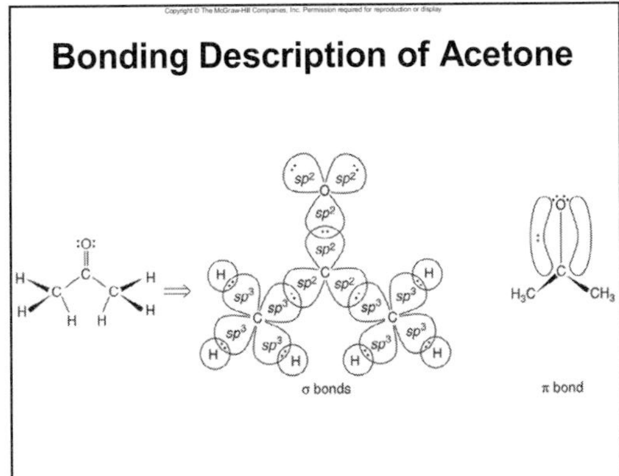
Bonding Description of Acetone
σ bonds
π bond

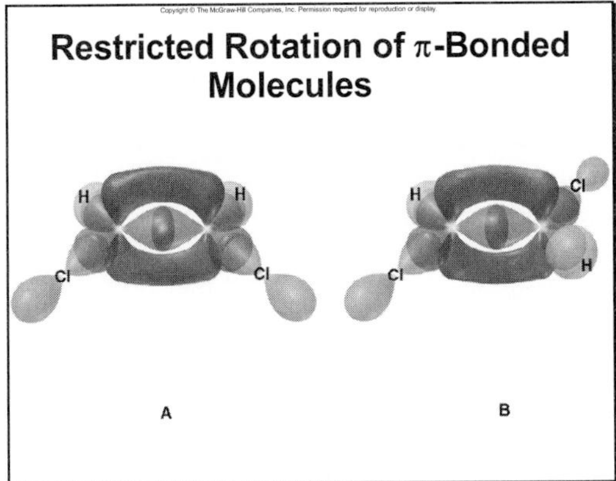
Restricted Rotation of π-Bonded Molecules
A
B

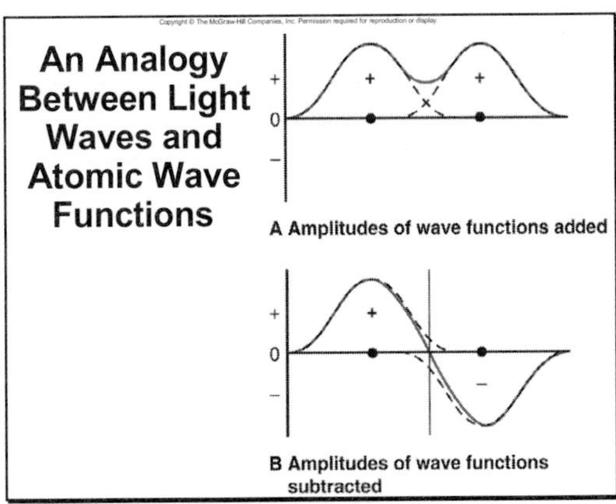
An Analogy Between Light Waves and Atomic Wave Functions
A Amplitudes of wave functions added
B Amplitudes of wave functions subtracted

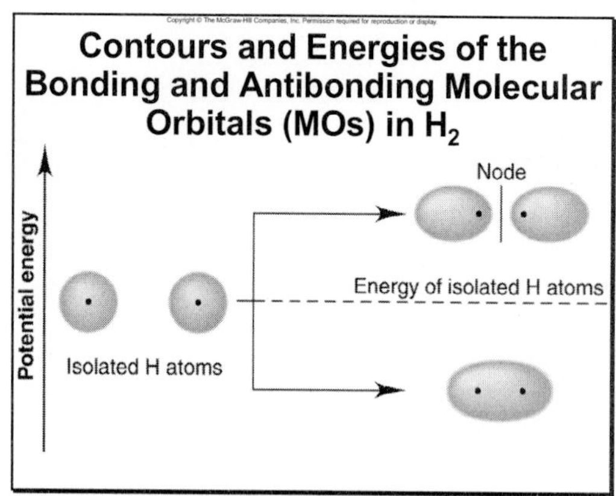
Contours and Energies of the Bonding and Antibonding Molecular Orbitals (MOs) in H_2
Potential energy
Node
Energy of isolated H atoms
Isolated H atoms

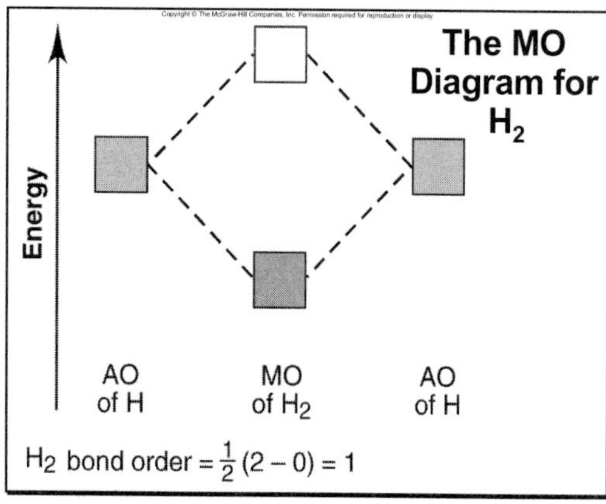
The MO Diagram for H_2
Energy
AO of H
MO of H_2
AO of H
H_2 bond order = $\frac{1}{2}(2 - 0) = 1$

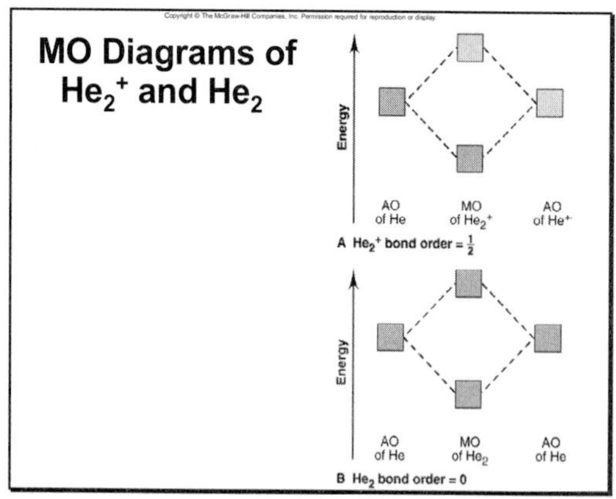
MO Diagrams of He_2^+ and He_2
Energy
AO of He
MO of He_2^+
AO of He^+
A He_2^+ bond order = $\frac{1}{2}$
Energy
AO of He
MO of He_2
AO of He
B He_2 bond order = 0

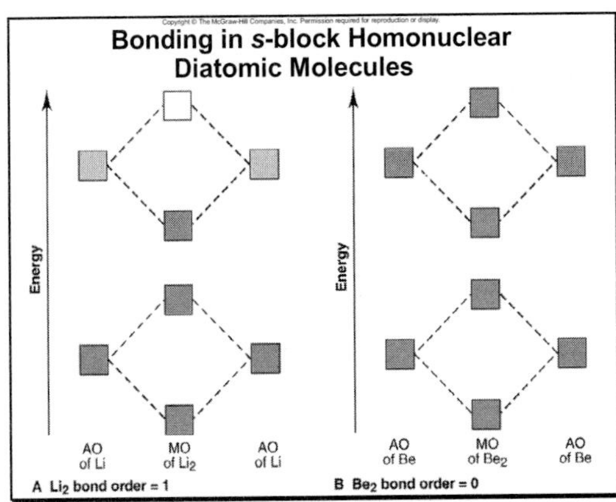
Copyright © The McGraw-Hill Companies, Inc. Permission required for reproduction or display.
Bonding in s-block Homonuclear Diatomic Molecules
Energy
AO of Li
MO of Li_2
AO of Li
A Li_2 bond order = 1
AO of Be
MO of Be_2
AO of Be
B Be_2 bond order = 0

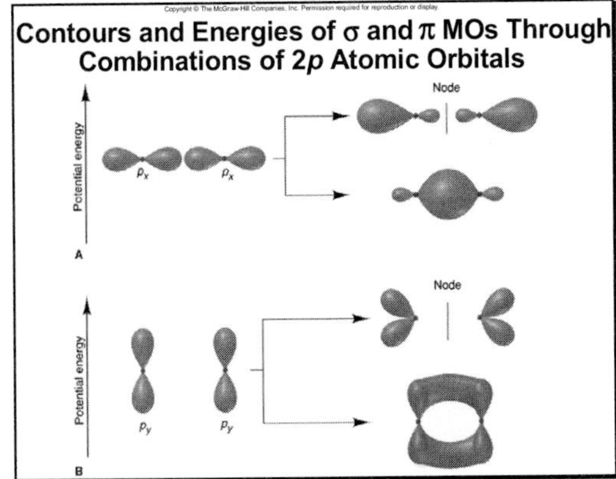
Copyright © The McGraw-Hill Companies, Inc. Permission required for reproduction or display.
Contours and Energies of σ and π MOs Through Combinations of 2p Atomic Orbitals
Potential energy
p_x
p_x
Node
A
Potential energy
p_y
p_y
Node
B

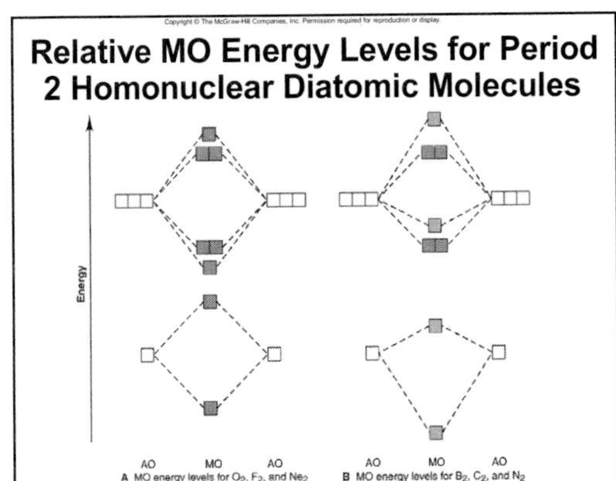
Copyright © The McGraw-Hill Companies, Inc. Permission required for reproduction or display.
Relative MO Energy Levels for Period 2 Homonuclear Diatomic Molecules
Energy
AO
MO
AO
A MO energy levels for O_2, F_2, and Ne_2
AO
MO
AO
B MO energy levels for B_2, C_2, and N_2

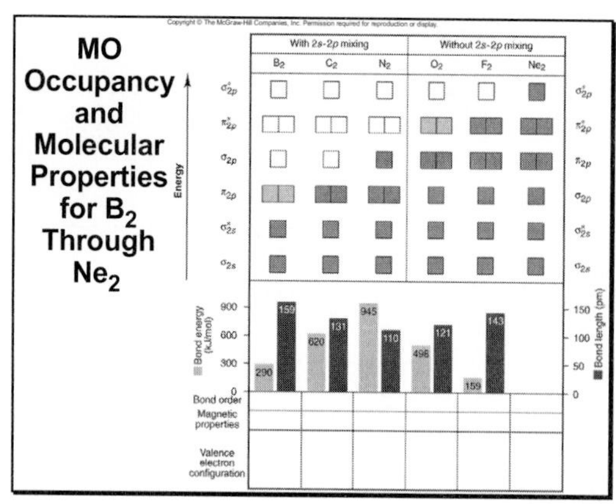
MO Occupancy and Molecular Properties for B_2 Through Ne_2
With 2s-2p mixing
Without 2s-2p mixing
Energy
Bond energy (kJ/mol)
Bond length (pm)
Bond order
Magnetic properties
Valence electron configuration

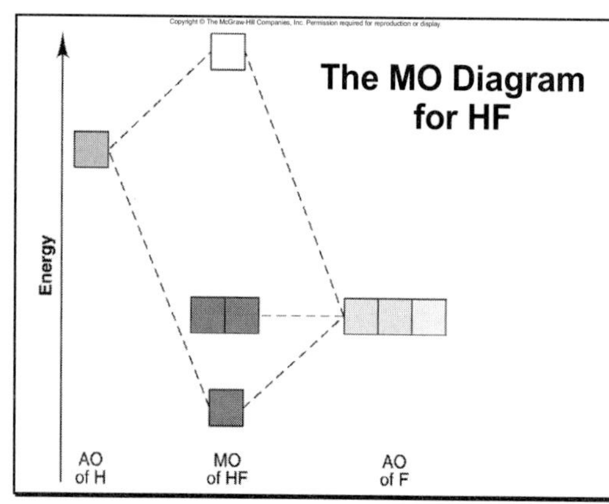
The MO Diagram for HF
Energy
AO of H
MO of HF
AO of F

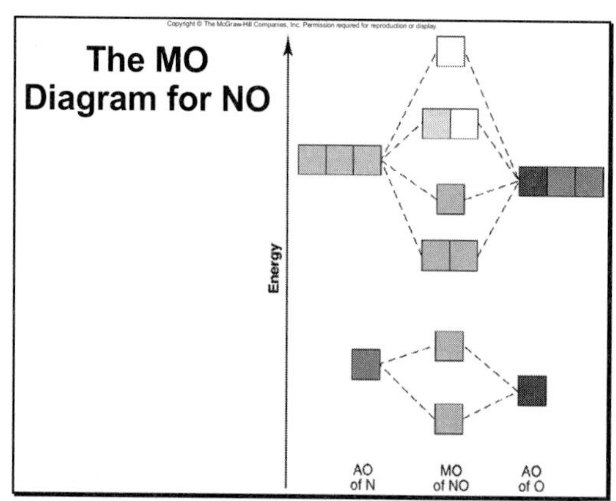
The MO Diagram for NO
Energy
AO of N
MO of NO
AO of O

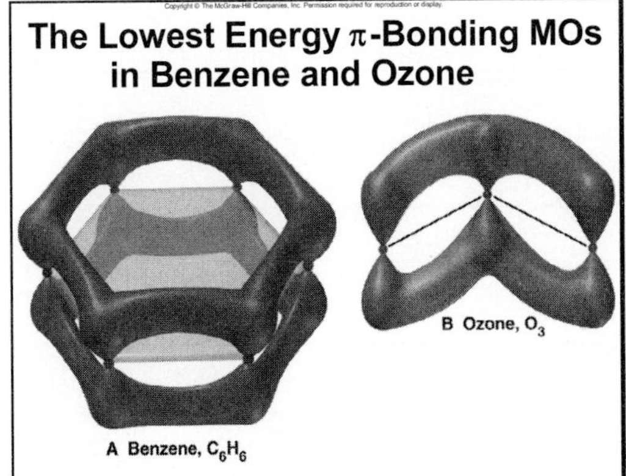
The Lowest Energy π-Bonding MOs in Benzene and Ozone
B Ozone, O3
A Benzene, C6H6

Chapter 12

Chemistry: The Molecular Nature of Matter and Change

Third Edition

Martin S. Silberberg

Table 12.1 A Macroscopic Comparison of Gases, Liquids, and Solids

State	Shape and Volume	Compressibility	Ability to Flow
Gas			
Liquid			
Solid			

Heats of Vaporization and Fusion for Several Common Substances

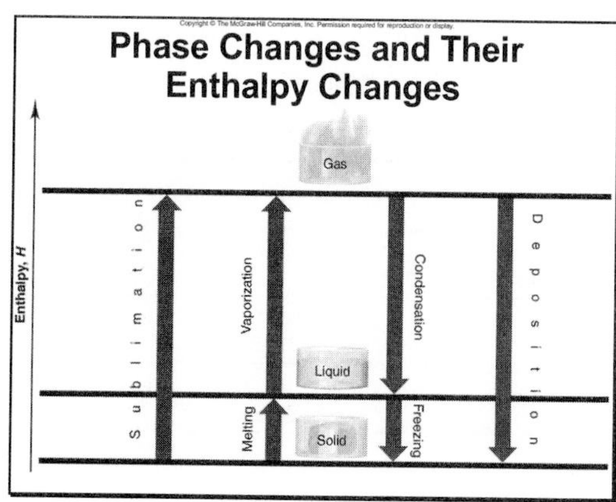
Copyright © The McGraw-Hill Companies, Inc. Permission required for reproduction or display.
Phase Changes and Their Enthalpy Changes
Enthalpy, H
Gas
Liquid
Solid
Sublimation
Vaporization
Condensation
Deposition
Melting
Freezing

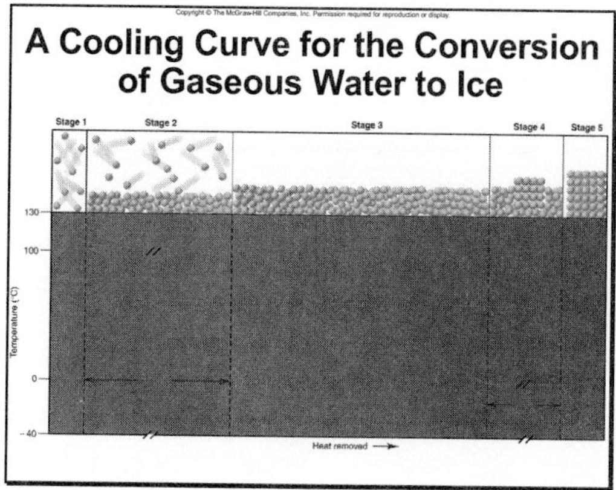
Copyright © The McGraw-Hill Companies, Inc. Permission required for reproduction or display.
A Cooling Curve for the Conversion of Gaseous Water to Ice
Stage 1
Stage 2
Stage 3
Stage 4
Stage 5
130
100
0
-40
Temperature (°C)
Heat removed

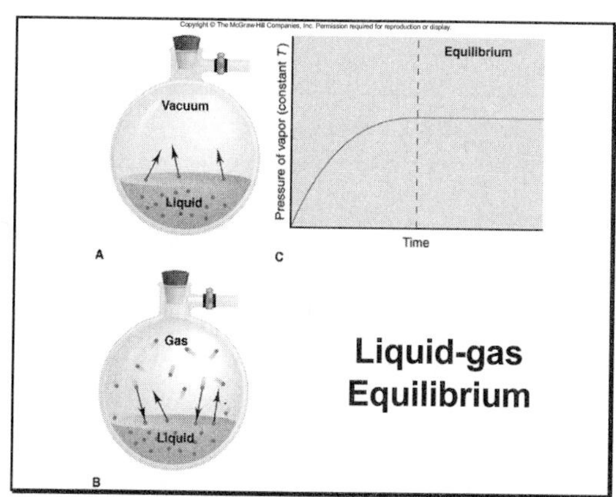
Copyright © The McGraw-Hill Companies, Inc. Permission required for reproduction or display.
Vacuum
Liquid
A
Gas
Liquid
B
Equilibrium
Pressure of vapor (constant T)
Time
C
Liquid-gas Equilibrium

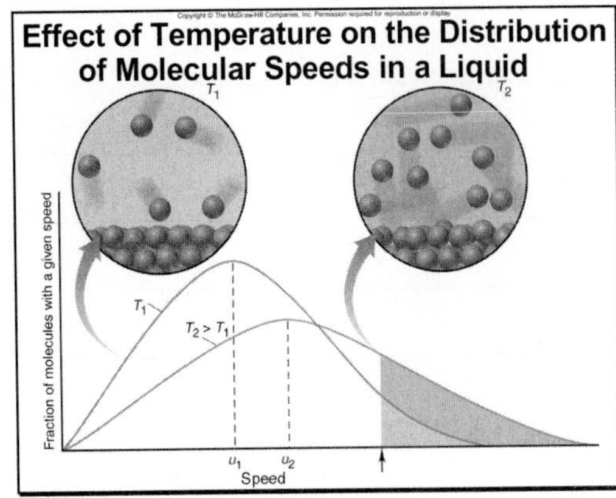
Copyright © The McGraw-Hill Companies, Inc. Permission required for reproduction or display.
Effect of Temperature on the Distribution of Molecular Speeds in a Liquid
T_1
T_2
Fraction of molecules with a given speed
T_1
$T_2 > T_1$
u_1
u_2
Speed

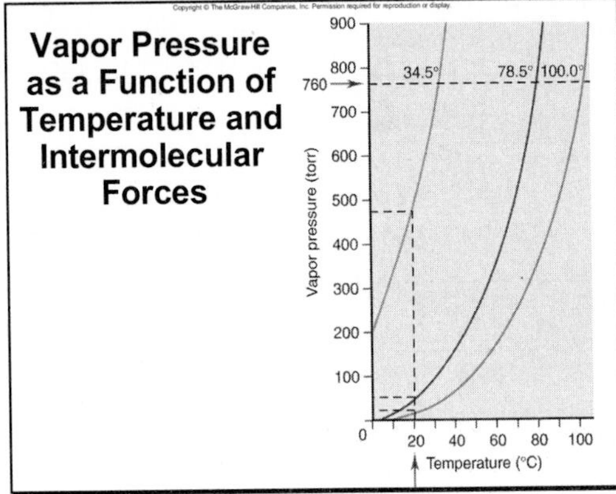
Copyright © The McGraw-Hill Companies, Inc. Permission required for reproduction or display.
Vapor Pressure as a Function of Temperature and Intermolecular Forces
Vapor pressure (torr)
900
800
760
700
600
500
400
300
200
100
0
34.5°
78.5°
100.0°
20
40
60
80
100
Temperature (°C)

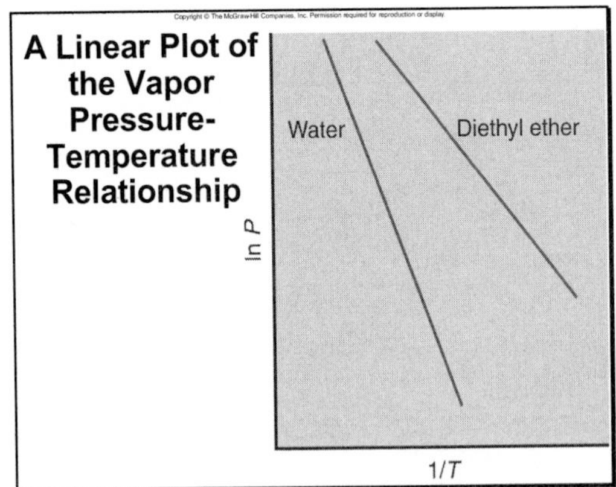
Copyright © The McGraw-Hill Companies, Inc. Permission required for reproduction or display.
A Linear Plot of the Vapor Pressure-Temperature Relationship
Water
Diethyl ether
ln P
1/T

Determination of Heat of Vaporization

$$\ln P = \frac{-\Delta H_{vap}}{R}\left(\frac{1}{T}\right) + C$$

$$y = m \quad x + b$$

$$\ln \frac{P_2}{P_1} = \frac{-\Delta H_{vap}}{R}\left(\frac{1}{T_2} - \frac{1}{T_1}\right) \qquad (12.1)$$

Phase Diagrams for CO_2 and H_2O

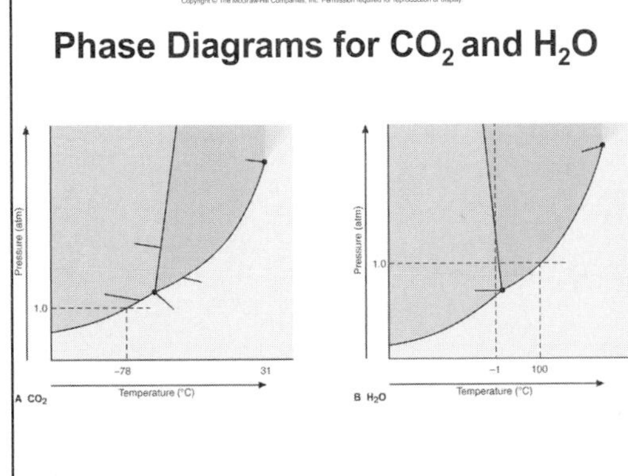

Covalent and van der Waals Radii

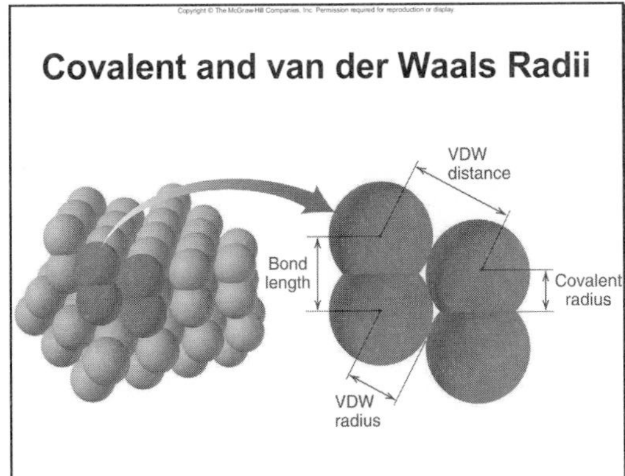

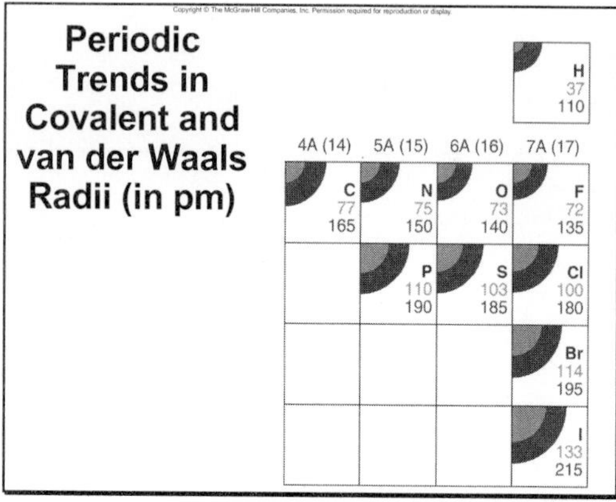

Table 12.2 Comparison of Bonding and Nonbonding (Intermolecular) Forces

Force	Model	Basis of Attraction	Energy (kJ/mol)	Example
Bonding				
Ionic				
Covalent				
Metallic				

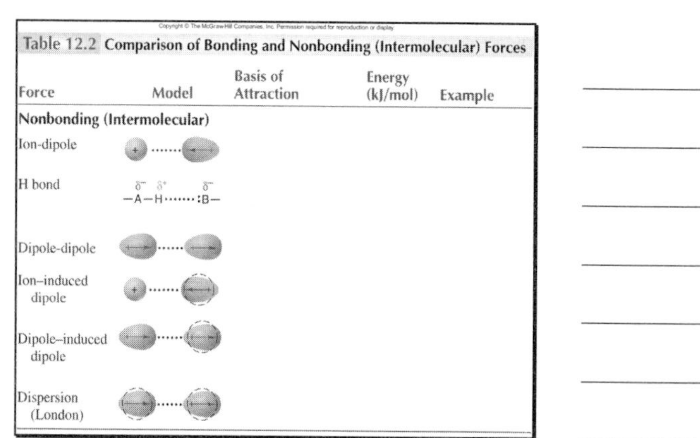

Table 12.2 Comparison of Bonding and Nonbonding (Intermolecular) Forces

Force	Model	Basis of Attraction	Energy (kJ/mol)	Example
Nonbonding (Intermolecular)				
Ion-dipole				
H bond	δ⁻ δ⁺ δ⁻ —A—H⋯⋯:B—			
Dipole-dipole				
Ion–induced dipole				
Dipole–induced dipole				
Dispersion (London)				

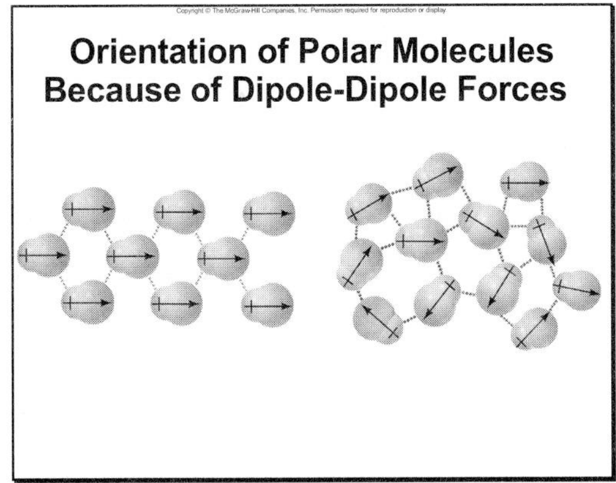

Dipole Moment and Boiling Point

Compound	Formula	Molar mass	Dipole moment (D x 100)	Boiling point (K)
Propane	$CH_3CH_2CH_3$	44.09 g/mol	8	231
Dimethyl ether	CH_3OCH_3	46.07 g/mol	130	248
Methyl chloride	CH_3Cl	50.48 g/mol	187	249
Acetaldehyde	CH_3CHO	44.05 g/mol	269	294
Acetonitrile	CH_3CN	41.05 g/mol	392	355

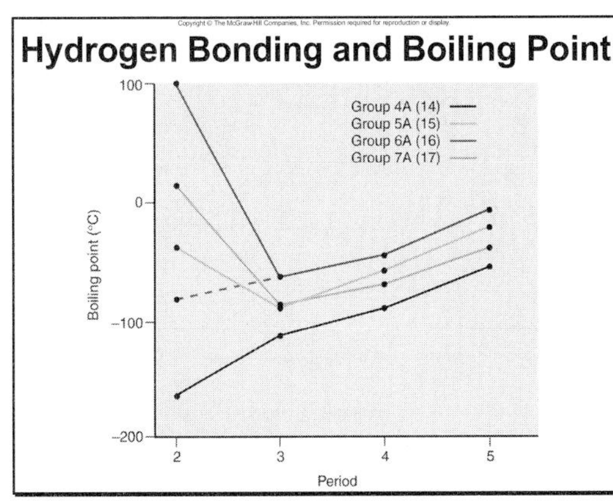

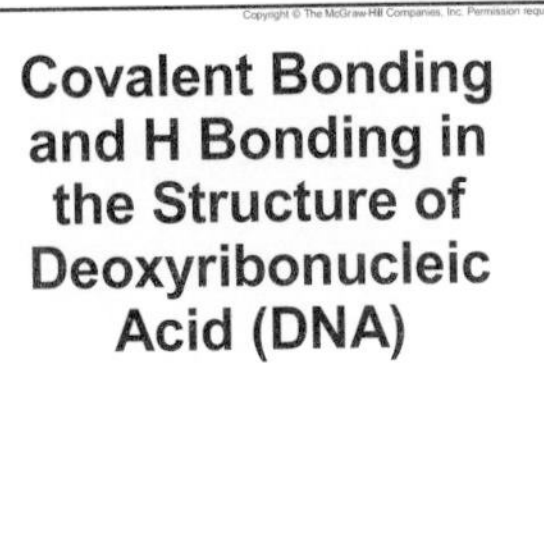

Covalent Bonding and H Bonding in the Structure of Deoxyribonucleic Acid (DNA)

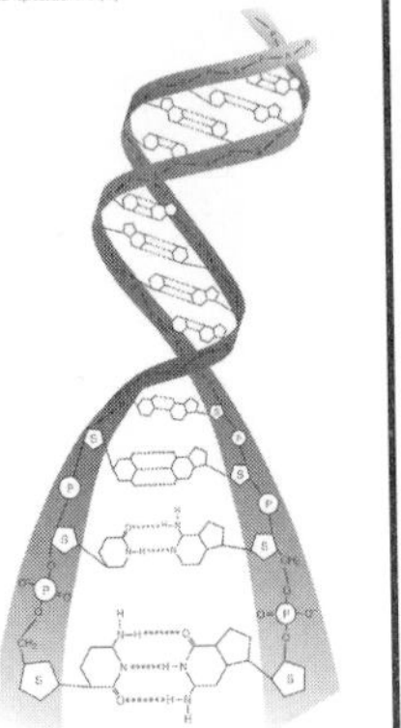

Dispersion Forces Among Nonpolar Molecules

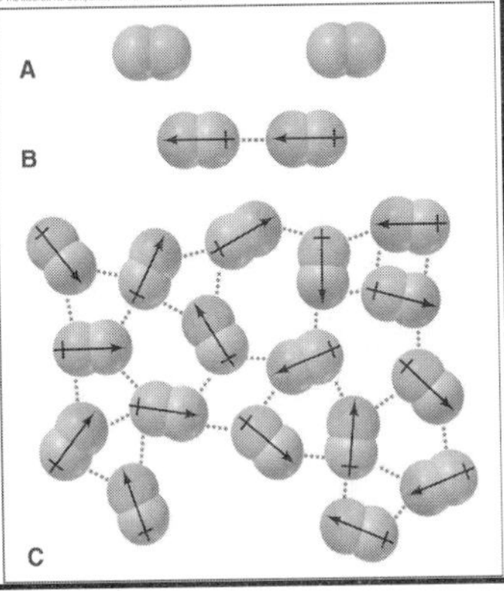

Molar Mass and Boiling Point

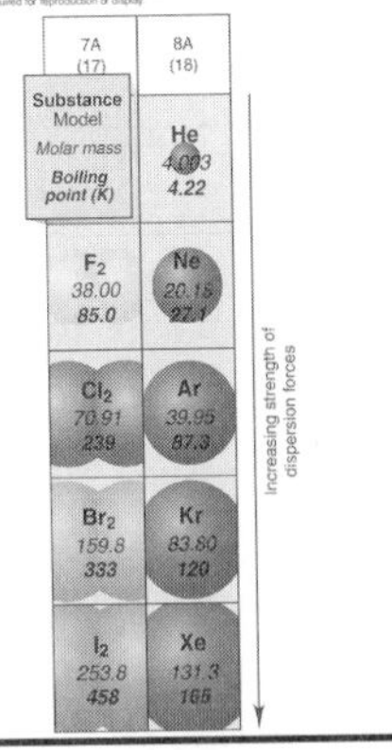

Molecular Shape and Boiling Point

n-Pentane, bp = 36.1°C

Neopentane, bp = 9.5°C

The Molecular Basis of Surface Tension

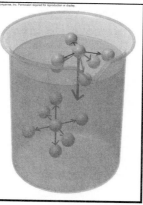

Table 12.3 Surface Tension and Forces Between Particles

Substance	Formula	Surface Tension (J/m^2) at 20°C	Major Force(s)
Diethyl ether	$CH_3CH_2OCH_2CH_3$	1.7×10^{-2}	
Ethanol	CH_3CH_2OH	2.3×10^{-2}	
Butanol	$CH_3CH_2CH_2CH_2OH$	2.5×10^{-2}	
Water	H_2O	7.3×10^{-2}	
Mercury	Hg	48×10^{-2}	

Shape of the Water or Mercury Meniscus in Glass

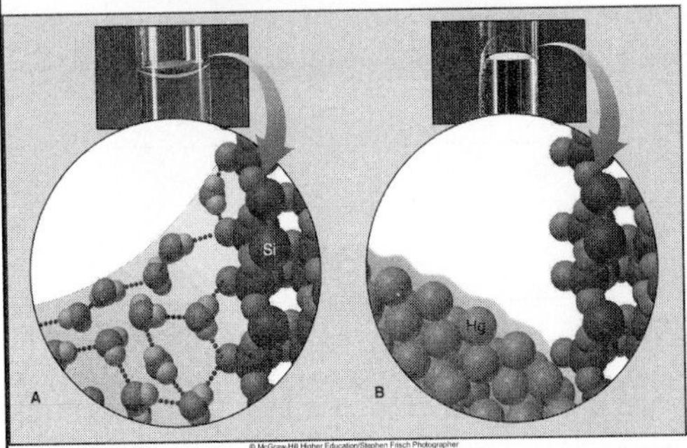

Table 12.4 Viscosity of Water at Several Temperatures

Temperature (°C)	Viscosity $(N\cdot s/m^2)$*
20	1.00×10^{-3}
40	0.65×10^{-3}
60	0.47×10^{-3}
80	0.35×10^{-3}

*The units of viscosity are newton-seconds per square meter.

The H-bonding Ability of The Water Molecule

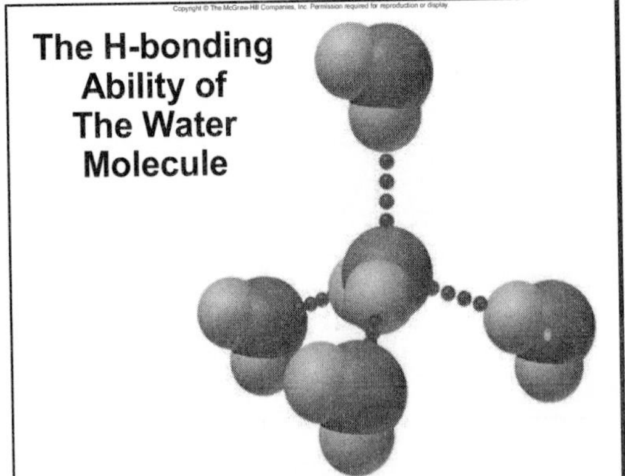

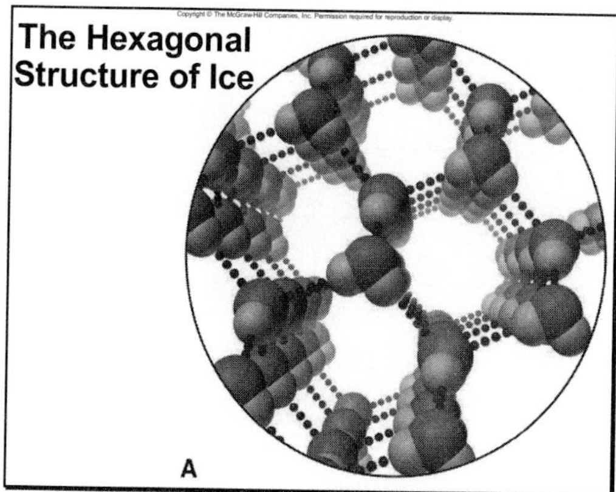
Copyright © The McGraw-Hill Companies, Inc. Permission required for reproduction or display.
The Hexagonal Structure of Ice
A

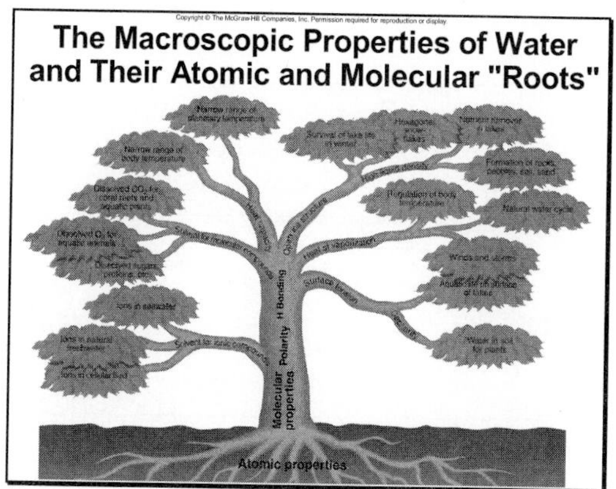
Copyright © The McGraw-Hill Companies, Inc. Permission required for reproduction or display.
The Macroscopic Properties of Water and Their Atomic and Molecular "Roots"
Narrow range of body temperature
Heat of vaporization
Natural water cycle
Winds and storms
Surface tension
H Bonding
Polarity
Molecular properties
Atomic properties

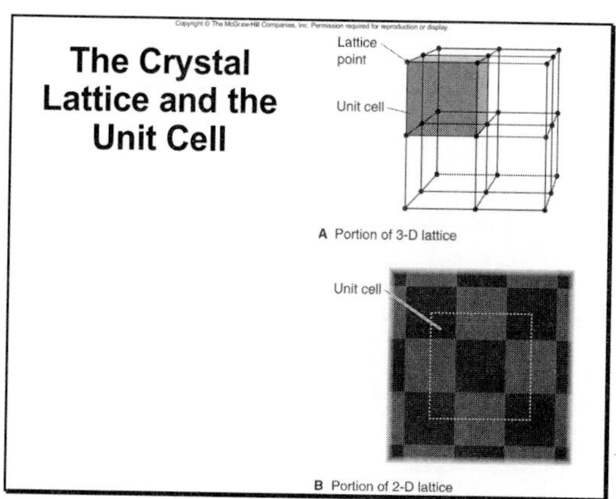
Copyright © The McGraw-Hill Companies, Inc. Permission required for reproduction or display.
The Crystal Lattice and the Unit Cell
Lattice point
Unit cell
A Portion of 3-D lattice
Unit cell
B Portion of 2-D lattice

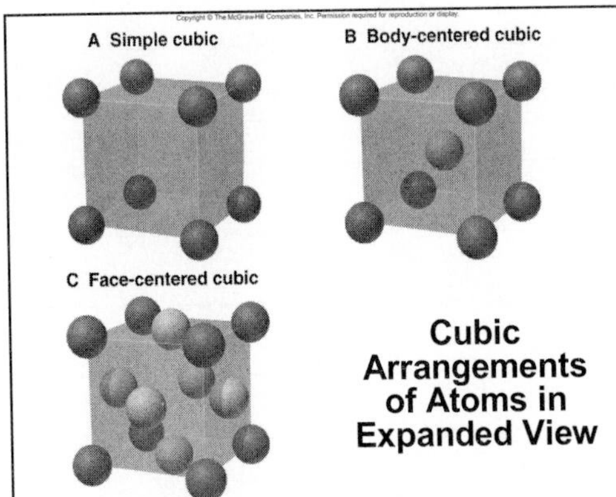
A Simple cubic
B Body-centered cubic
C Face-centered cubic
Cubic Arrangements of Atoms in Expanded View

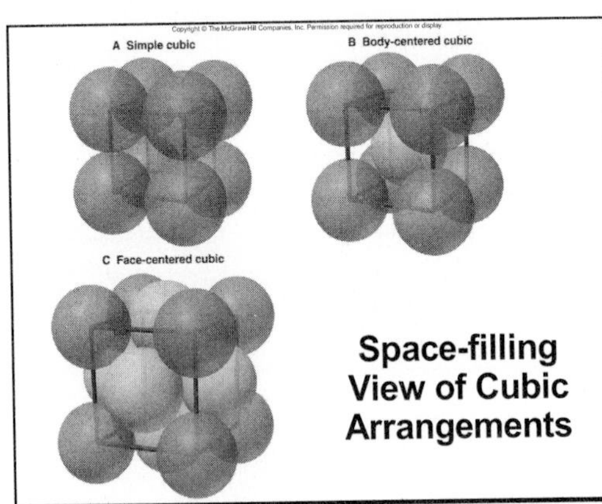
A Simple cubic
B Body-centered cubic
C Face-centered cubic
Space-filling View of Cubic Arrangements

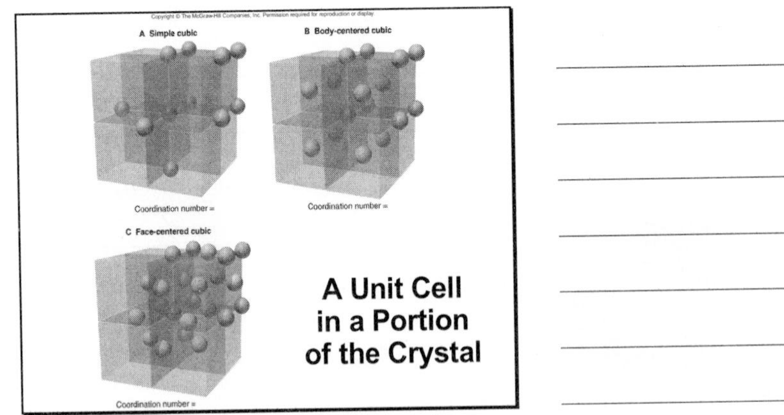
A Simple cubic
B Body-centered cubic
Coordination number =
Coordination number =
C Face-centered cubic
Coordination number =
A Unit Cell in a Portion of the Crystal

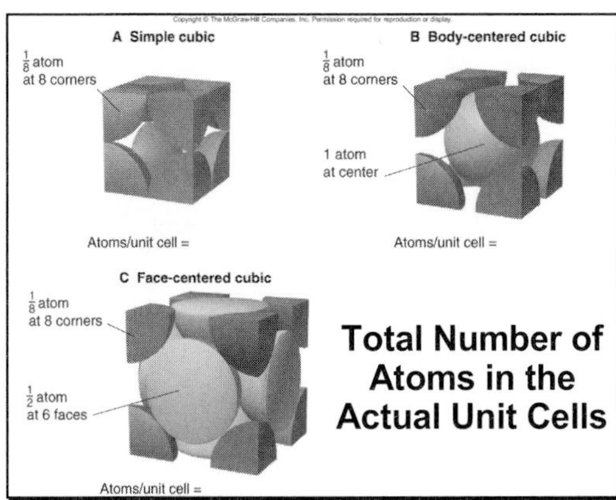
Copyright © The McGraw-Hill Companies, Inc. Permission required for reproduction or display.
A Simple cubic
$\frac{1}{8}$ atom
at 8 corners
Atoms/unit cell =
B Body-centered cubic
$\frac{1}{8}$ atom
at 8 corners
1 atom
at center
Atoms/unit cell =
C Face-centered cubic
$\frac{1}{8}$ atom
at 8 corners
$\frac{1}{2}$ atom
at 6 faces
Atoms/unit cell =
Total Number of Atoms in the Actual Unit Cells

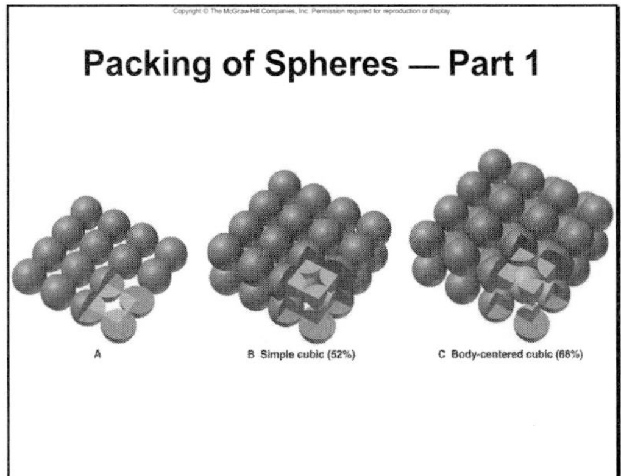
Copyright © The McGraw-Hill Companies, Inc. Permission required for reproduction or display.
Packing of Spheres — Part 1
A
B Simple cubic (52%)
C Body-centered cubic (68%)

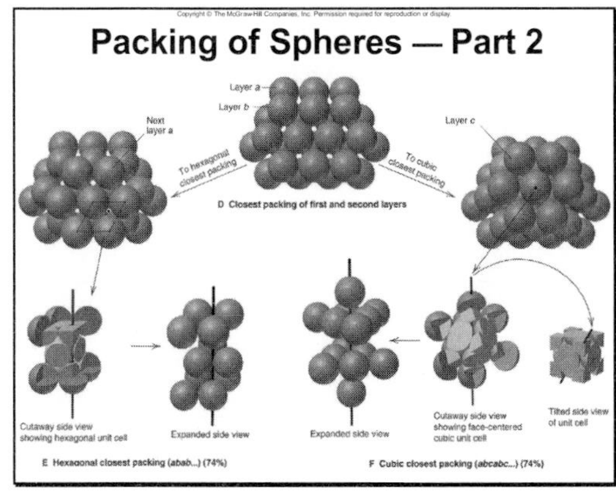
Copyright © The McGraw-Hill Companies, Inc. Permission required for reproduction or display.
Packing of Spheres — Part 2
Layer a
Layer b
Next layer a
Layer c
To hexagonal closest packing
To cubic closest packing
D Closest packing of first and second layers
Cutaway side view showing hexagonal unit cell
Expanded side view
Expanded side view
Cutaway side view showing face-centered cubic unit cell
Tilted side view of unit cell
E Hexagonal closest packing (abab...) (74%)
F Cubic closest packing (abcabc...) (74%)

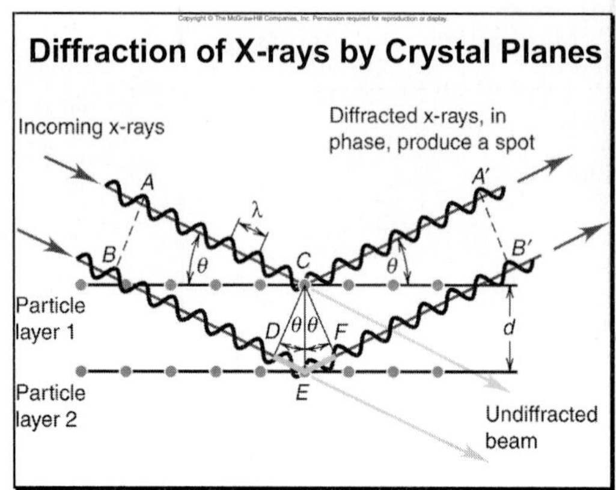
Copyright © The McGraw-Hill Companies, Inc. Permission required for reproduction or display.
Diffraction of X-rays by Crystal Planes
Incoming x-rays
Diffracted x-rays, in phase, produce a spot
A
A′
λ
B
B′
C
θ
θ
Particle layer 1
D
θ
θ
F
d
Particle layer 2
E
Undiffracted beam

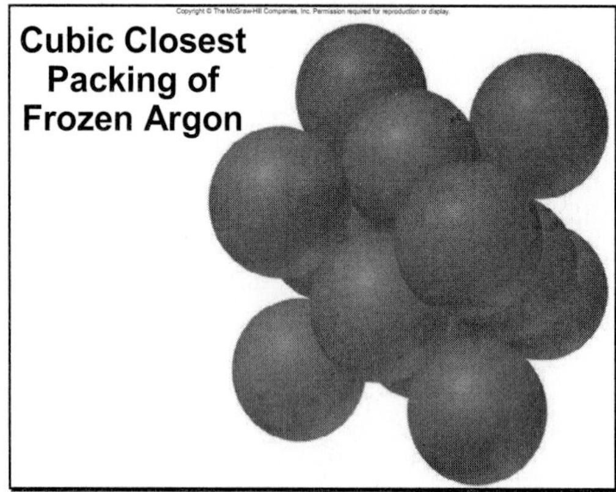
Copyright © The McGraw-Hill Companies, Inc. Permission required for reproduction or display.
Cubic Closest Packing of Frozen Argon

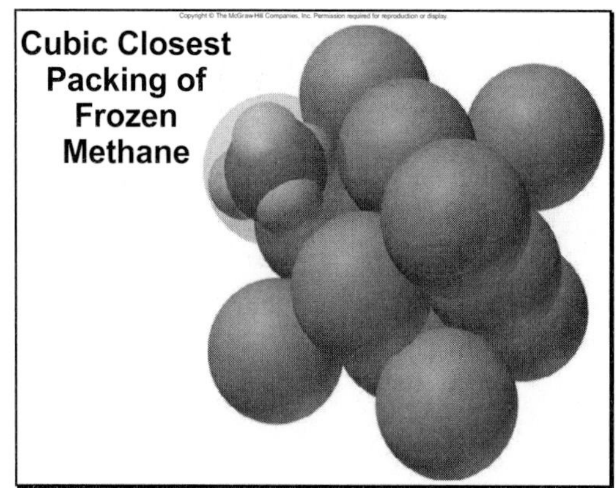
Copyright © The McGraw-Hill Companies, Inc. Permission required for reproduction or display.
Cubic Closest Packing of Frozen Methane

Table 12.5 Characteristics of the Major Types of Crystalline Solids

	Particle(s)	Interparticle Forces	Physical Behavior	Examples [mp, °C]
Atomic	Atoms			Group 8A(18) [Ne −249 to Rn −71]
Molecular	Molecules			*Nonpolar** O_2 [−219], C_4H_{10} [−138] Cl_2 [−101], C_6H_{14} [−95] P_4 [44.1] *Polar* SO_2 [−73], $CHCl_3$ [−64] HNO_3 [−42], H_2O [0.0] CH_3COOH [17]
Ionic	Positive and negative ions			NaCl [801] CaF_2 [1423] MgO [2852]
Metallic	Atoms			Na [97.8] Zn [420] Fe [1535]
Network	Atoms			SiO_2 (quartz) [1610] C(diamond) [~4000]

*Nonpolar molecular solids are arranged in order of increasing molar mass. Note the correlation with increasing melting point (mp).

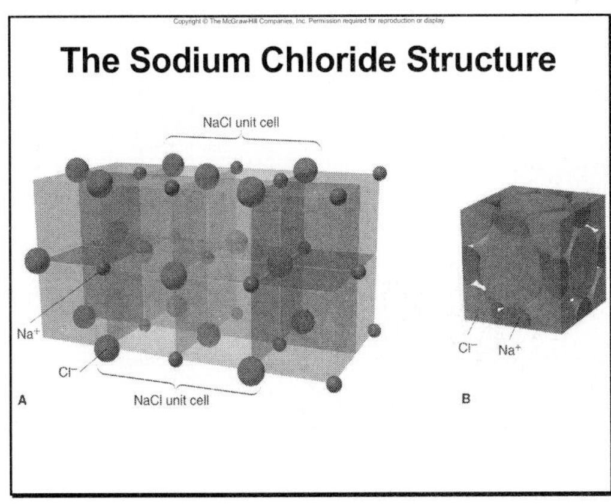

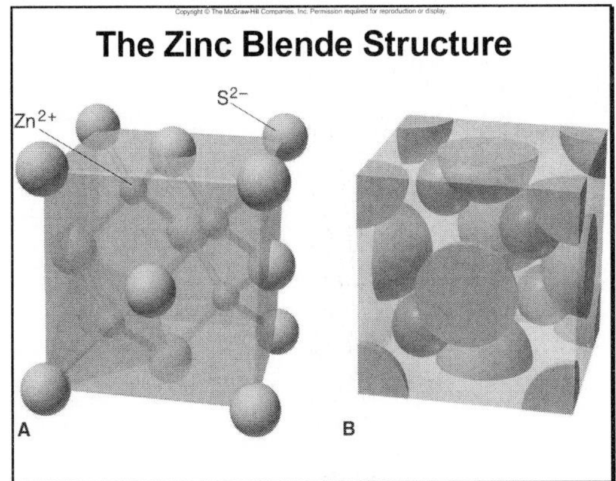

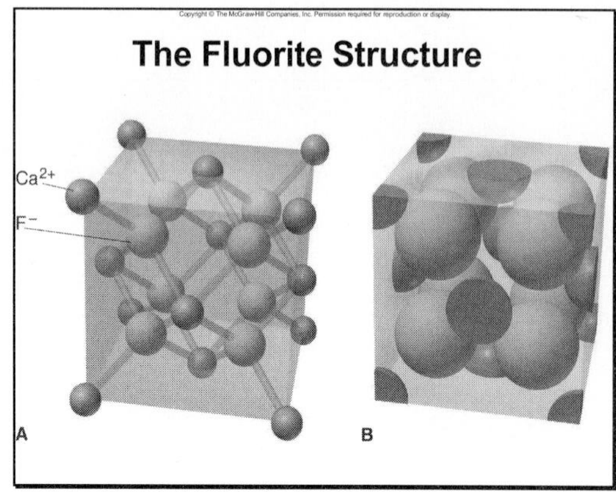

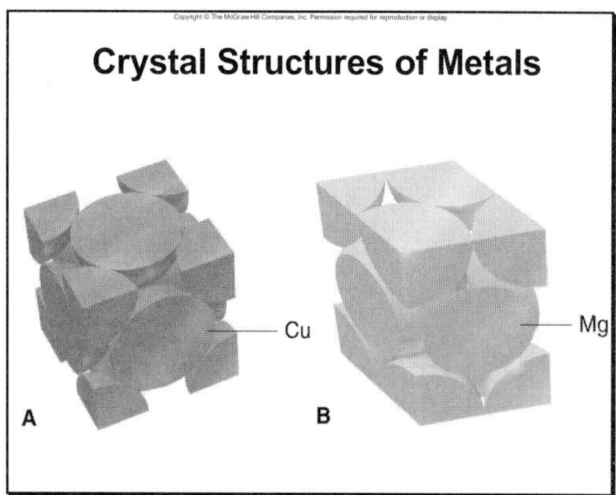

Table 12.6 Comparison of the Properties of Diamond and Graphite

Property	Graphite	Diamond
Density (g/cm^3)	2.27	3.51
Hardness	<1 (very soft)	10 (hardest)
Melting point (K)	4100	4100
Color	Shiny black	Colorless transparent
Electrical conductivity	High (along sheet)	None
ΔH^0_{comb} (kJ/mol)	−393.5	−395.4
ΔH^0_f (kJ/mol)	0 (standard state)	1.90

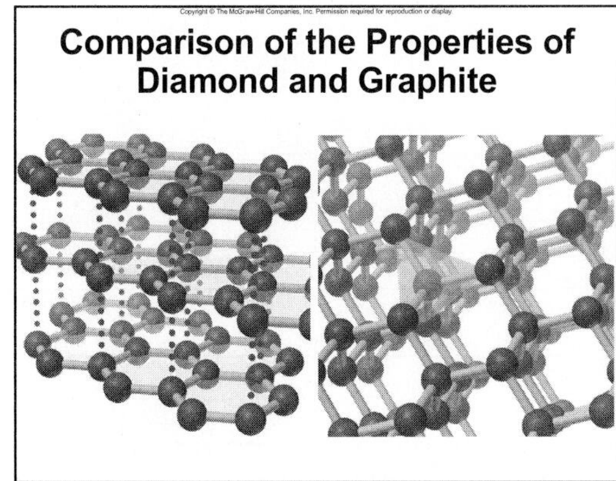
Copyright © The McGraw-Hill Companies, Inc. Permission required for reproduction or display.
Comparison of the Properties of Diamond and Graphite

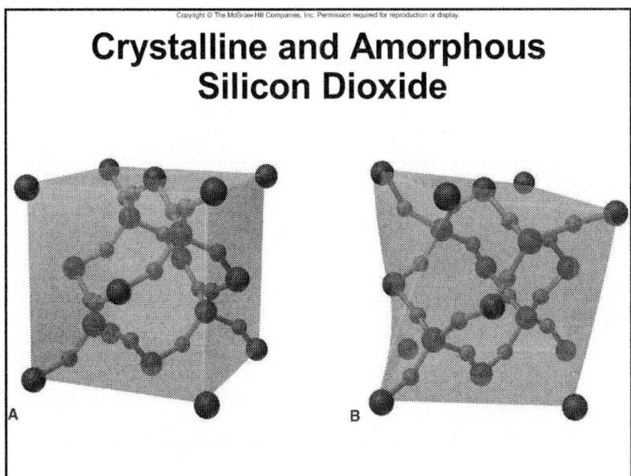
Copyright © The McGraw-Hill Companies, Inc. Permission required for reproduction or display.
Crystalline and Amorphous Silicon Dioxide
A
B

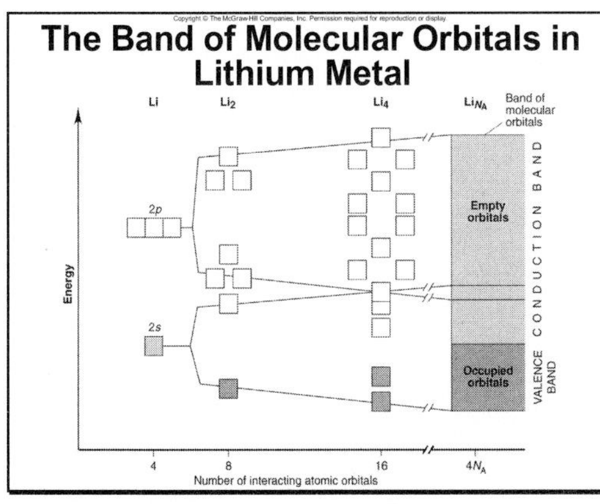
Copyright © The McGraw-Hill Companies, Inc. Permission required for reproduction or display.
The Band of Molecular Orbitals in Lithium Metal
Li
Li2
Li4
LiNA
Band of molecular orbitals
Energy
2p
2s
Empty orbitals
Occupied orbitals
CONDUCTION BAND
VALENCE BAND
4
8
16
4NA
Number of interacting atomic orbitals

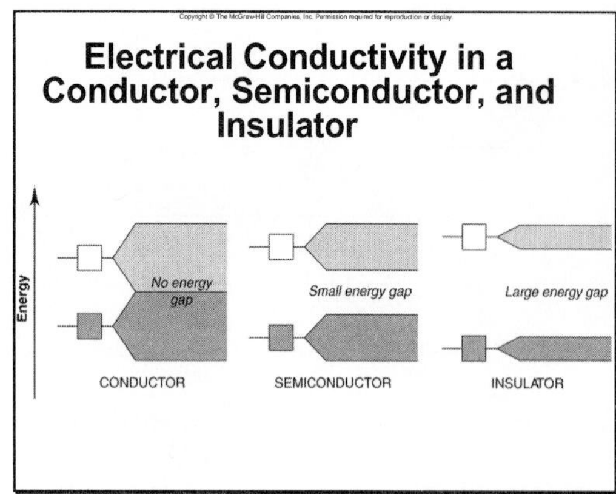
Copyright © The McGraw-Hill Companies, Inc. Permission required for reproduction or display.
Electrical Conductivity in a Conductor, Semiconductor, and Insulator
Energy
No energy gap
Small energy gap
Large energy gap
CONDUCTOR
SEMICONDUCTOR
INSULATOR

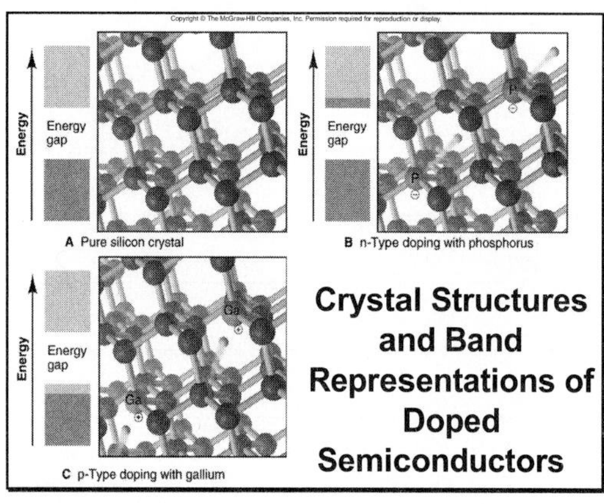
Copyright © The McGraw-Hill Companies, Inc. Permission required for reproduction or display.
Energy
Energy gap
A Pure silicon crystal
B n-Type doping with phosphorus
P
Ga
C p-Type doping with gallium
Crystal Structures and Band Representations of Doped Semiconductors

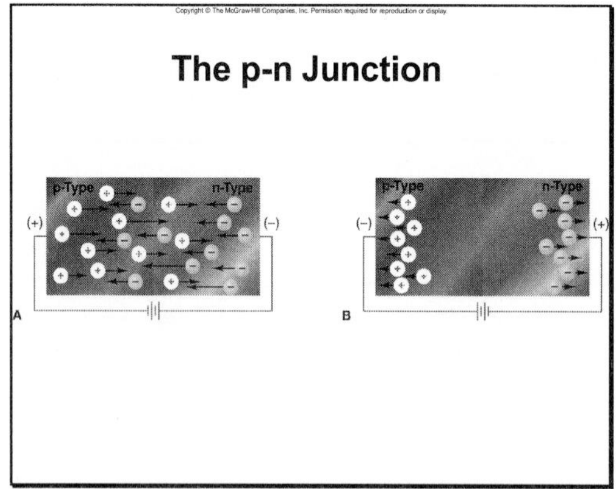
Copyright © The McGraw-Hill Companies, Inc. Permission required for reproduction or display.
The p-n Junction
p-Type
n-Type
(+)
(–)
A
B

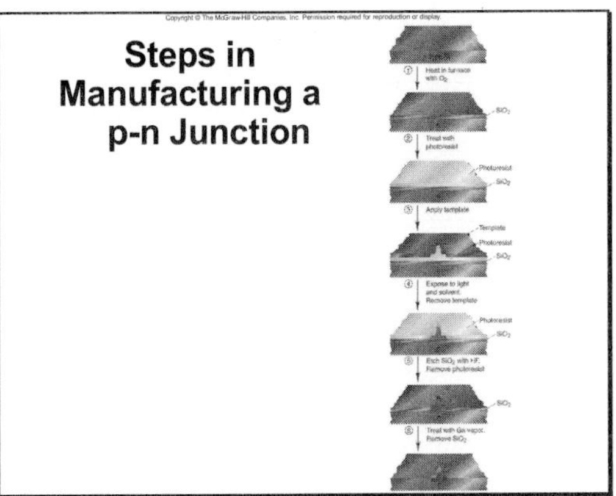
Steps in Manufacturing a p-n Junction

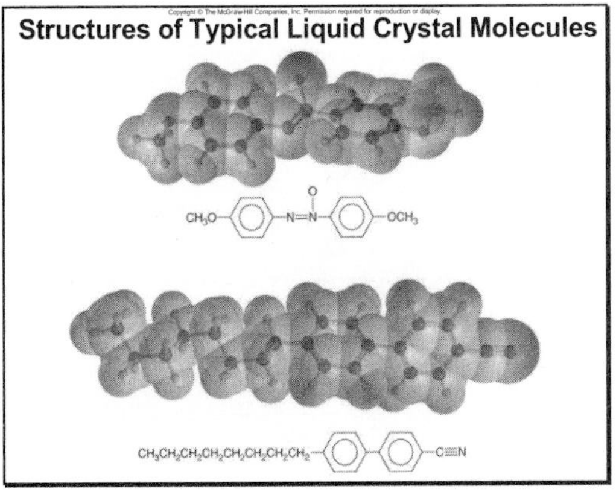
Structures of Typical Liquid Crystal Molecules
CH₃O–C₆H₄–N=N(O)–C₆H₄–OCH₃
CH₃CH₂CH₂CH₂CH₂CH₂CH₂CH₂–C₆H₄–C₆H₄–C≡N

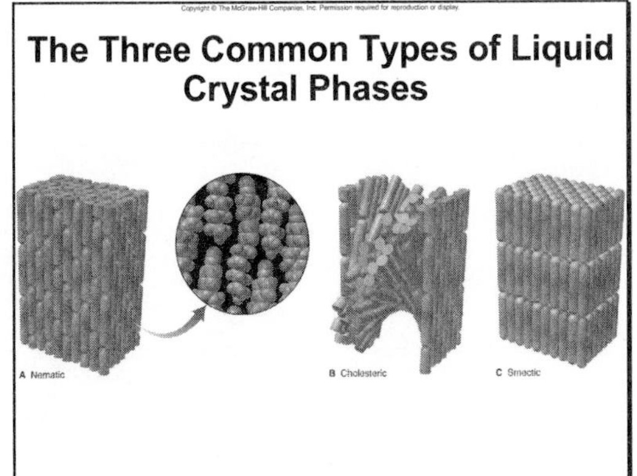
The Three Common Types of Liquid Crystal Phases
A Nematic
B Cholesteric
C Smectic

Schematic of a Liquid Crystal Display (LCD)

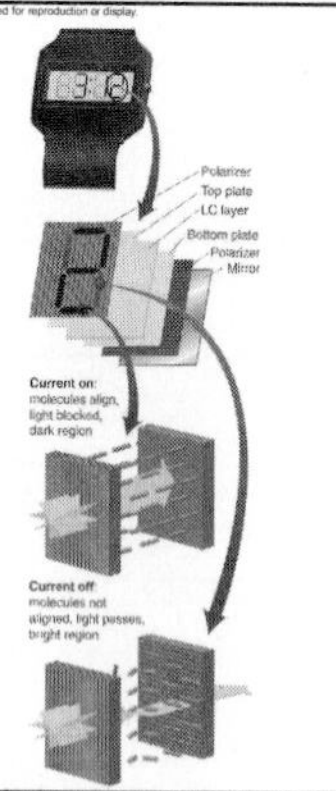

Table 12.7 Some Uses of New Ceramics and Ceramic Mixtures

Ceramic	Applications
SiC, Si_3N_4, TiB_2, Al_2O_3	Whiskers (fibers) to strengthen Al and other ceramics
Si_3N_4	Car engine parts; turbine rotors for "turbo" cars; electronic sensor units
Si_3N_4, BN, Al_2O_3	Supports or layering materials (as insulators) in electronic microchips
SiC, Si_3N_4, TiB_2, ZrO_2, Al_2O_3, BN	Cutting tools, edge sharpeners (as coatings and whole devices), scissors, surgical tools, industrial "diamond"
BN, SiC	Armor-plating reinforcement fibers (as in Kevlar composites)
ZrO_2, Al_2O_3	Surgical implants (hip and knee joints)

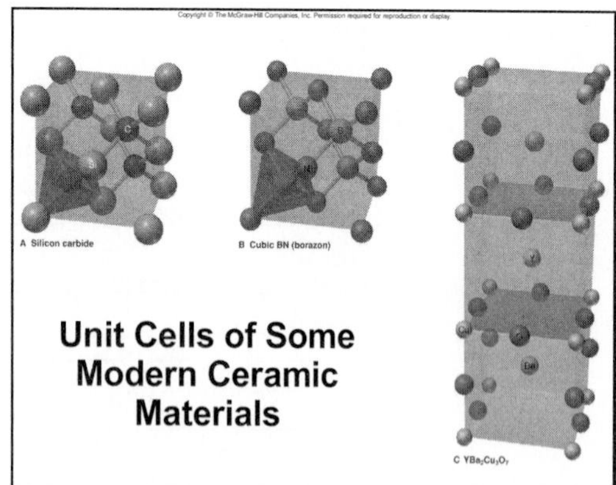

Unit Cells of Some Modern Ceramic Materials

C $YBa_2Cu_3O_7$

Table 12.8 Molar Masses of Some Common Polymers

Name	$\mathcal{M}_{polymer}$ (g/mol)	n	Uses
Acrylates	2×10^5	2×10^3	Rugs, carpets
Polyamide (nylons)	1.5×10^4	1.2×10^2	Tires, fishing line
Polycarbonate	1×10^5	4×10^2	Compact disks
Polyethylene	3×10^5	1×10^4	Grocery bags
Polyethylene (ultra-high molecular weight)	5×10^6	2×10^5	Hip joints
Poly(ethylene terephthalate)	2×10^4	1×10^2	Soda bottles
Polystyrene	3×10^5	3×10^3	Packing; coffee cups
Poly(vinyl chloride)	1×10^5	1.5×10^3	Plumbing

The Random-Coil Shape of a Polymer Chain

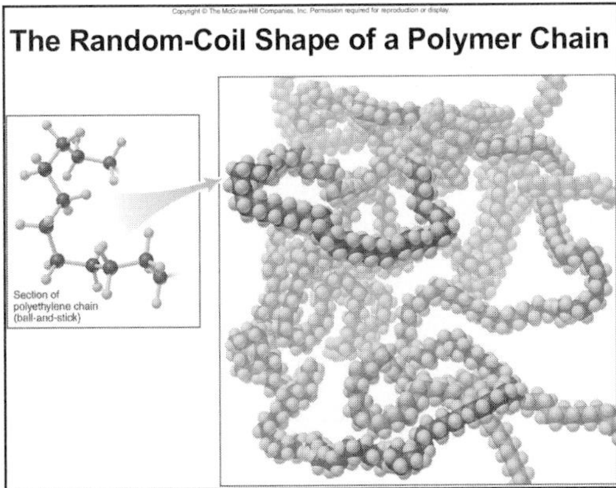

The Semicrystallinity of a Polymer Chain

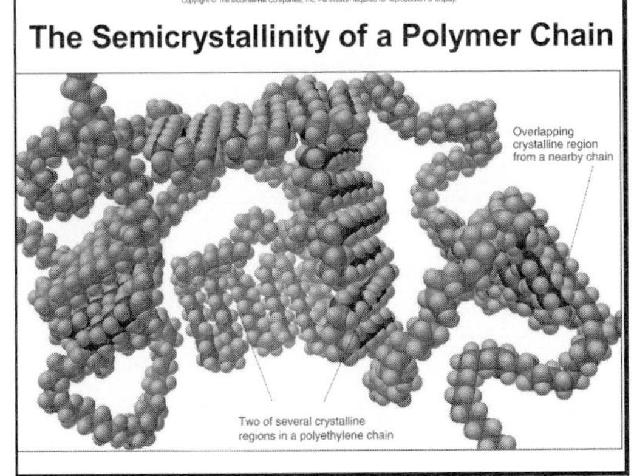

Chapter 13

Chemistry: The Molecular Nature of Matter and Change

Third Edition

Martin S. Silberberg

Table 13.1 Approximate Composition of a Bacterium

Substance	Mass % of Cell	Number of Types	Number of Molecules
Water	~70	1	5×10^{10}
Ions	1	20	?
Sugars*	3	200	3×10^{8}
Amino acids*	0.4	100	5×10^{7}
Lipids*	2	50	3×10^{7}
Nucleotides*	0.4	200	1×10^{7}
Other small molecules	0.2	~200	?
Macromolecules (proteins, nucleic acids, polysaccharides)	23	~5000	6×10^{6}

*Includes precursors and metabolites.

The Major Types of Intermolecular Forces in Solutions — Part 1

Ion-dipole
(40–600)

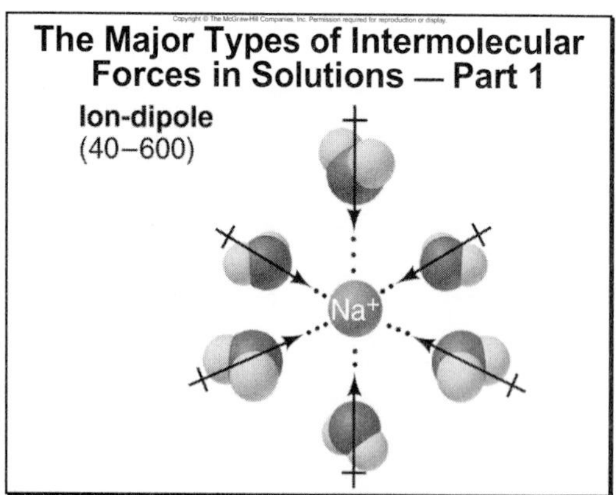

The Major Types of Intermolecular Forces in Solutions — Part 2

H bond
(10–40)

Methanol
(CH_3OH)

H_2O

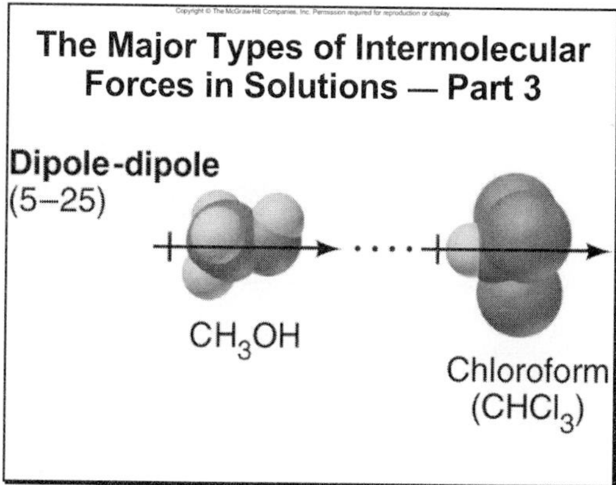

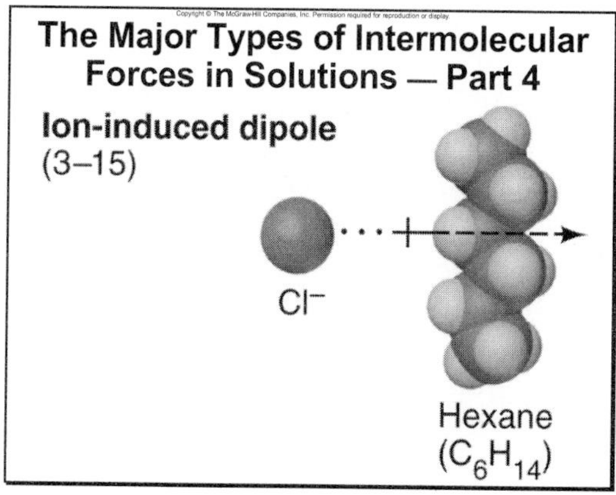

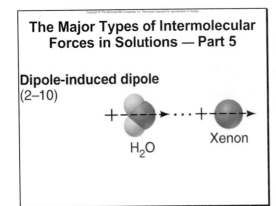

The Major Types of Intermolecular Forces in Solutions — Part 5

Dipole-induced dipole
(2–10)

H_2O Xenon

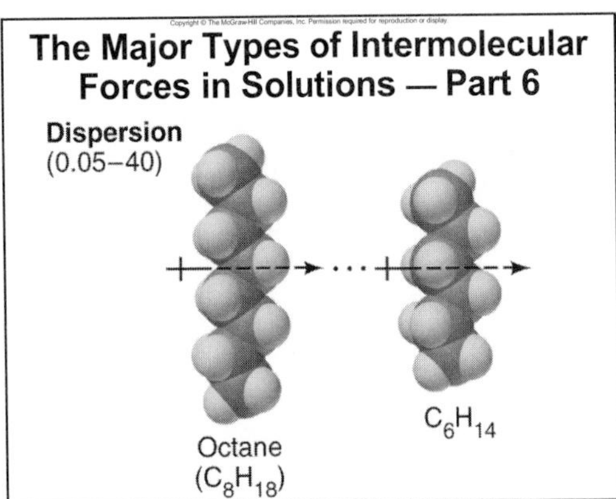

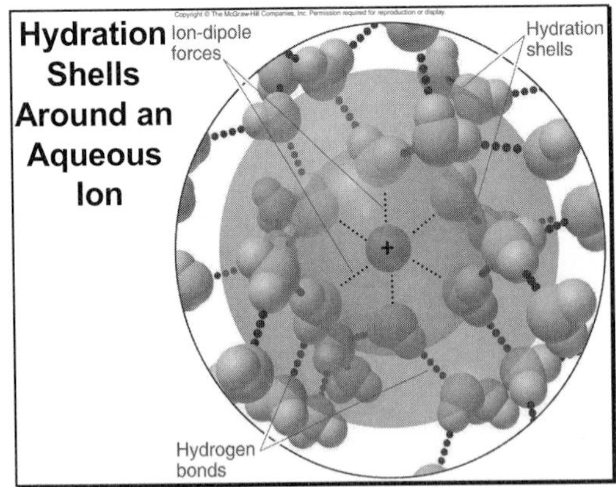

Table 13.2 Solubility* of a Series of Alcohols in Water and Hexane

Alcohol	Model	Solubility in Water	Solubility in Hexane
CH_3OH (methanol)		∞	1.2
CH_3CH_2OH (ethanol)		∞	∞
$CH_3(CH_2)_2OH$ (propanol)		∞	∞
$CH_3(CH_2)_3OH$ (butanol)		1.1	∞
$CH_3(CH_2)_4OH$ (pentanol)		0.30	∞
$CH_3(CH_2)_5OH$ (hexanol)		0.058	∞

*Expressed in mol alcohol/1000 g solvent at 20°C.

Like Dissolves Like: Solubility of Methanol in Water

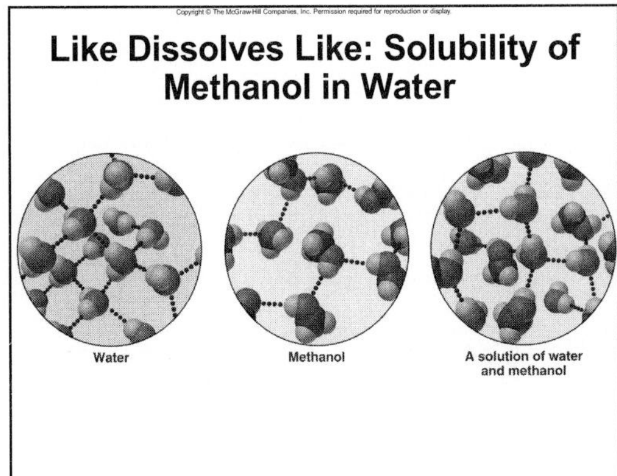

The Structure and Function of a Soap

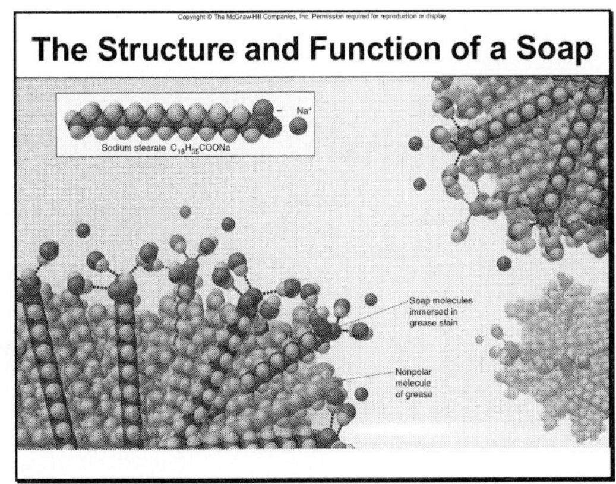

The Mode of Action of an Antibiotic

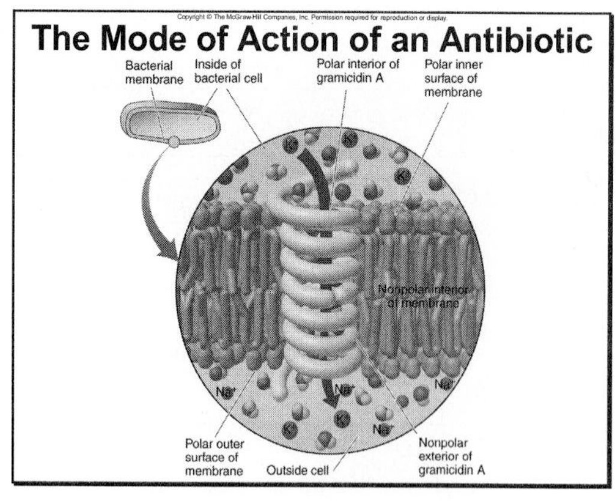

Table 13.3 Correlation Between Boiling Point and Solubility in Water

Gas	Solubility (*M*)*	bp (K)
He	4.2×10^{-4}	4.2
Ne	6.6×10^{-4}	27.1
N_2	10.4×10^{-4}	77.4
CO	15.6×10^{-4}	81.6
O_2	21.8×10^{-4}	90.2
NO	32.7×10^{-4}	121.4

*At 273 K and 1 atm.

Arrangement of Atoms in Two Types of Alloys

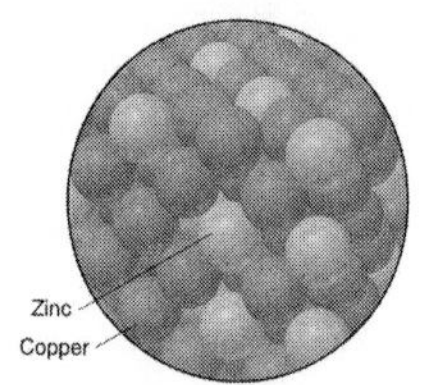

A Brass, a substitutional alloy

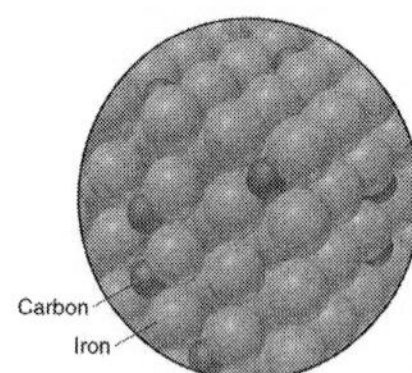

B Carbon steel, an interstitial alloy

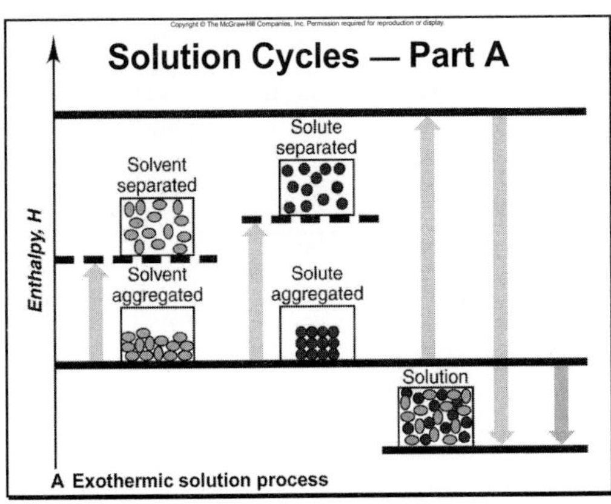

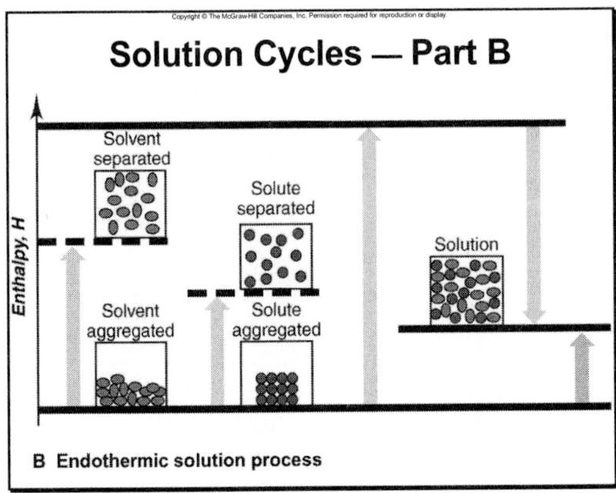

Table 13.4 Trends in Ionic Heats of Hydration

Ion	Ionic Radius (pm)	ΔH_{hydr} (kJ/mol)
Group 1A(1)		
Li^+	76	−510
Na^+	102	−410
K^+	138	−336
Rb^+	152	−315
Cs^+	167	−282
Group 2A(2)		
Mg^{2+}	72	−1903
Ca^{2+}	100	−1591
Sr^{2+}	118	−1424
Ba^{2+}	135	−1317
Group 7A(17)		
F^-	133	−431
Cl^-	181	−313
Br^-	196	−284
I^-	220	−247

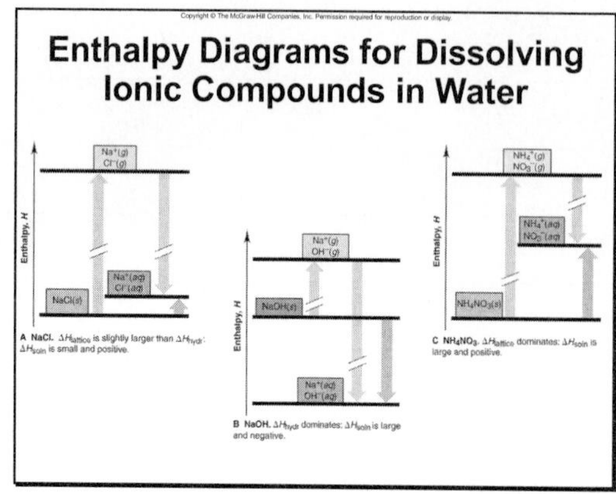
Copyright © The McGraw-Hill Companies, Inc. Permission required for reproduction or display.
Enthalpy Diagrams for Dissolving Ionic Compounds in Water
Enthalpy, H
Na⁺(g) Cl⁻(g)
Na⁺(aq) Cl⁻(aq)
NaCl(s)
A NaCl. ΔH_lattice is slightly larger than ΔH_hydr: ΔH_soln is small and positive.
Na⁺(g) OH⁻(g)
NaOH(s)
Na⁺(aq) OH⁻(aq)
B NaOH. ΔH_hydr dominates: ΔH_soln is large and negative.
NH₄⁺(g) NO₃⁻(g)
NH₄⁺(aq) NO₃⁻(aq)
NH₄NO₃(s)
C NH₄NO₃. ΔH_lattice dominates: ΔH_soln is large and positive.

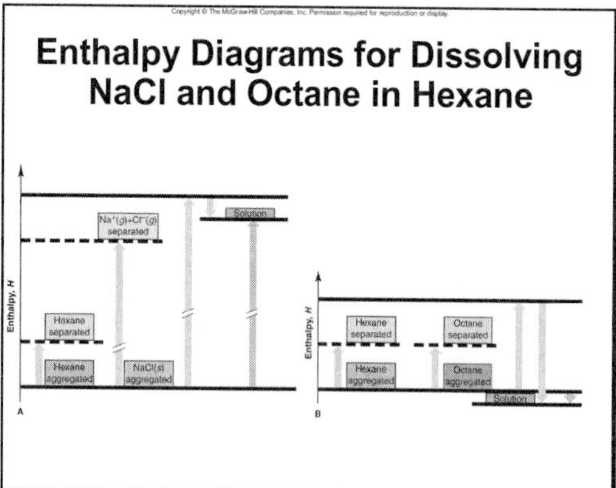
Copyright © The McGraw-Hill Companies, Inc. Permission required for reproduction or display.
Enthalpy Diagrams for Dissolving NaCl and Octane in Hexane
Enthalpy, H
Solution
Na⁺(g)+Cl⁻(g) separated
Hexane separated
Hexane aggregated
NaCl(s) aggregated
A
Hexane separated
Octane separated
Hexane aggregated
Octane aggregated
Solution
B

Copyright © The McGraw-Hill Companies, Inc. Permission required for reproduction or display.
Equilibrium in a Saturated Solution

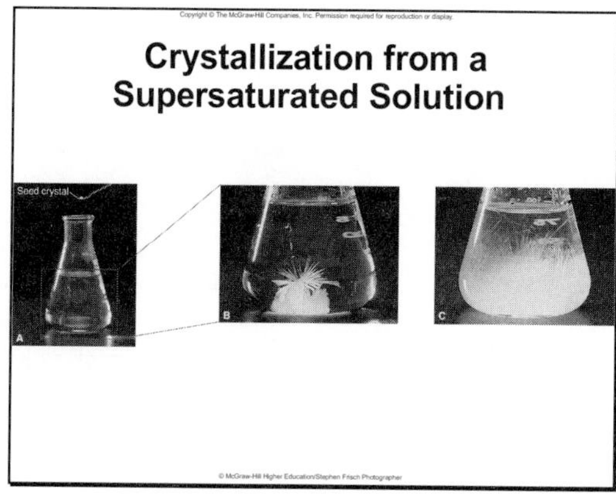
Crystallization from a Supersaturated Solution
Seed crystal
A
B
C

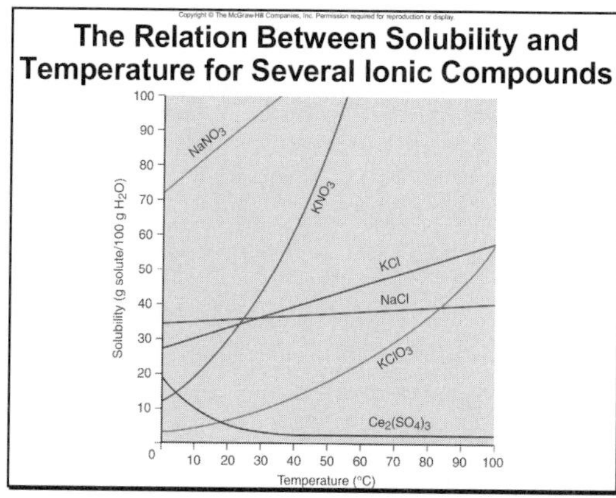
The Relation Between Solubility and Temperature for Several Ionic Compounds
Solubility (g solute/100 g H2O)
Temperature (°C)
NaNO3
KNO3
KCl
NaCl
KClO3
Ce2(SO4)3

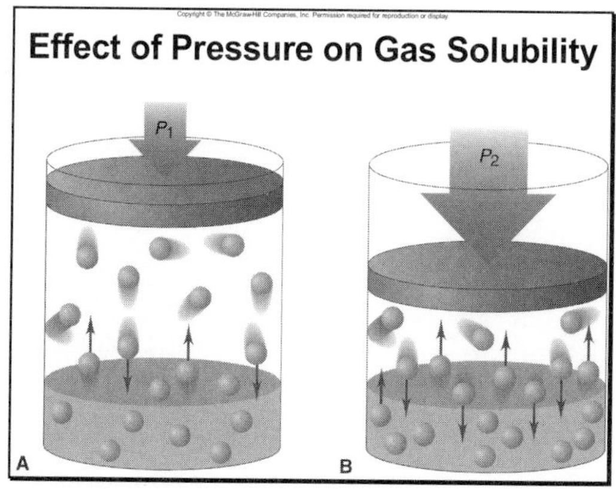
Effect of Pressure on Gas Solubility
P1
P2
A
B

Table 13.5 Concentration Definitions

Concentration Term	Ratio
Molarity (M)	
Molality (m)	
Parts by mass	
Parts by volume	
Mole fraction (X)	

The Three Types of Electrolytes

A B C

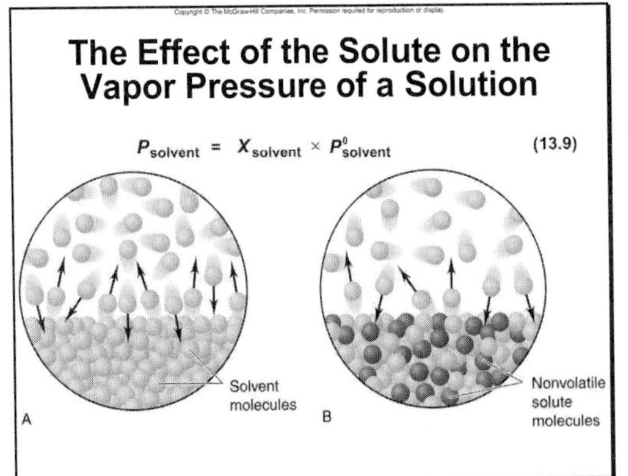

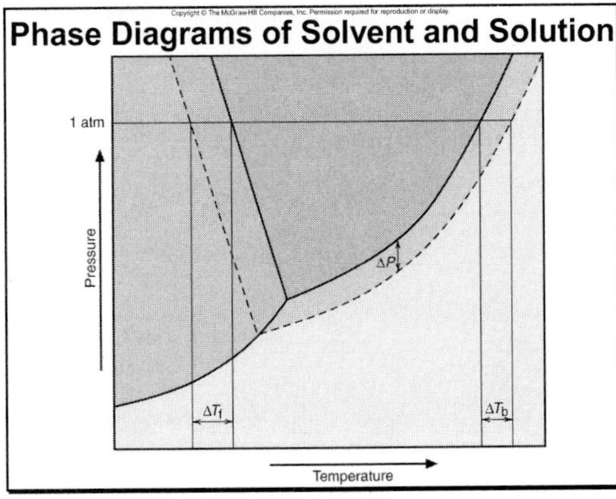

Table 13.6 Molal Boiling Point Elevation and Freezing Point Depression Constants of Several Solvents

Solvent	Boiling Point (°C)*	K_b (°C/m)	Melting Point (°C)	K_f (°C/m)
Acetic acid	117.9	3.07	16.6	3.90
Benzene	80.1	2.53	5.5	4.90
Carbon disulfide	46.2	2.34	−111.5	3.83
Carbon tetrachloride	76.5	5.03	−23	30.
Chloroform	61.7	3.63	−63.5	4.70
Diethyl ether	34.5	2.02	−116.2	1.79
Ethanol	78.5	1.22	−117.3	1.99
Water	100.0	0.512	0.0	1.86

*At 1 atm.

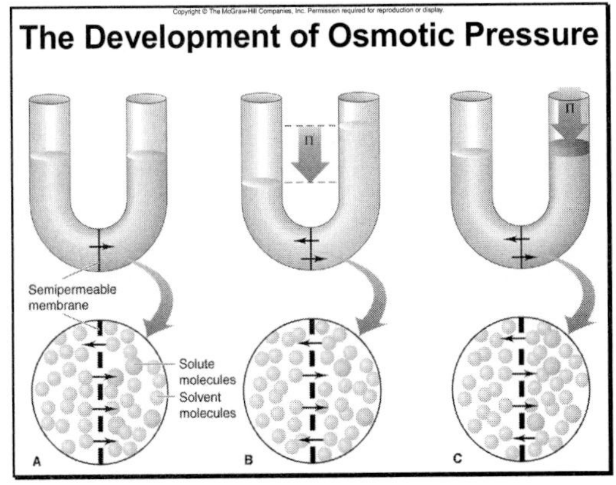

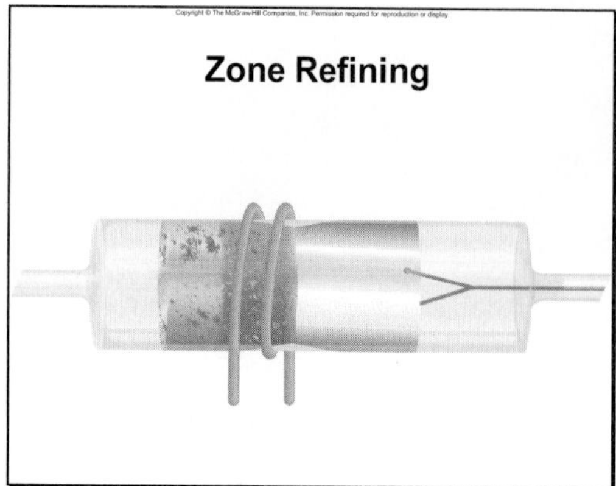
Zone Refining

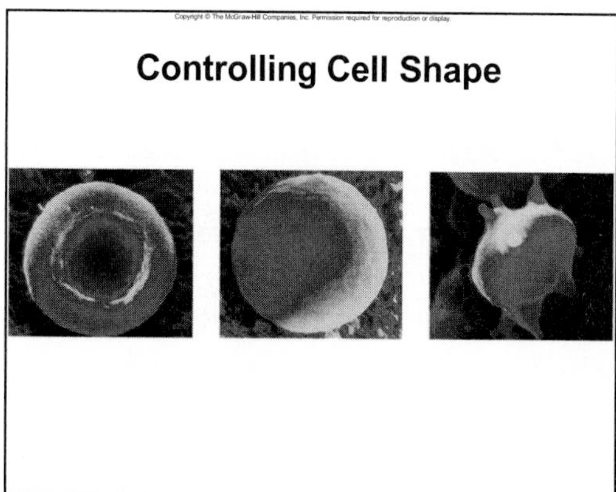
Controlling Cell Shape

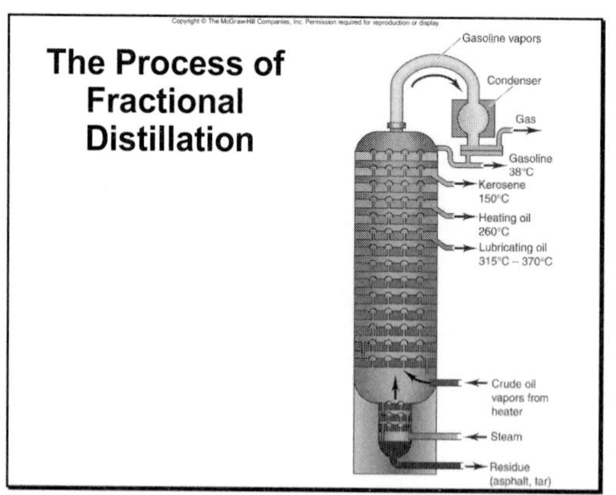
The Process of Fractional Distillation
Gasoline vapors
Condenser
Gas
Gasoline 38°C
Kerosene 150°C
Heating oil 260°C
Lubricating oil 315°C – 370°C
Crude oil vapors from heater
Steam
Residue (asphalt, tar)

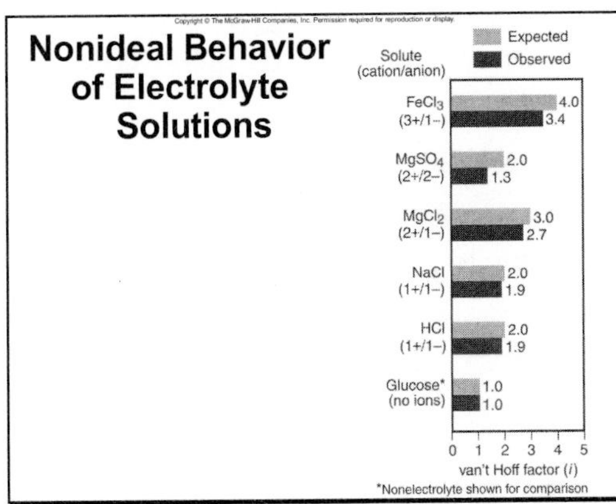

An Ionic Atmosphere Model for Nonideal Behavior of Electrolyte Solutions

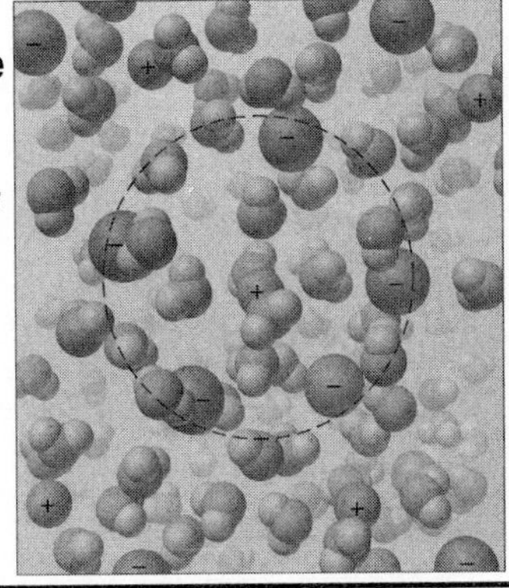

Table 13.7 Types of Colloids

Colloid Type	Dispersed Substance	Dispersing Medium	Example
Aerosol			Fog
Aerosol			Smoke
Foam			Whipped cream
Solid foam			Marshmallow
Emulsion			Milk
Solid emulsion			Butter
Sol			Paint; cell fluid
Solid sol			Opal

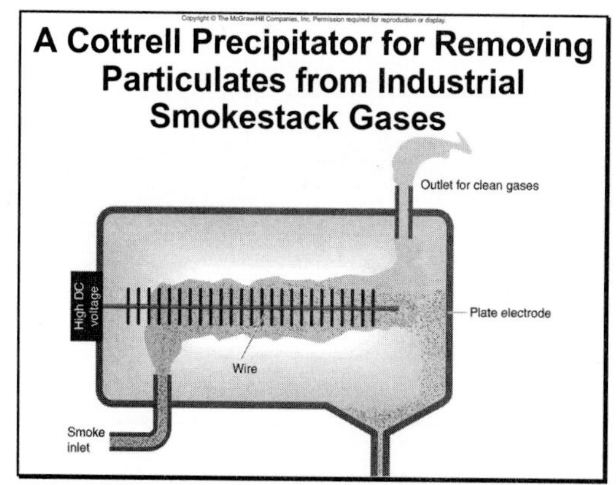
A Cottrell Precipitator for Removing Particulates from Industrial Smokestack Gases
Outlet for clean gases
High DC voltage
Plate electrode
Wire
Smoke inlet

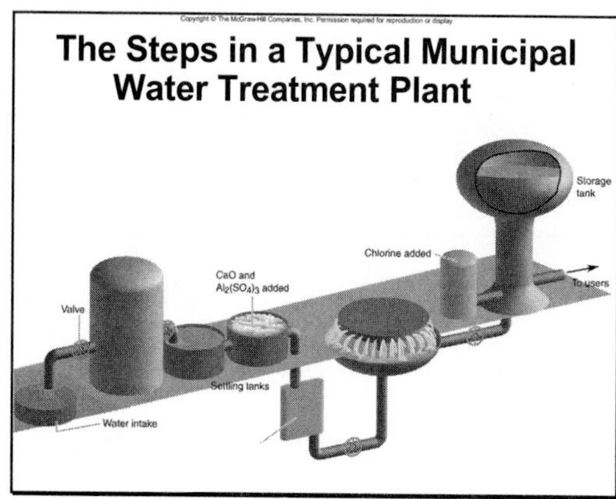
The Steps in a Typical Municipal Water Treatment Plant
Storage tank
Chlorine added
CaO and $Al_2(SO_4)_3$ added
To users
Valve
Settling tanks
Water intake

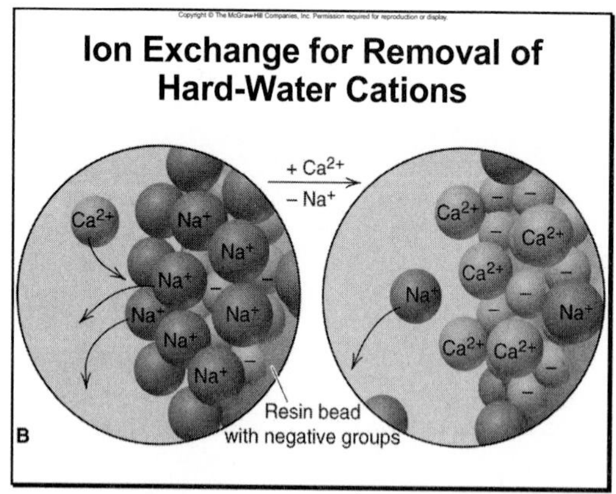
Ion Exchange for Removal of Hard-Water Cations
+ Ca^{2+}
− Na^+
Ca^{2+}
Na^+
Resin bead with negative groups
B

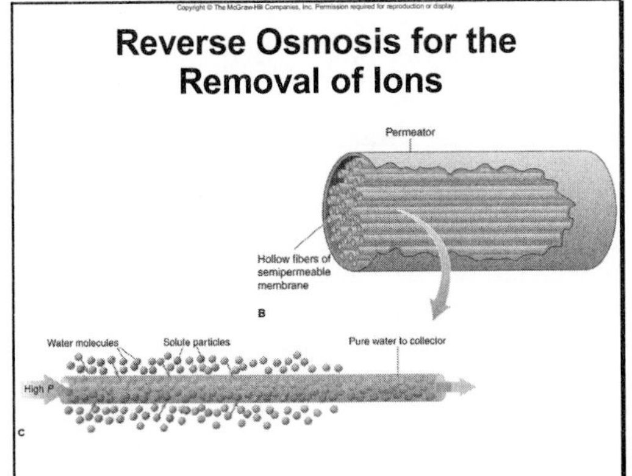
Copyright © The McGraw-Hill Companies, Inc. Permission required for reproduction or display
Reverse Osmosis for the Removal of Ions
Permeator
Hollow fibers of semipermeable membrane
B
Water molecules
Solute particles
Pure water to collector
High P
C

Interchapter

Chemistry: The Molecular Nature of Matter and Change

Third Edition

Martin S. Silberberg

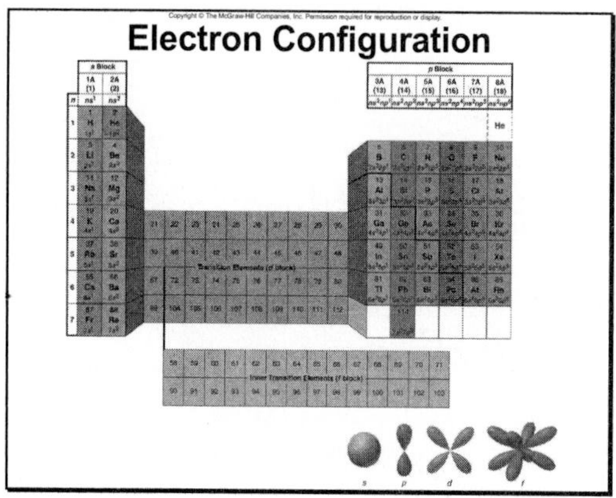

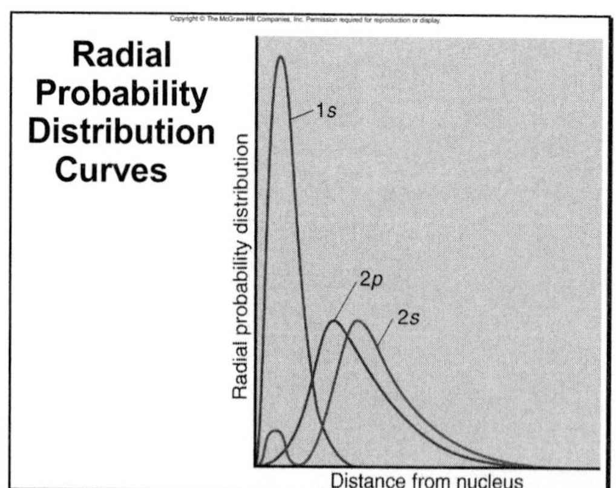

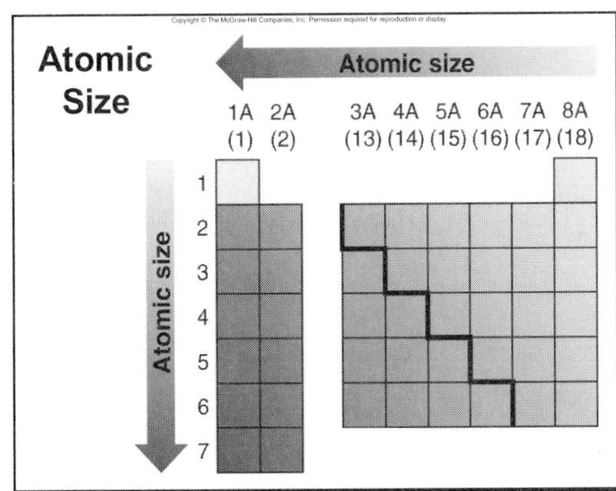
Atomic Size
Atomic size
1A (1)
2A (2)
3A (13)
4A (14)
5A (15)
6A (16)
7A (17)
8A (18)
Atomic size
1
2
3
4
5
6
7

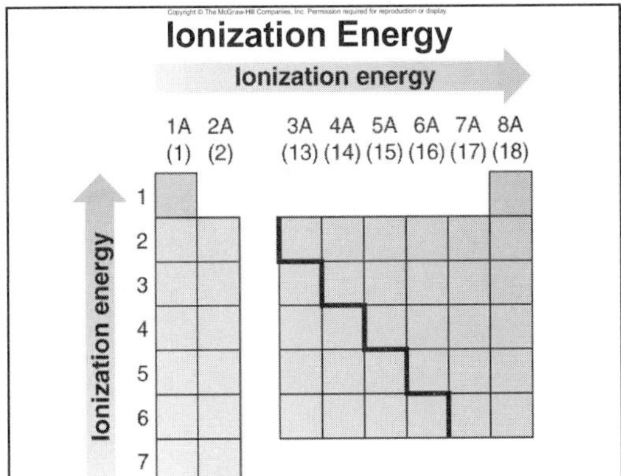
Ionization Energy
Ionization energy
1A (1)
2A (2)
3A (13)
4A (14)
5A (15)
6A (16)
7A (17)
8A (18)
Ionization energy
1
2
3
4
5
6
7

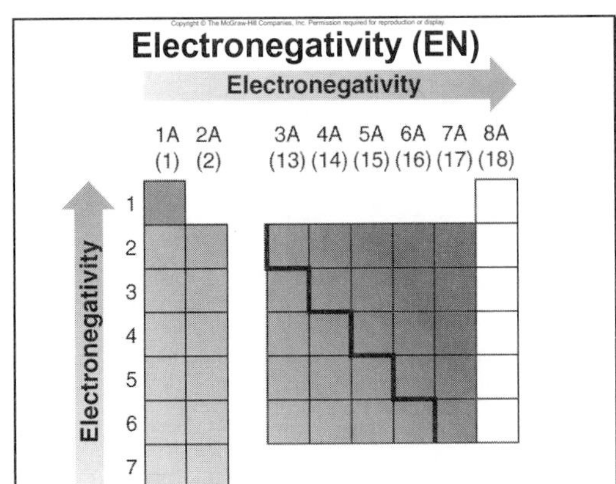
Electronegativity (EN)
Electronegativity
1A (1)
2A (2)
3A (13)
4A (14)
5A (15)
6A (16)
7A (17)
8A (18)
Electronegativity
1
2
3
4
5
6
7

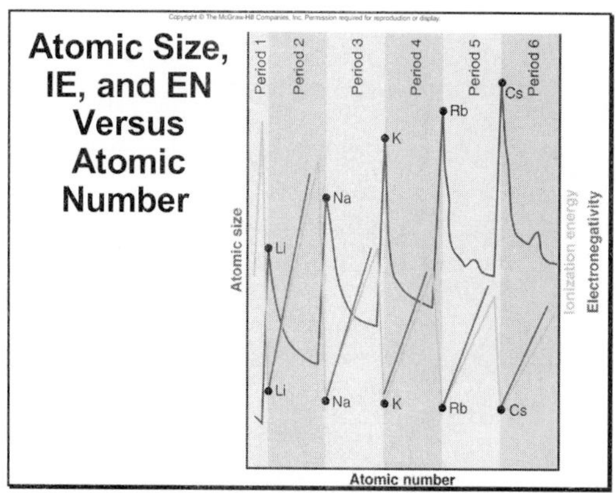
Copyright © The McGraw-Hill Companies, Inc. Permission required for reproduction or display.
Atomic Size, IE, and EN Versus Atomic Number
Period 1
Period 2
Period 3
Period 4
Period 5
Period 6
Li
Na
K
Rb
Cs
Atomic size
Ionization energy
Electronegativity
Atomic number

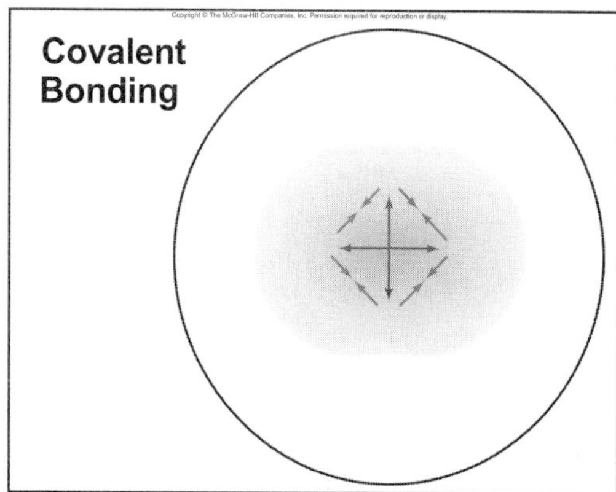
Copyright © The McGraw-Hill Companies, Inc. Permission required for reproduction or display.
Covalent Bonding

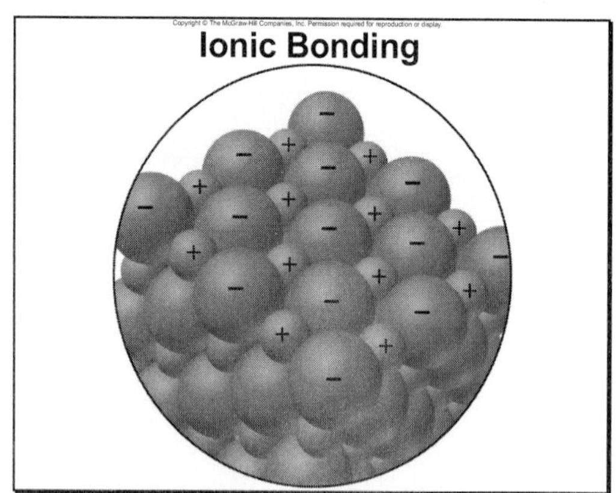
Copyright © The McGraw-Hill Companies, Inc. Permission required for reproduction or display.
Ionic Bonding

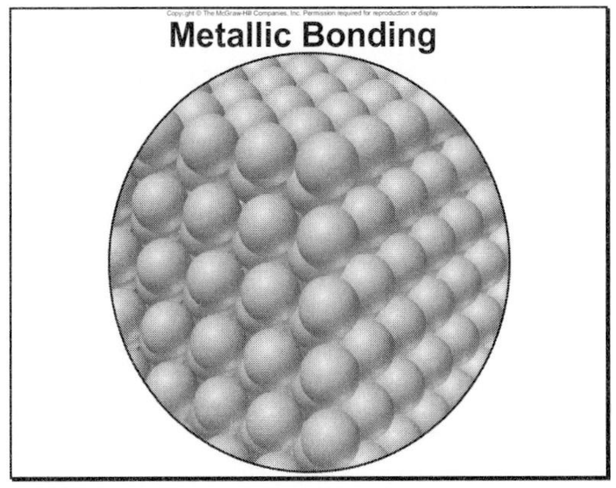
Copyright © The McGraw-Hill Companies, Inc. Permission required for reproduction or display.
Metallic Bonding

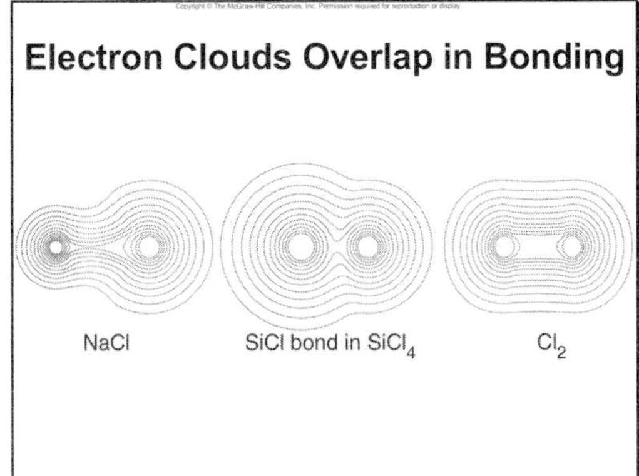
Copyright © The McGraw-Hill Companies, Inc. Permission required for reproduction or display.
Electron Clouds Overlap in Bonding
NaCl
SiCl bond in SiCl4
Cl2

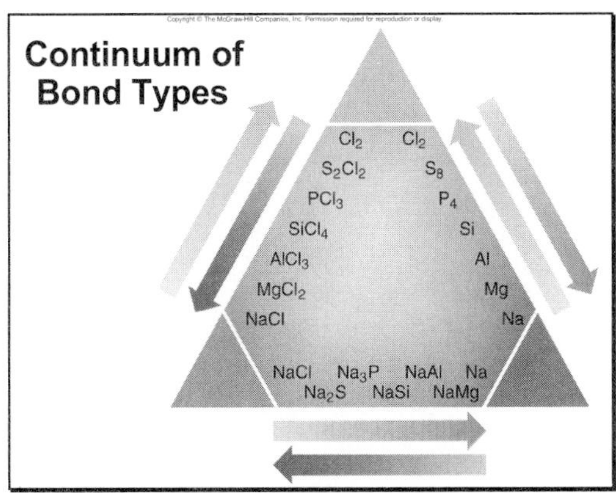
Copyright © The McGraw-Hill Companies, Inc. Permission required for reproduction or display.
Continuum of Bond Types
Cl2
Cl2
S2Cl2
S8
PCl3
P4
SiCl4
Si
AlCl3
Al
MgCl2
Mg
NaCl
Na
NaCl Na3P NaAl Na
Na2S NaSi NaMg

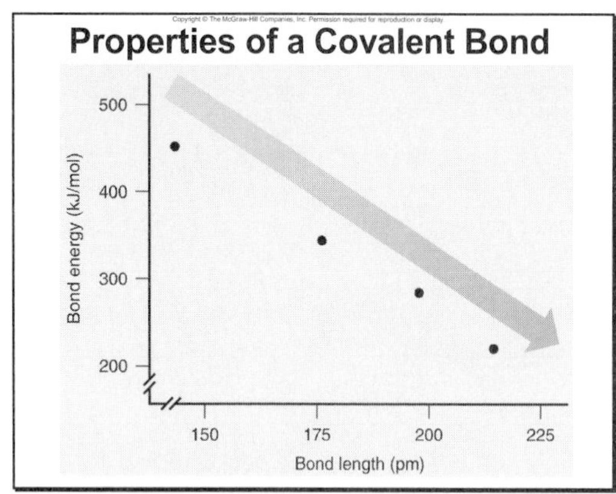
Copyright © The McGraw-Hill Companies, Inc. Permission required for reproduction or display.
Properties of a Covalent Bond
Bond energy (kJ/mol)
500
400
300
200
150
175
200
225
Bond length (pm)

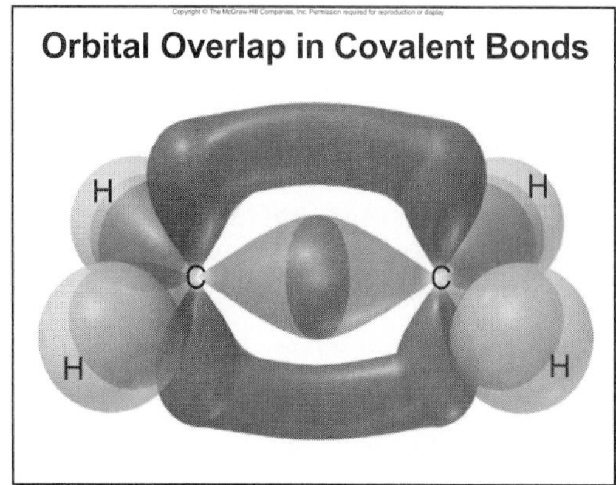
Copyright © The McGraw-Hill Companies, Inc. Permission required for reproduction or display.
Orbital Overlap in Covalent Bonds
H
H
C
C
H
H

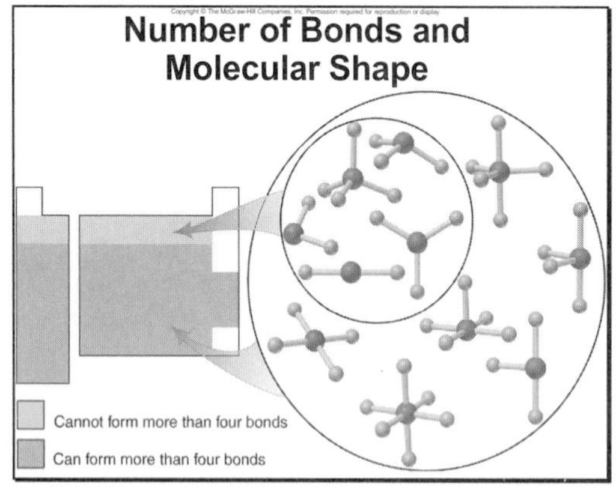
Copyright © The McGraw-Hill Companies, Inc. Permission required for reproduction or display.
Number of Bonds and Molecular Shape
Cannot form more than four bonds
Can form more than four bonds

Metals Versus Nonmetals

	Metals	Nonmetals
Atomic Properties	Have fewer valence electrons (in period) Have larger atomic size Have lower ionization energies Have lower electronegativities	Have more valence electrons (in period) Have smaller atomic size Have higher ionization energies Have higher electronegativities
Physical Properties	Occur as solids at room temperature Conduct electricity and heat well Are malleable and ductile	Occur in all three physical states Conduct electricity and heat poorly Are not malleable or ductile
Chemical Properties	Lose electron(s) to become cations React with nonmetals to form ionic compounds Mix with other metals to form solid solutions (alloys)	Gain electron(s) to become anions React with metals to form ionic compounds React with other nonmetals to form covalent compounds

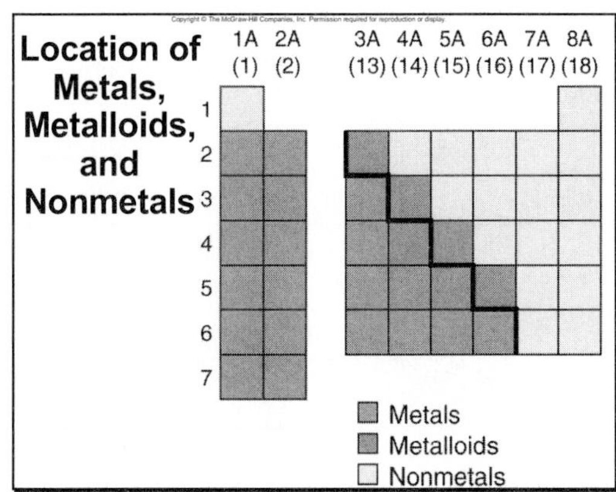

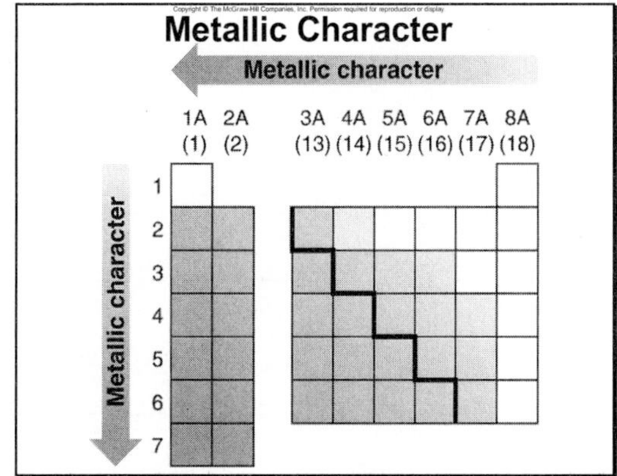

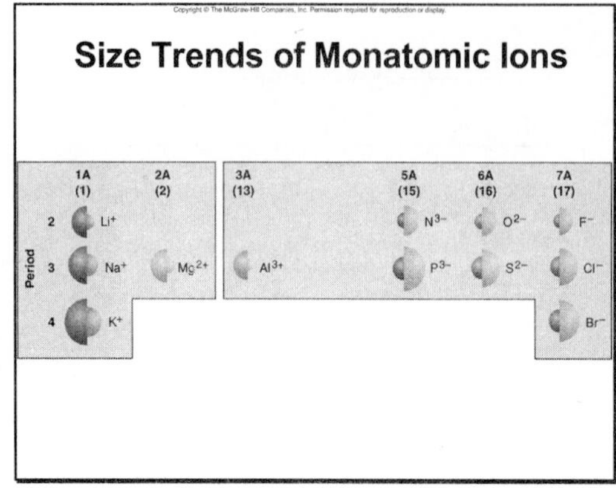

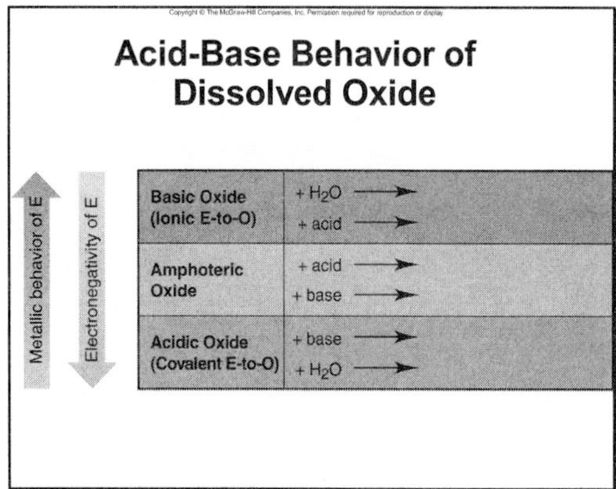

Acid-Base Behavior of Main-Group Oxides

Period	1A (1)	2A (2)	3A (13)	4A (14)	5A (15)	6A (16)	7A (17)	8A (18)
1								
2	Li_2O	BeO	B_2O_3	CO_2	N_2O_5 N_2O_3			
3	Na_2O	MgO	Al_2O_3	SiO_2	P_4O_{10} P_4O_6	SO_3 SO_2	Cl_2O_7 Cl_2O	
4	K_2O	CaO	Ga_2O_3	GeO_2	As_2O_5 As_4O_6	SeO_3 SeO_2	Br_2O	
5	Rb_2O	SrO	In_2O_3 In_2O	SnO_2 SnO	Sb_2O_5 Sb_4O_6	TeO_3 TeO_2	I_2O_5	
6	Cs_2O	BaO	Tl_2O	PbO_2 PbO	Bi_2O_3	PoO_2 PoO		
7	Fr_2O	RaO						

Strongly basic
Weakly basic
Amphoteric
Strongly acidic
Moderately acidic
Weakly acidic

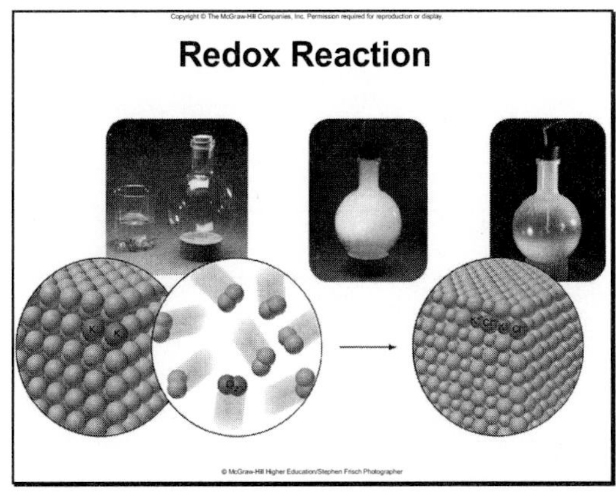
Copyright © The McGraw-Hill Companies, Inc. Permission required for reproduction or display.
Redox Reaction
© McGraw-Hill Higher Education/Stephen Frisch Photographer

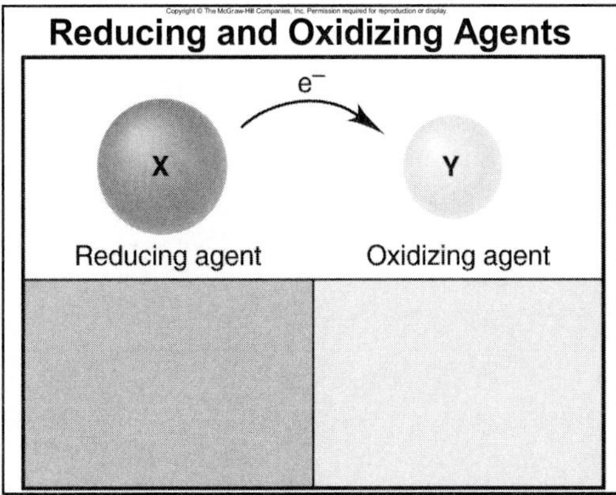
Copyright © The McGraw-Hill Companies, Inc. Permission required for reproduction or display.
Reducing and Oxidizing Agents
e⁻
X
Y
Reducing agent
Oxidizing agent

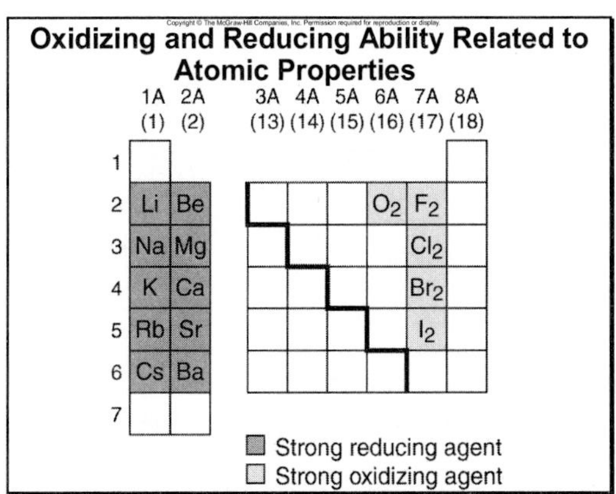
Copyright © The McGraw-Hill Companies, Inc. Permission required for reproduction or display.
Oxidizing and Reducing Ability Related to Atomic Properties
1A (1) 2A (2) 3A (13) 4A (14) 5A (15) 6A (16) 7A (17) 8A (18)
1 2 3 4 5 6 7
Li Be Na Mg K Ca Rb Sr Cs Ba
O2 F2 Cl2 Br2 I2
Strong reducing agent
Strong oxidizing agent

Oxidation States of the Main-Group Elements

Metals
Metalloids
Nonmetals

Period	1A (1)	2A (2)	3A (13)	4A (14)	5A (15)	6A (16)	7A (17)	8A (18)
1	H −1, +1							He
2	Li +1	Be +2	B +3	C −4, +4, +2	N −3, +5, +4, +3, +2, +1	O −1, −2	F −1	Ne
3	Na +1	Mg +2	Al +3	Si −4, +4, +2	P −3, +5, +3	S −2, +6, +4, +2	Cl −1, +7, +5, +3, +1	Ar
4	K +1	Ca +2	Ga +3, +1	Ge +4, +2	As −3, +5, +3	Se −2, +6, +4, +2	Br −1, +7, +5, +3, +1	Kr +2
5	Rb +1	Sr +2	In +3, +1	Sn +4, +2	Sb −3, +5, +3	Te −2, +6, +4, +2	I −1, +7, +5, +3, +1	Xe +6, +6, +4, +2
6	Cs +1	Ba +2	Tl +1	Pb +4, +2	Bi +3	Po +4, +2	At −1	Rn +2
7	Fr +1	Ra +2						

Most common oxidation states shown in **bold**.

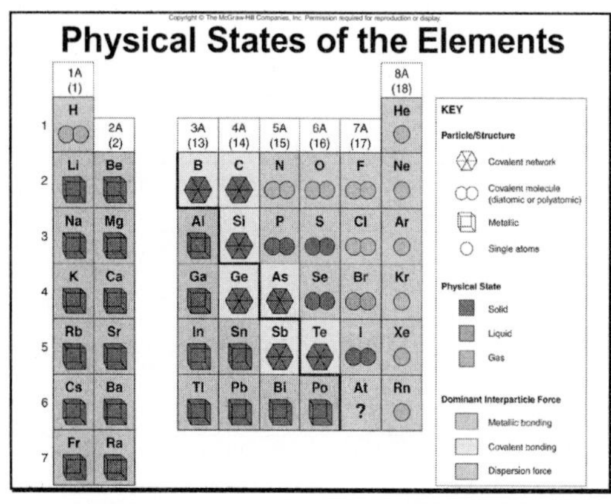

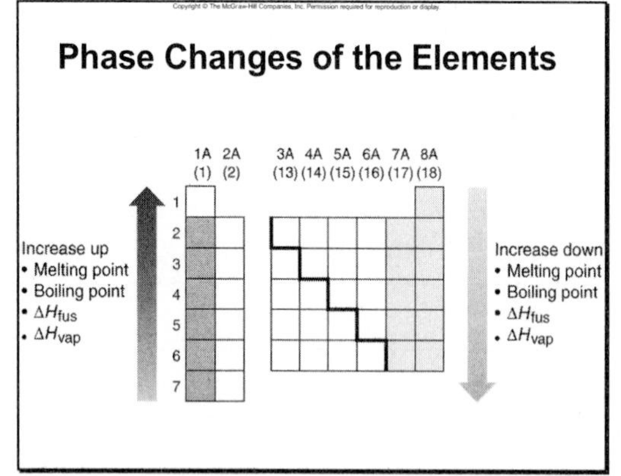

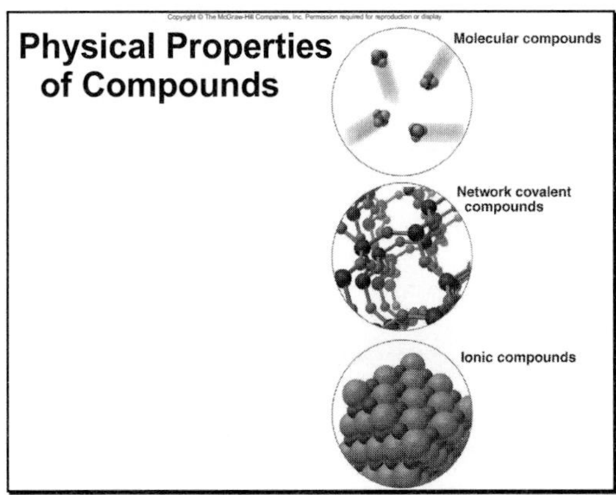
Physical Properties of Compounds
Molecular compounds
Network covalent compounds
Ionic compounds

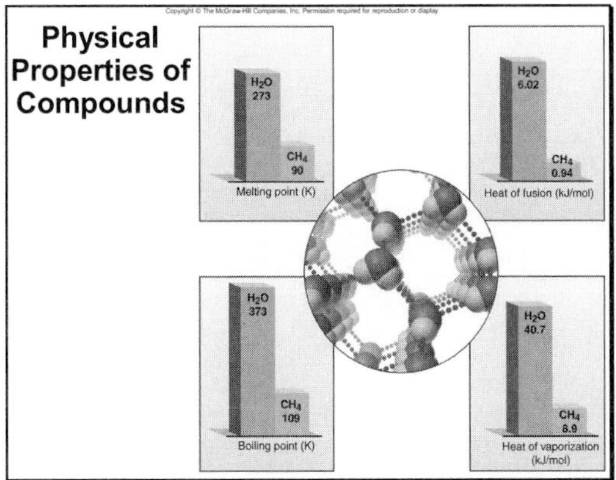
Physical Properties of Compounds
H2O 273
CH4 90
Melting point (K)
H2O 6.02
CH4 0.94
Heat of fusion (kJ/mol)
H2O 373
CH4 109
Boiling point (K)
H2O 40.7
CH4 8.9
Heat of vaporization (kJ/mol)

Chapter 14

Chemistry: The Molecular Nature of Matter and Change

Third Edition

Martin S. Silberberg

Where Does Hydrogen Belong?

1A (1) 2A (2) 3A (13) 4A (14) 5A (15) 6A (16) 7A (17) 8A (18)

Periods 1–7

H (group 1A, period 1) H (group 7A, period 1)

Lattice Energies of the Group 1A(1) and 2A(2) Chlorides

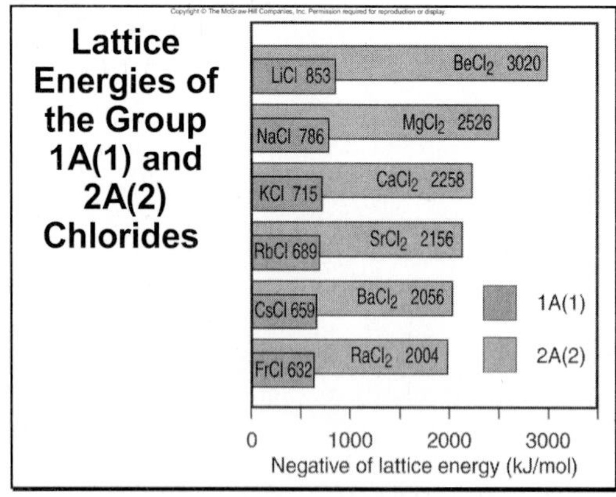

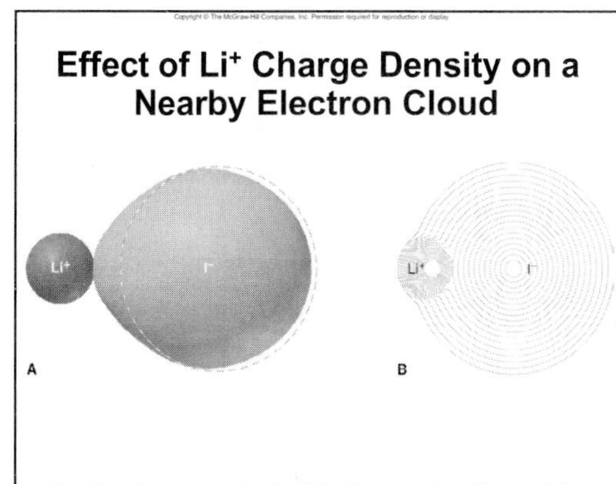
Effect of Li⁺ Charge Density on a Nearby Electron Cloud
Li⁺
I⁻
A
B

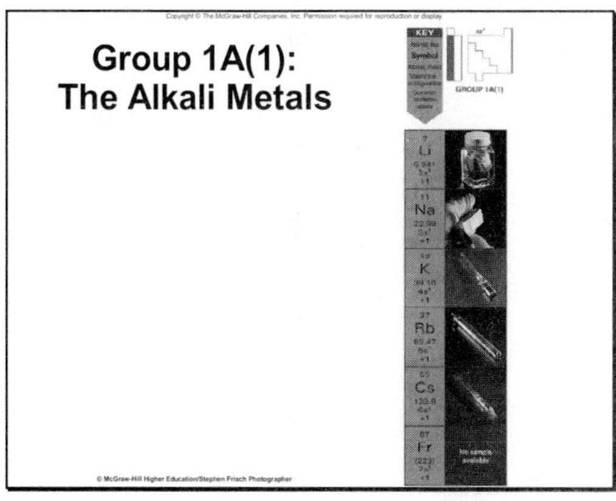
Group 1A(1): The Alkali Metals
KEY
GROUP 1A(1)
Li
Na
K
Rb
Cs
Fr
No sample available

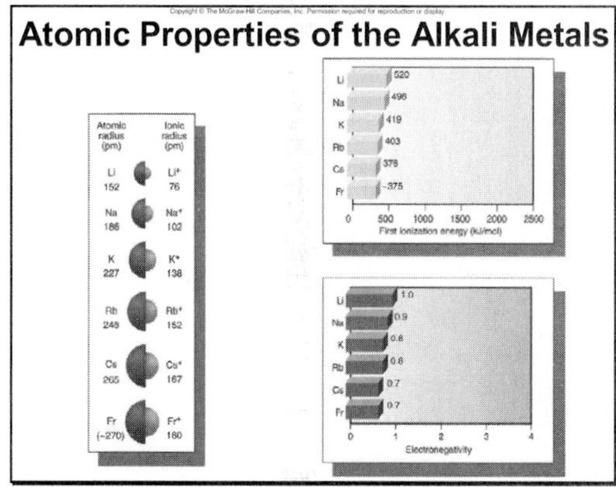
Copyright © The McGraw-Hill Companies, Inc. Permission required for reproduction or display.
Atomic Properties of the Alkali Metals
Atomic radius (pm)
Ionic radius (pm)
Li 152
Li⁺ 76
Na 186
Na⁺ 102
K 227
K⁺ 138
Rb 248
Rb⁺ 152
Cs 265
Cs⁺ 167
Fr (~270)
Fr⁺ 180
Li 520
Na 496
K 419
Rb 403
Cs 376
Fr ~375
0 500 1000 1500 2000 2500
First ionization energy (kJ/mol)
Li 1.0
Na 0.9
K 0.8
Rb 0.8
Cs 0.7
Fr 0.7
0 1 2 3 4
Electronegativity

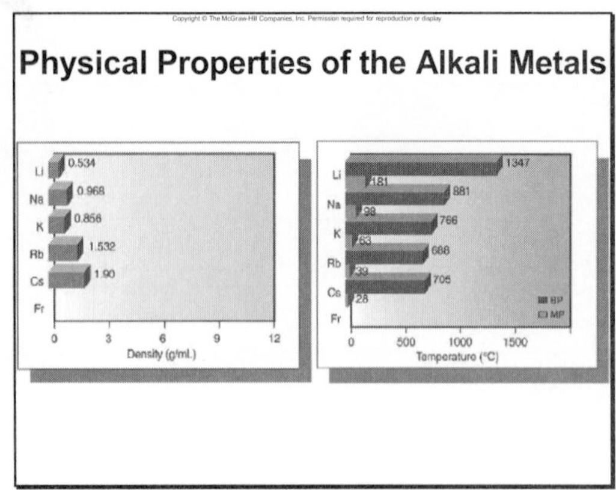
Physical Properties of the Alkali Metals
Li
Na
K
Rb
Cs
Fr
0.534
0.968
0.856
1.532
1.90
0
3
6
9
12
Density (g/mL)
1347
181
881
98
766
63
688
39
705
28
BP
MP
0
500
1000
1500
Temperature (°C)

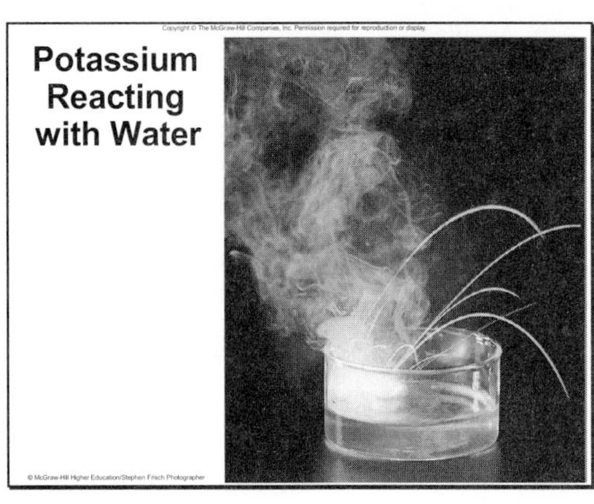
Potassium Reacting with Water

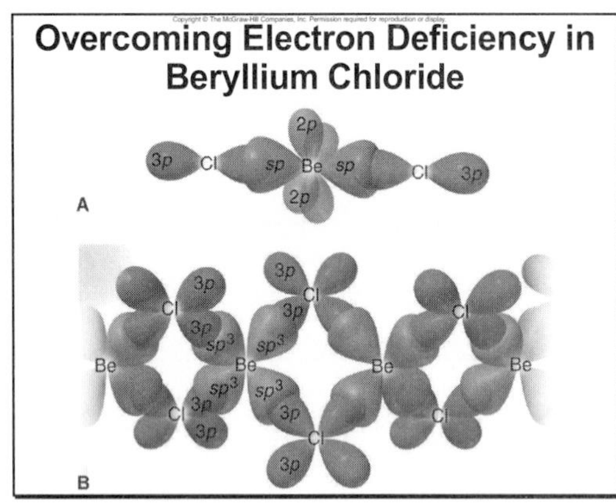
Overcoming Electron Deficiency in Beryllium Chloride
A
B
3p
Cl
sp
Be
2p
sp3

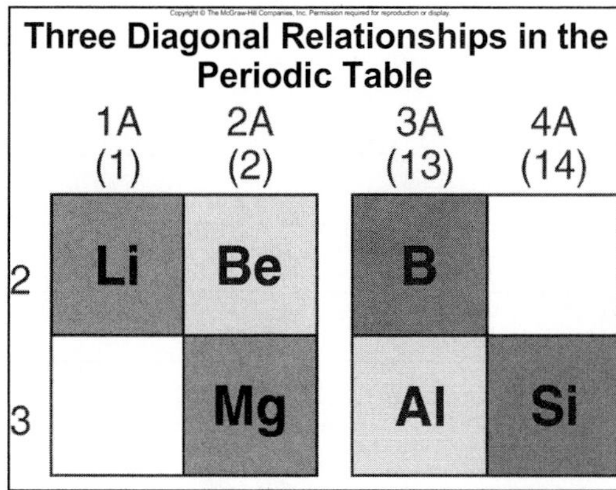
Copyright © The McGraw-Hill Companies, Inc. Permission required for reproduction or display.
Three Diagonal Relationships in the Periodic Table
1A (1)
2A (2)
3A (13)
4A (14)
2
3
Li
Be
B
Mg
Al
Si

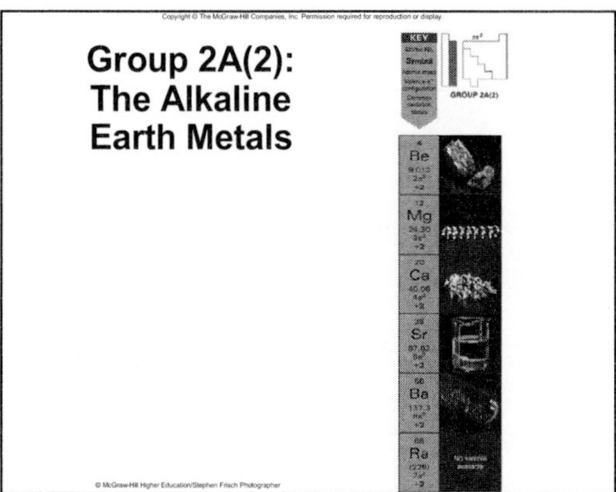
Copyright © The McGraw-Hill Companies, Inc. Permission required for reproduction or display.
Group 2A(2): The Alkaline Earth Metals
KEY
GROUP 2A(2)
Be
Mg
Ca
Sr
Ba
Ra
© McGraw-Hill Higher Education/Stephen Frisch Photographer

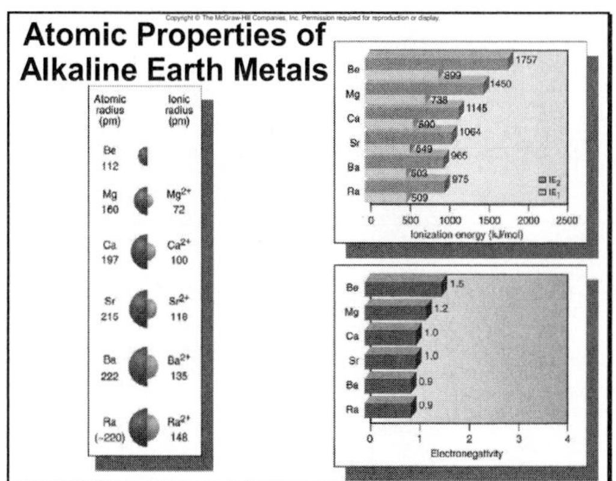
Copyright © The McGraw-Hill Companies, Inc. Permission required for reproduction or display.
Atomic Properties of Alkaline Earth Metals
Atomic radius (pm)
Ionic radius (pm)
Be 112
Mg 160 Mg2+ 72
Ca 197 Ca2+ 100
Sr 215 Sr2+ 118
Ba 222 Ba2+ 135
Ra (~220) Ra2+ 148
Be 899 1757
Mg 738 1450
Ca 590 1145
Sr 549 1064
Ba 503 965
Ra 509 975
IE2
IE1
Ionization energy (kJ/mol)
Be 1.5
Mg 1.2
Ca 1.0
Sr 1.0
Ba 0.9
Ra 0.9
Electronegativity

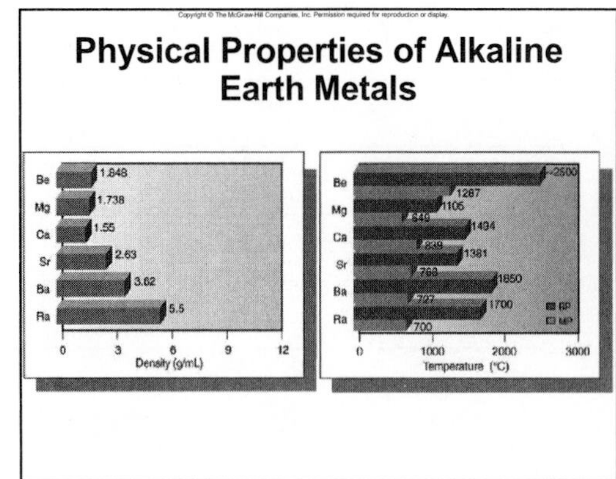
Physical Properties of Alkaline Earth Metals
Be
Mg
Ca
Sr
Ba
Ra
1.848
1.738
1.55
2.63
3.62
5.5
0
3
6
9
12
Density (g/mL)
2500
1287
1105
649
1494
839
1381
768
1850
727
1700
700
BP
MP
0
1000
2000
3000
Temperature (°C)

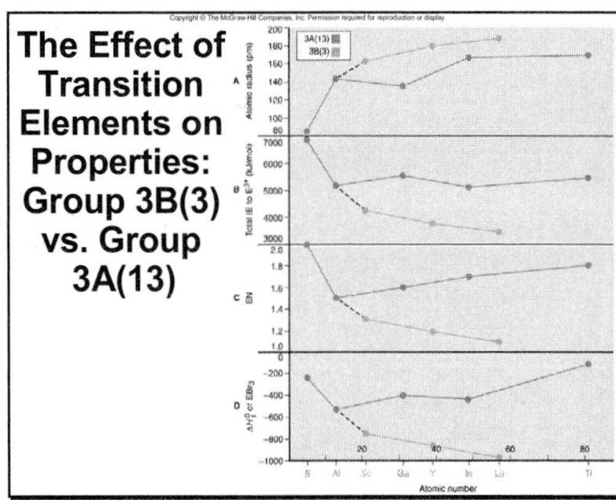
The Effect of Transition Elements on Properties: Group 3B(3) vs. Group 3A(13)
Atomic number

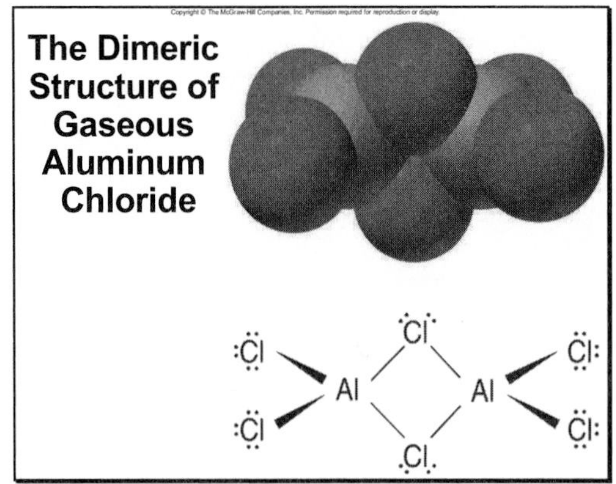
The Dimeric Structure of Gaseous Aluminum Chloride
:Cl
:Cl
Cl
Al
Al
Cl
Cl:
Cl:

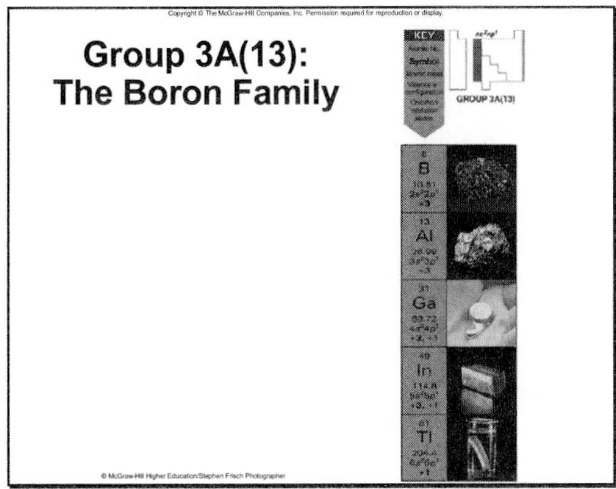
Group 3A(13):
The Boron Family
KEY
GROUP 3A(13)
B
Al
Ga
In
Tl

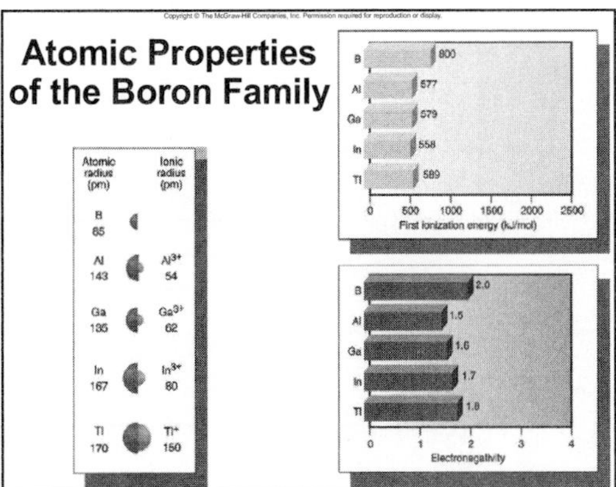
Atomic Properties of the Boron Family
Atomic radius (pm)
Ionic radius (pm)
B 85
Al 143
Al^{3+} 54
Ga 135
Ga^{3+} 62
In 167
In^{3+} 80
Tl 170
Tl^{+} 150
B 800
Al 577
Ga 579
In 558
Tl 589
0 500 1000 1500 2000 2500
First ionization energy (kJ/mol)
B 2.0
Al 1.5
Ga 1.6
In 1.7
Tl 1.8
0 1 2 3 4
Electronegativity

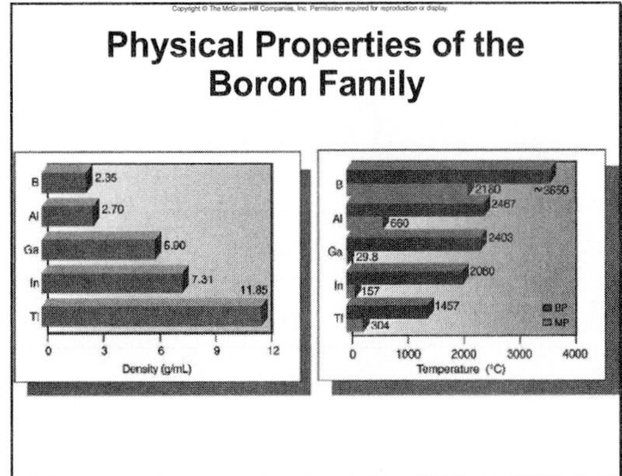
Physical Properties of the Boron Family
B 2.35
Al 2.70
Ga 5.90
In 7.31
Tl 11.85
0 3 6 9 12
Density (g/mL)
B ~3650 2180
Al 2467 660
Ga 2403 29.8
In 2080 157
Tl 1457 304
BP
MP
0 1000 2000 3000 4000
Temperature (°C)

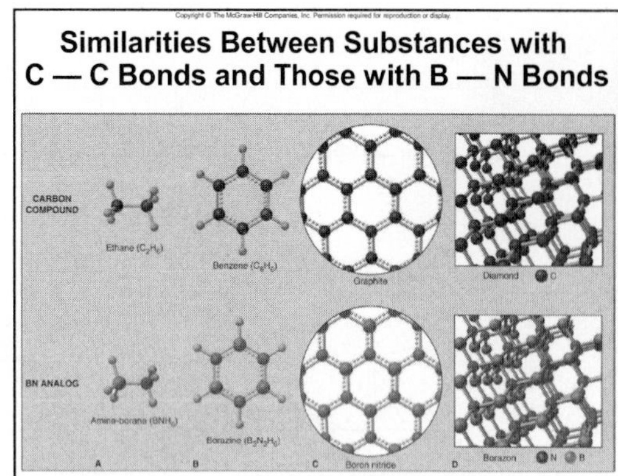
Similarities Between Substances with
C — C Bonds and Those with B — N Bonds
CARBON COMPOUND
Ethane (C_2H_6)
Benzene (C_6H_6)
Graphite
Diamond
C
BN ANALOG
Amine-borane (BNH_6)
Borazine ($B_3N_3H_6$)
Boron nitride
Borazon
N
B
A
B
C
D

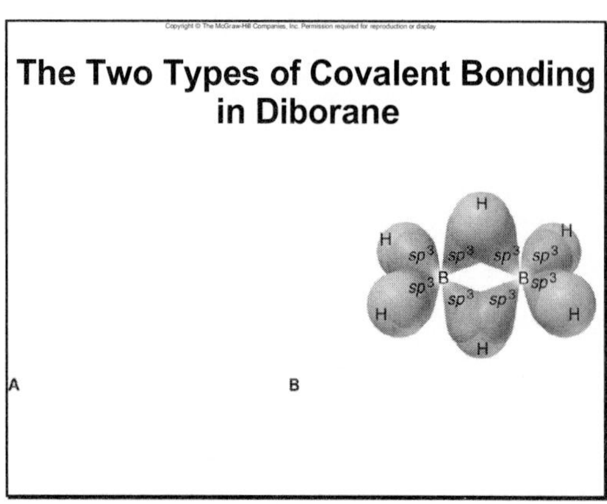
The Two Types of Covalent Bonding
in Diborane
H
H
H
sp^3
sp^3
sp^3
sp^3
sp^3
B
B
sp^3
sp^3
sp^3
H
H
H
A
B

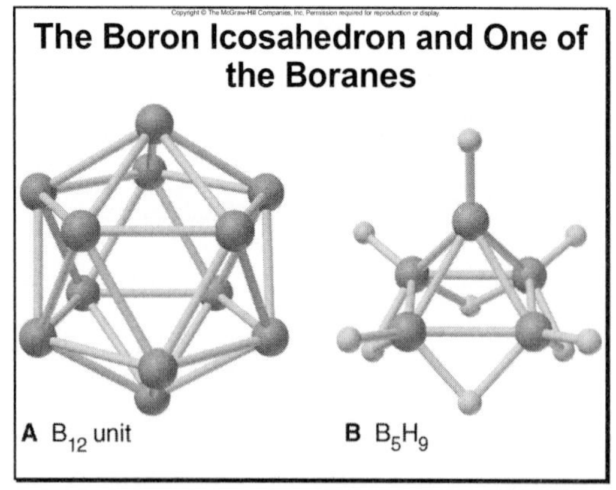
The Boron Icosahedron and One of
the Boranes
A B_{12} unit
B B_5H_9

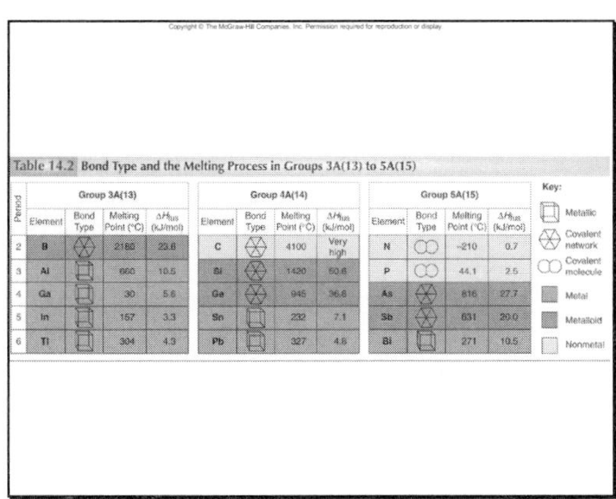

Table 14.2 Bond Type and the Melting Process in Groups 3A(13) to 5A(15)

Period	Group 3A(13) Element	Bond Type	Melting Point (°C)	ΔH_{fus} (kJ/mol)	Group 4A(14) Element	Bond Type	Melting Point (°C)	ΔH_{fus} (kJ/mol)	Group 5A(15) Element	Bond Type	Melting Point (°C)	ΔH_{fus} (kJ/mol)
2	B	Covalent network	2180	23.6	C	Covalent network	4100	Very high	N	Covalent molecule	−210	0.7
3	Al	Metallic	660	10.5	Si	Covalent network	1420	50.6	P	Covalent molecule	44.1	2.5
4	Ga	Metallic	30	5.6	Ge	Covalent network	945	36.8	As	Covalent network	816	27.7
5	In	Metallic	157	3.3	Sn	Metallic	232	7.1	Sb	Covalent network	631	20.0
6	Tl	Metallic	304	4.3	Pb	Metallic	327	4.8	Bi	Metallic	271	10.5

Key: Metallic; Covalent network; Covalent molecule; Metal; Metalloid; Nonmetal

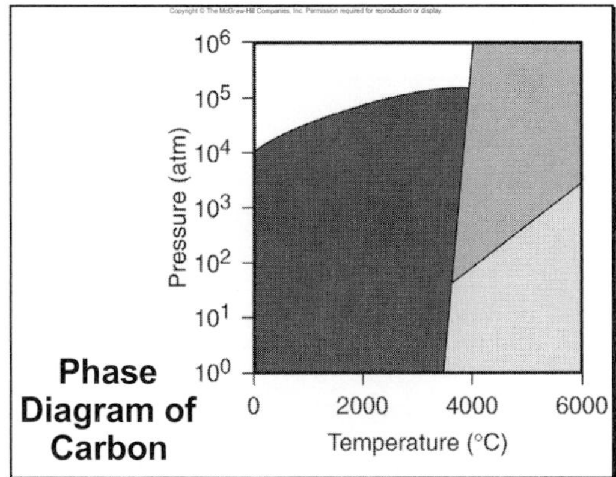

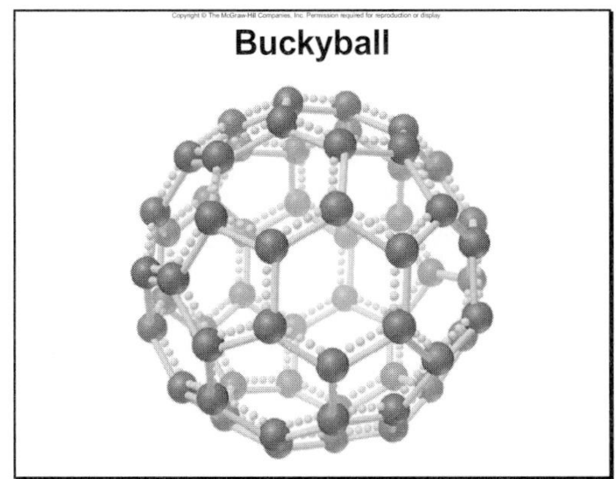

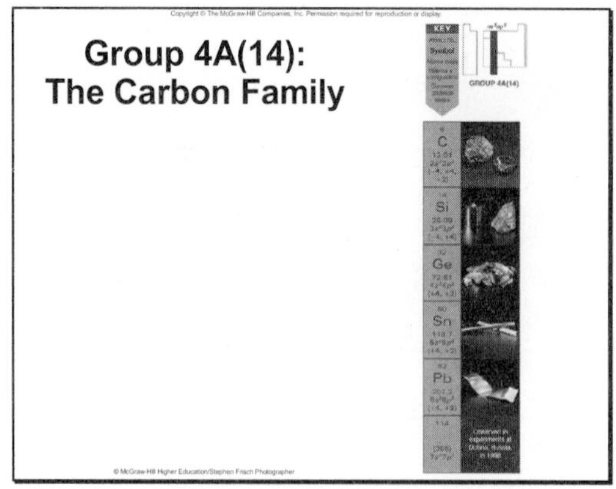
Group 4A(14):
The Carbon Family
KEY
GROUP 4A(14)
C
Si
Ge
Sn
Pb

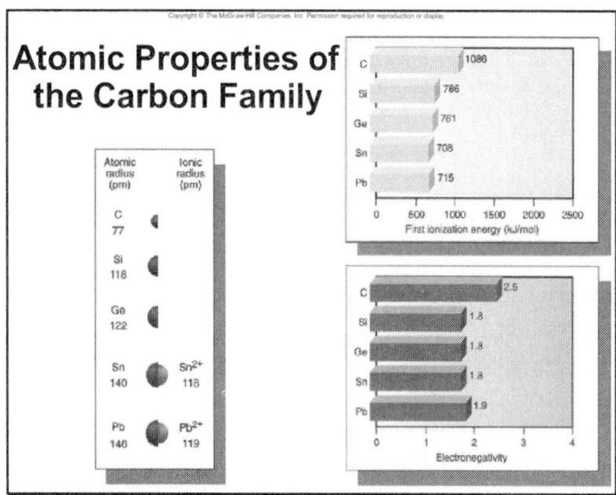
Atomic Properties of the Carbon Family
Atomic radius (pm)
Ionic radius (pm)
C 77
Si 118
Ge 122
Sn 140
Sn2+ 118
Pb 146
Pb2+ 119
1086
786
761
708
715
First ionization energy (kJ/mol)
2.5
1.8
1.8
1.8
1.9
Electronegativity

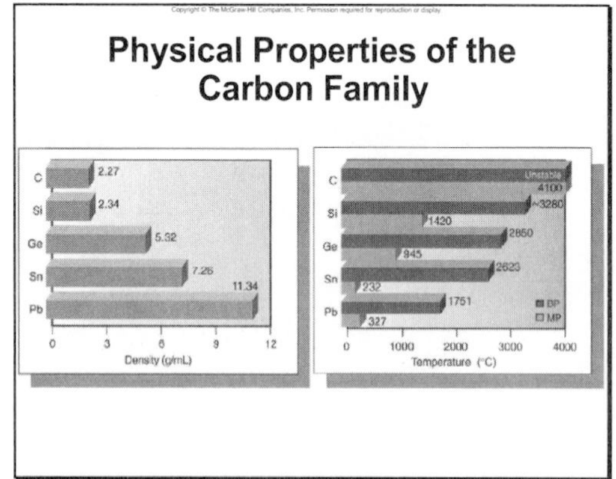
Physical Properties of the Carbon Family
2.27
2.34
5.32
7.26
11.34
Density (g/mL)
Unstable
4100
~3280
1420
2850
945
2623
232
1751
327
BP
MP
Temperature (°C)

The Greater Metallic Character of Tin and Lead in the Lower Oxidation State

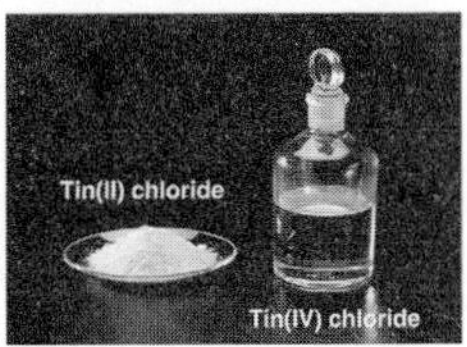

Three of the Several Million Known Organic Compounds of Carbon

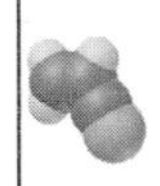

Acrylonitrile

PCB

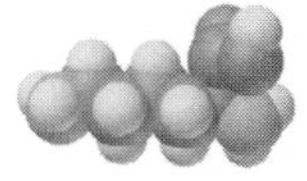

Lysine

The Impact of p,d-π Bonding on the Structure of Trisilylamine

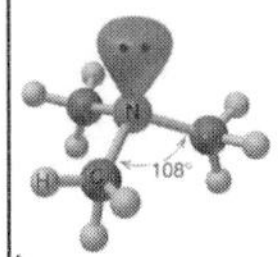

A

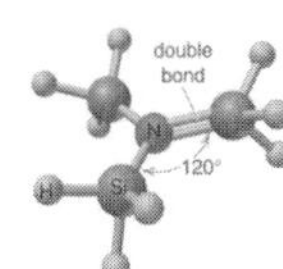

B

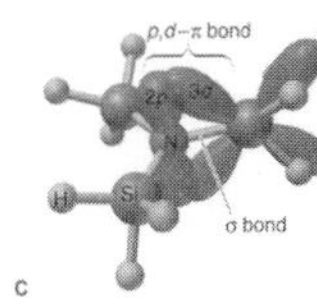

C

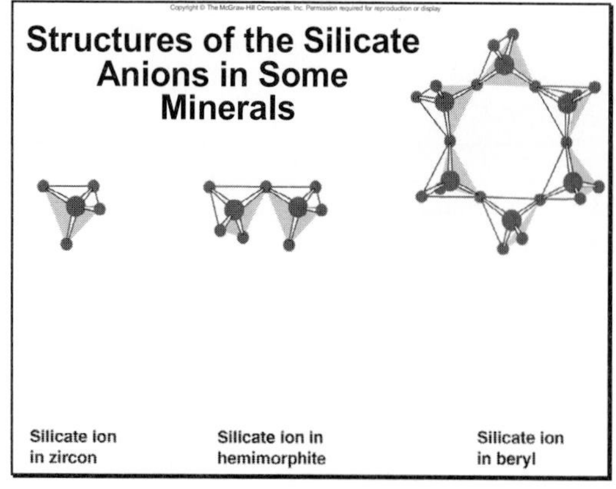
Copyright © The McGraw-Hill Companies, Inc. Permission required for reproduction or display.
Structures of the Silicate Anions in Some Minerals
Silicate ion in zircon
Silicate ion in hemimorphite
Silicate ion in beryl

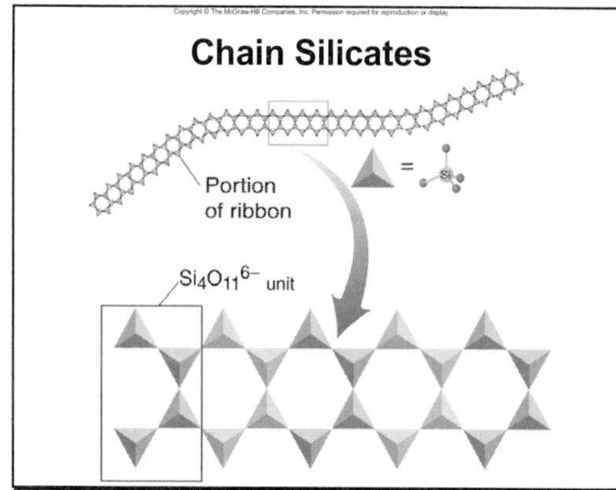
Copyright © The McGraw-Hill Companies, Inc. Permission required for reproduction or display.
Chain Silicates
Portion of ribbon
Si
$Si_4O_{11}^{6-}$ unit

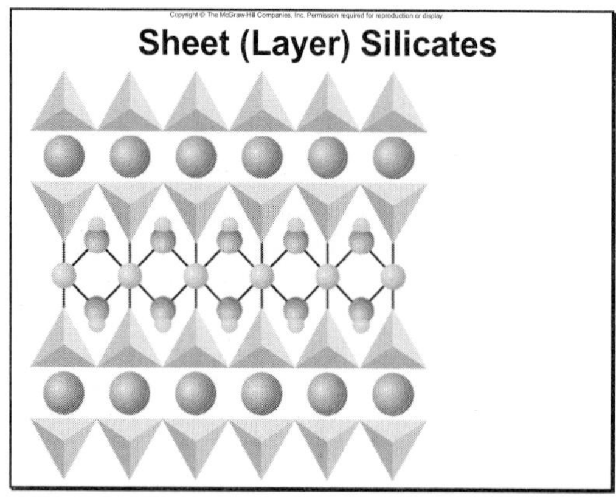
Copyright © The McGraw-Hill Companies, Inc. Permission required for reproduction or display.
Sheet (Layer) Silicates

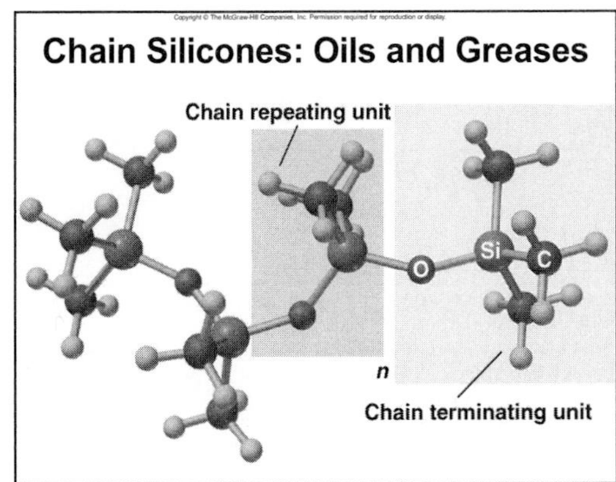
Copyright © The McGraw-Hill Companies, Inc. Permission required for reproduction or display.
Chain Silicones: Oils and Greases
Chain repeating unit
O
Si
C
n
Chain terminating unit

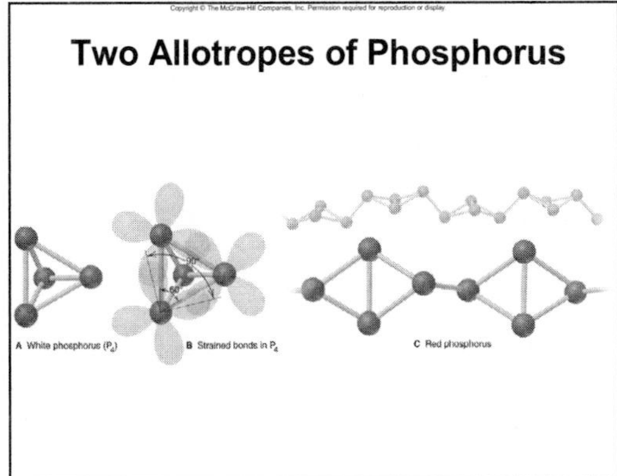
Copyright © The McGraw-Hill Companies, Inc. Permission required for reproduction or display.
Two Allotropes of Phosphorus
A White phosphorus (P_4)
B Strained bonds in P_4
C Red phosphorus

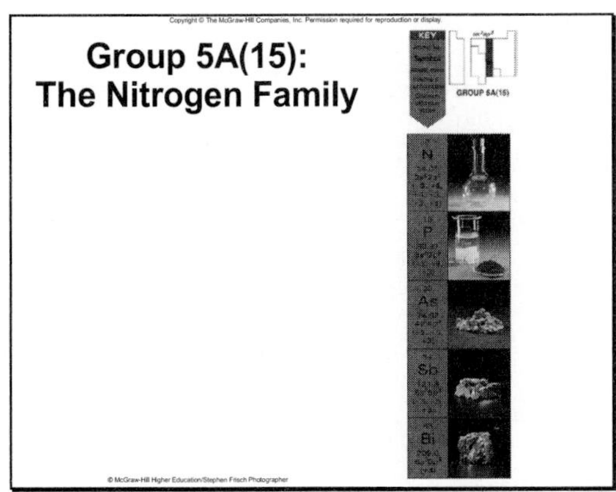
Copyright © The McGraw-Hill Companies, Inc. Permission required for reproduction or display.
Group 5A(15):
The Nitrogen Family
KEY
GROUP 5A(15)
N
P
As
Sb
Bi
© McGraw-Hill Higher Education/Stephen Frisch Photographer

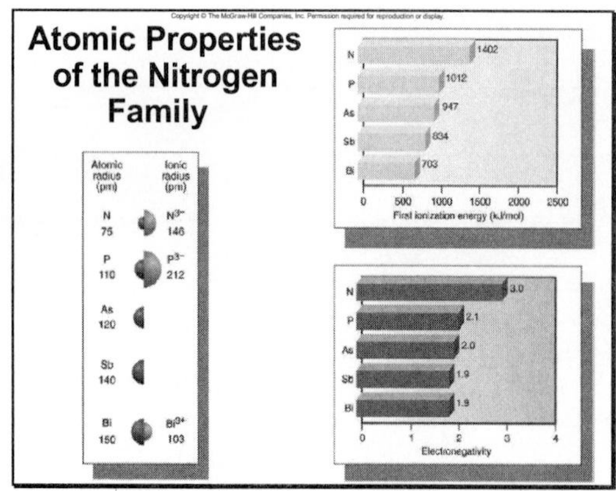
Copyright © The McGraw-Hill Companies, Inc. Permission required for reproduction or display.
Atomic Properties of the Nitrogen Family
Atomic radius (pm)
Ionic radius (pm)
N 75
N3− 146
P 110
P3− 212
As 120
Sb 140
Bi 150
Bi3+ 103
1402
1012
947
834
703
First ionization energy (kJ/mol)
3.0
2.1
2.0
1.9
1.9
Electronegativity

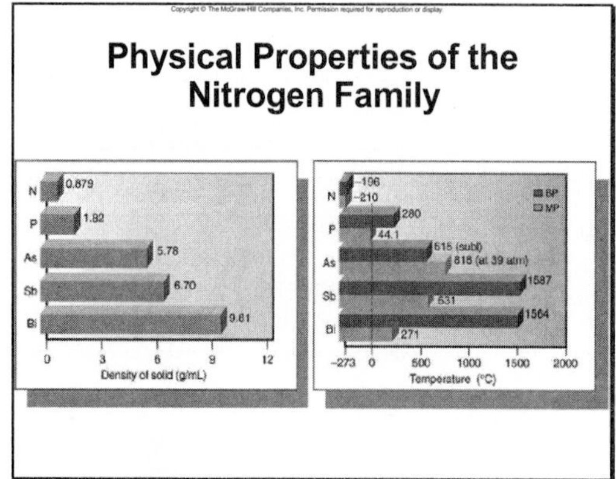
Copyright © The McGraw-Hill Companies, Inc. Permission required for reproduction or display.
Physical Properties of the Nitrogen Family
0.879
1.82
5.78
6.70
9.81
Density of solid (g/mL)
BP
MP
−196
−210
280
44.1
615 (subl)
816 (at 39 atm)
1587
631
1564
271
Temperature (°C)

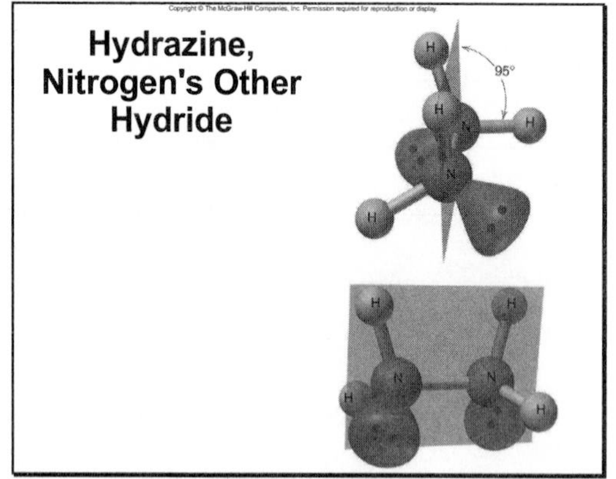
Copyright © The McGraw-Hill Companies, Inc. Permission required for reproduction or display.
Hydrazine, Nitrogen's Other Hydride
95°

Table 14.3 Structures and Properties of the Nitrogen Oxides

Formula	Name	Space-filling Model	Lewis Structure	Oxidation State of N	ΔH_f° (kJ/mol) at 298 K	Comment
N_2O	Dinitrogen monoxide (dinitrogen oxide; nitrous oxide)					
NO	Nitrogen monoxide (nitrogen oxide; nitric oxide)					
N_2O_3	Dinitrogen trioxide					
NO_2	Nitrogen dioxide					
N_2O_4	Dinitrogen tetraoxide					
N_2O_5	Dinitrogen pentaoxide					

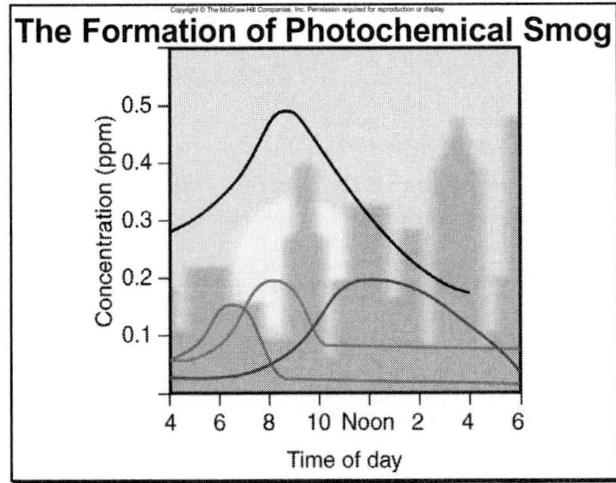

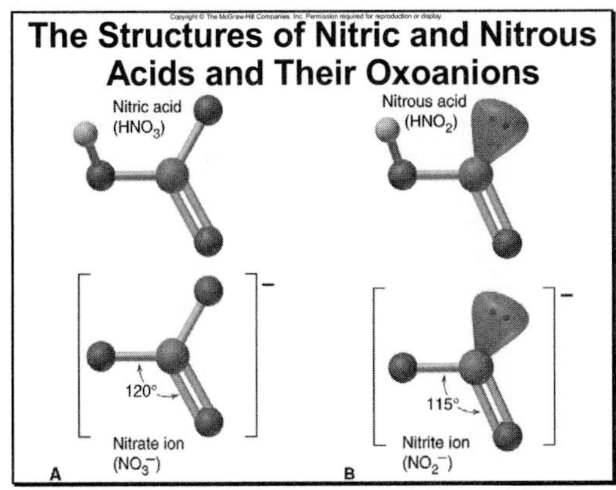

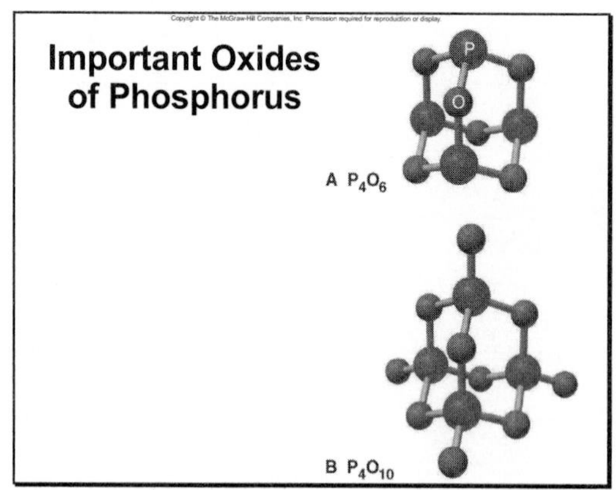
Important Oxides
of Phosphorus
P
O
A P_4O_6
B P_4O_{10}

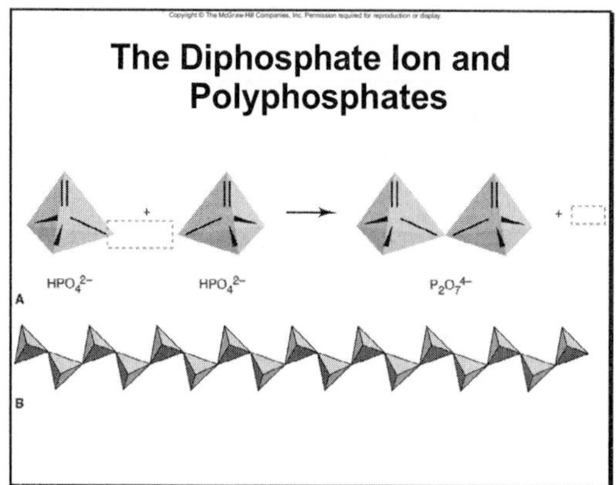
The Diphosphate Ion and
Polyphosphates
HPO_4^{2-}
HPO_4^{2-}
$P_2O_7^{4-}$
A
B

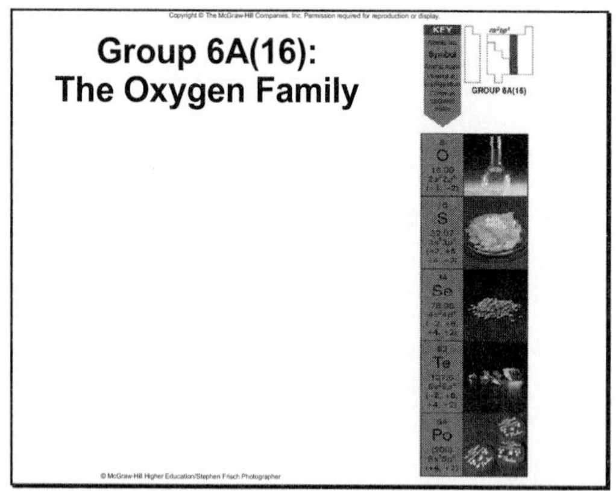
Group 6A(16):
The Oxygen Family
KEY
GROUP 6A(16)
O
S
Se
Te
Po

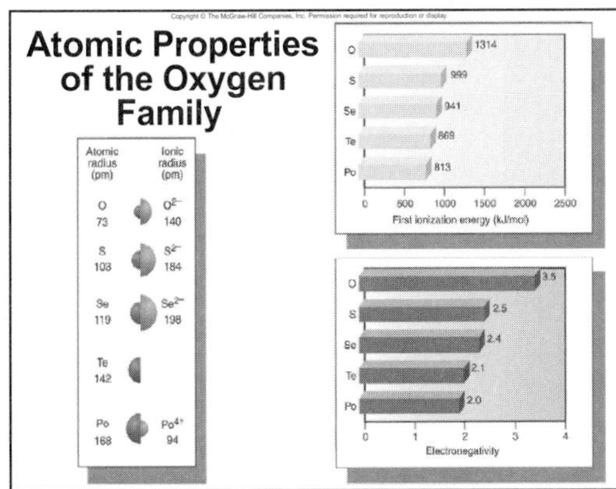
Copyright © The McGraw-Hill Companies, Inc. Permission required for reproduction or display.
Atomic Properties of the Oxygen Family
Atomic radius (pm)
Ionic radius (pm)
O 73
O2− 140
S 103
S2− 184
Se 119
Se2− 198
Te 142
Po 168
Po4+ 94
1314
999
941
869
813
First ionization energy (kJ/mol)
3.5
2.5
2.4
2.1
2.0
Electronegativity

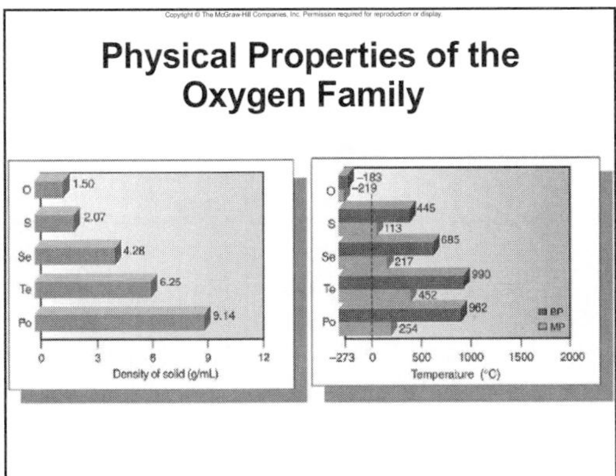
Copyright © The McGraw-Hill Companies, Inc. Permission required for reproduction or display.
Physical Properties of the Oxygen Family
1.50
2.07
4.28
6.25
9.14
Density of solid (g/mL)
−183
−219
445
113
685
217
990
452
962
254
BP
MP
Temperature (°C)

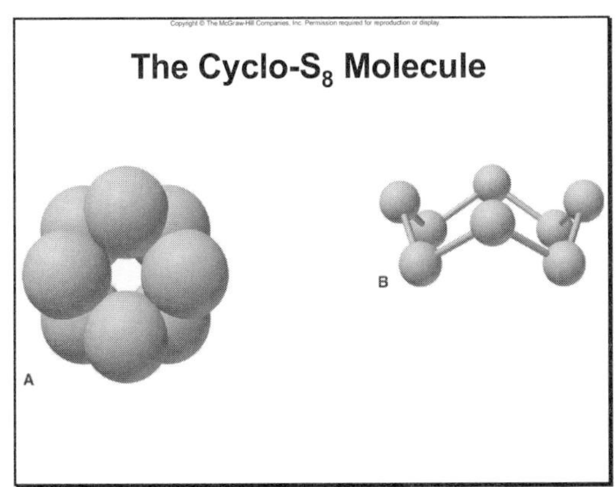
Copyright © The McGraw-Hill Companies, Inc. Permission required for reproduction or display.
The Cyclo-S8 Molecule
A
B

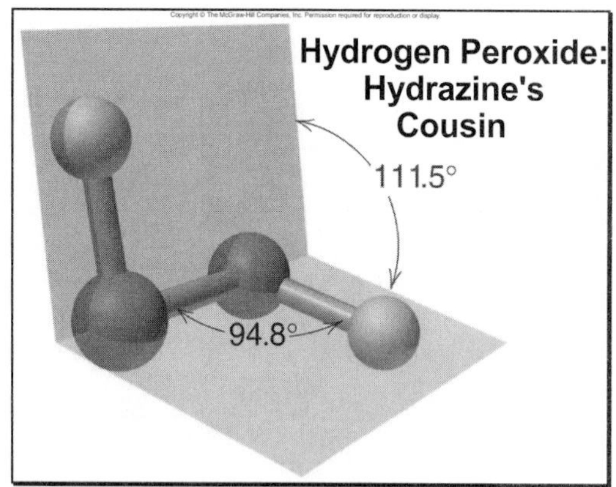
Copyright © The McGraw-Hill Companies, Inc. Permission required for reproduction or display.
Hydrogen Peroxide: Hydrazine's Cousin
111.5°
94.8°

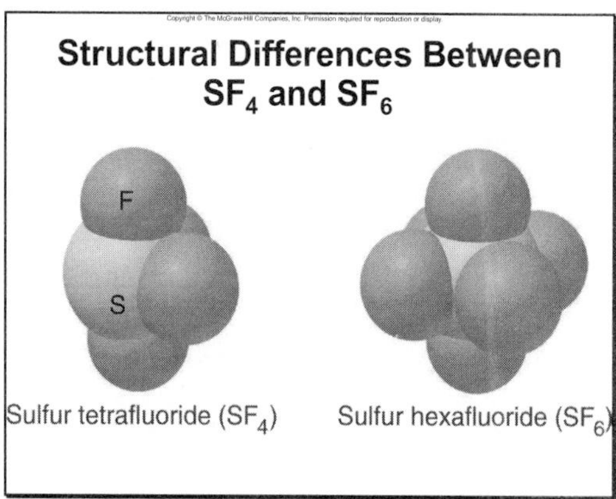
Copyright © The McGraw-Hill Companies, Inc. Permission required for reproduction or display.
Structural Differences Between SF_4 and SF_6
F
S
Sulfur tetrafluoride (SF_4)
Sulfur hexafluoride (SF_6)

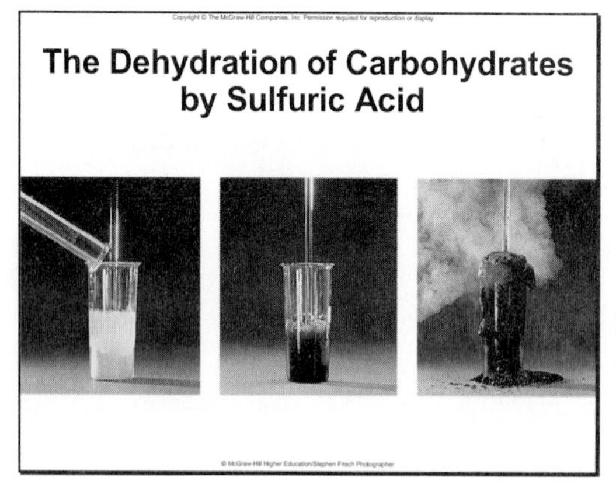
Copyright © The McGraw-Hill Companies, Inc. Permission required for reproduction or display.
The Dehydration of Carbohydrates by Sulfuric Acid
© McGraw-Hill Higher Education/Stephen Frisch Photographer

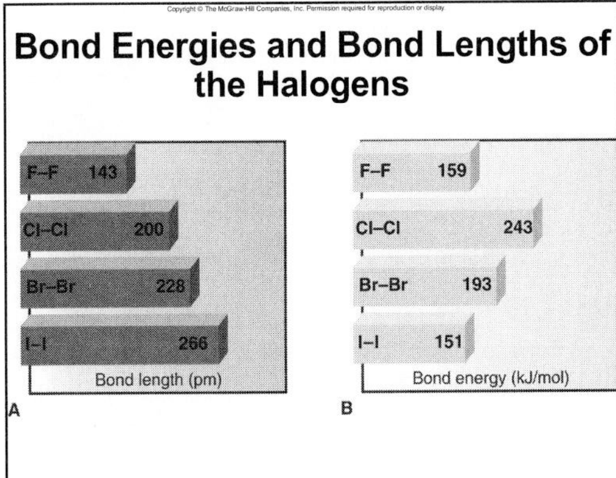
Copyright © The McGraw-Hill Companies, Inc. Permission required for reproduction or display.
Bond Energies and Bond Lengths of the Halogens
F–F 143
Cl–Cl 200
Br–Br 228
I–I 266
Bond length (pm)
A
F–F 159
Cl–Cl 243
Br–Br 193
I–I 151
Bond energy (kJ/mol)
B

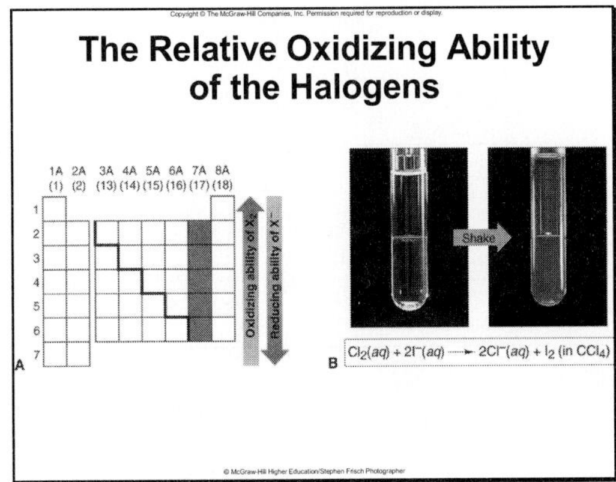
Copyright © The McGraw-Hill Companies, Inc. Permission required for reproduction or display.
The Relative Oxidizing Ability of the Halogens
1A 2A 3A 4A 5A 6A 7A 8A
(1) (2) (13) (14) (15) (16) (17) (18)
Oxidizing ability of X2
Reducing ability of X−
A
Shake
B
Cl2(aq) + 2I−(aq) → 2Cl−(aq) + I2 (in CCl4)
© McGraw-Hill Higher Education/Stephen Frisch Photographer

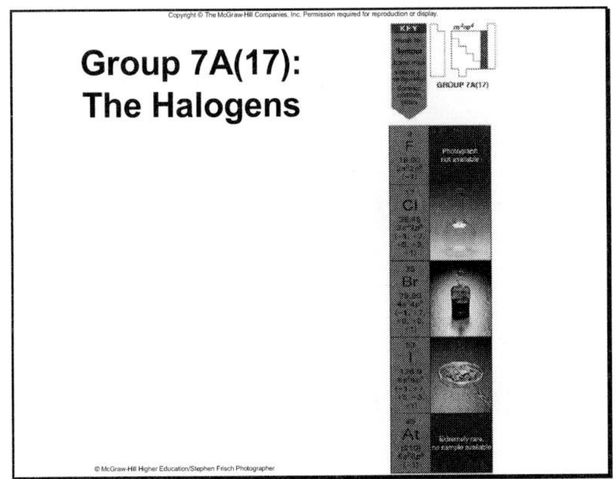
Copyright © The McGraw-Hill Companies, Inc. Permission required for reproduction or display.
Group 7A(17): The Halogens
KEY
GROUP 7A(17)
F
Cl
Br
I
At
© McGraw-Hill Higher Education/Stephen Frisch Photographer

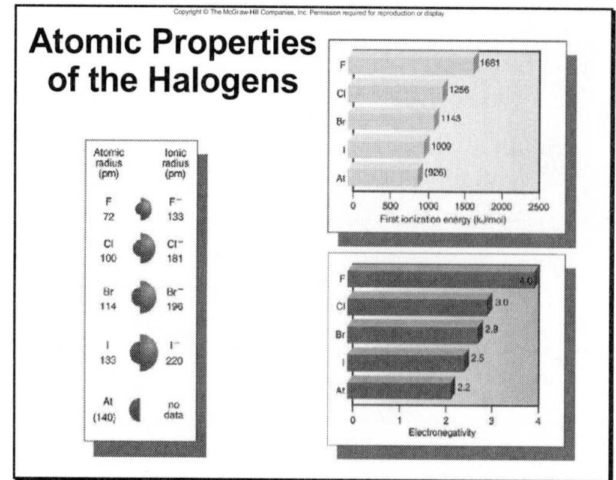
Atomic Properties of the Halogens
Atomic radius (pm)
Ionic radius (pm)
F 72
F⁻ 133
Cl 100
Cl⁻ 181
Br 114
Br⁻ 196
I 133
I⁻ 220
At (140)
no data
1681
1256
1143
1009
(926)
First ionization energy (kJ/mol)
4.0
3.0
2.8
2.5
2.2
Electronegativity

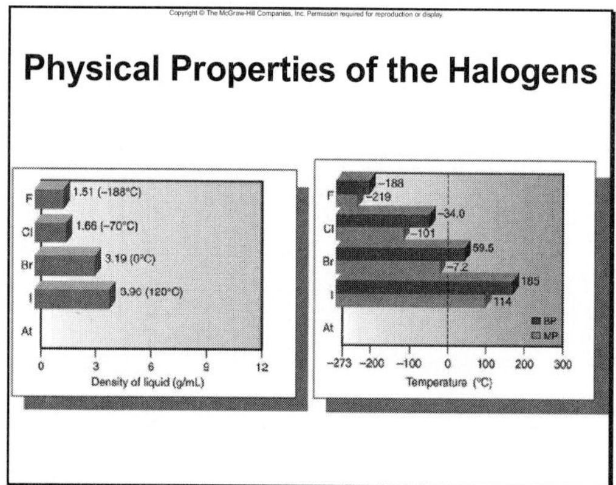
Physical Properties of the Halogens
1.51 (−188°C)
1.66 (−70°C)
3.19 (0°C)
3.96 (120°C)
Density of liquid (g/mL)
−188
−219
−34.0
−101
59.5
−7.2
185
114
BP
MP
Temperature (°C)

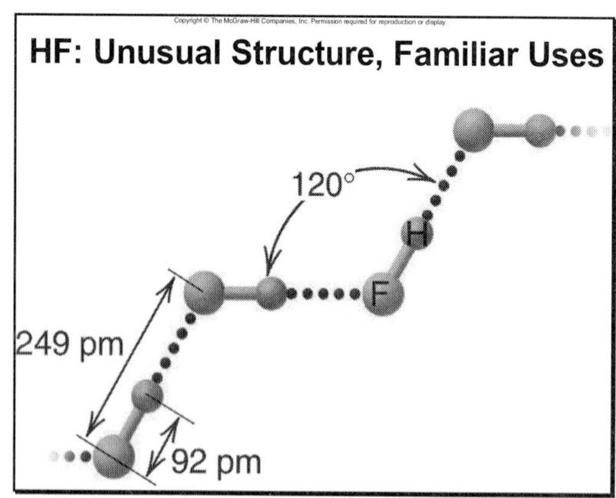
HF: Unusual Structure, Familiar Uses
120°
H
F
249 pm
92 pm

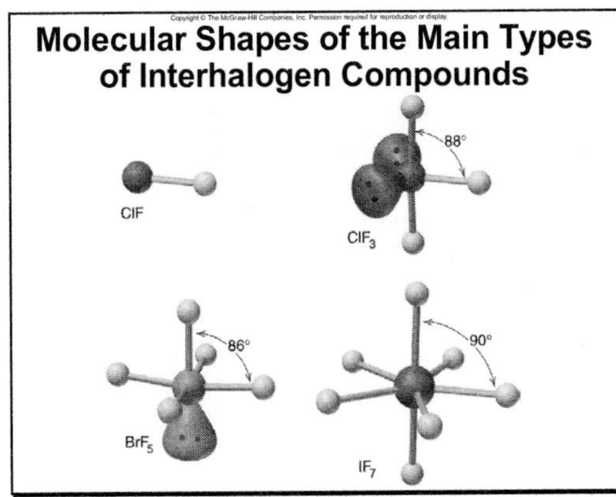

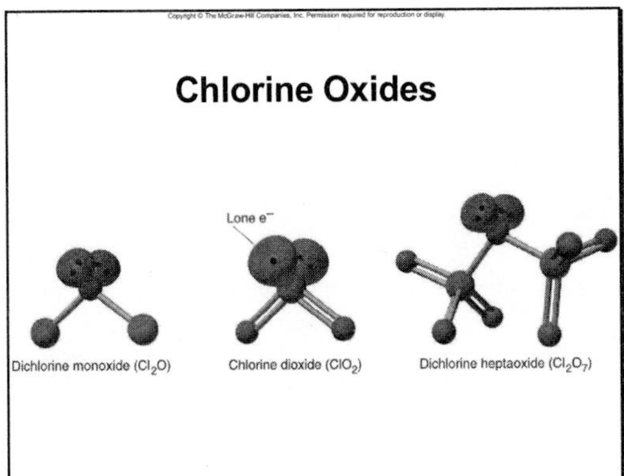

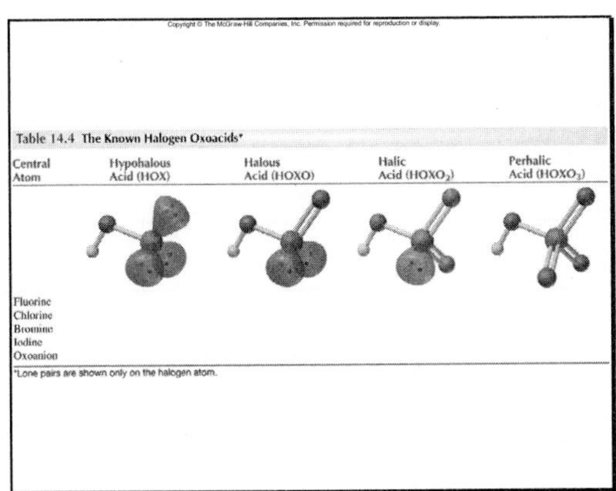

Table 14.4 The Known Halogen Oxoacids*

Central Atom	Hypohalous Acid (HOX)	Halous Acid (HOXO)	Halic Acid ($HOXO_2$)	Perhalic Acid ($HOXO_3$)
Fluorine				
Chlorine				
Bromine				
Iodine				
Oxoanion				

*Lone pairs are shown only on the halogen atom.

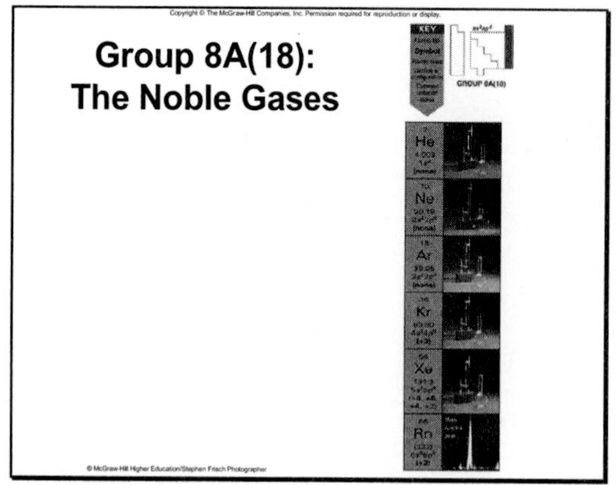
Group 8A(18):
The Noble Gases
He
Ne
Ar
Kr
Xe
Rn

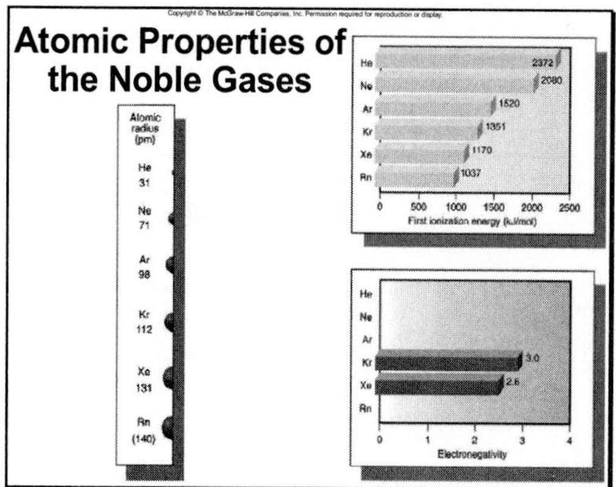
Atomic Properties of the Noble Gases
Atomic radius (pm)
He 31
Ne 71
Ar 98
Kr 112
Xe 131
Rn (140)
2372
2080
1520
1351
1170
1037
First ionization energy (kJ/mol)
3.0
2.6
Electronegativity

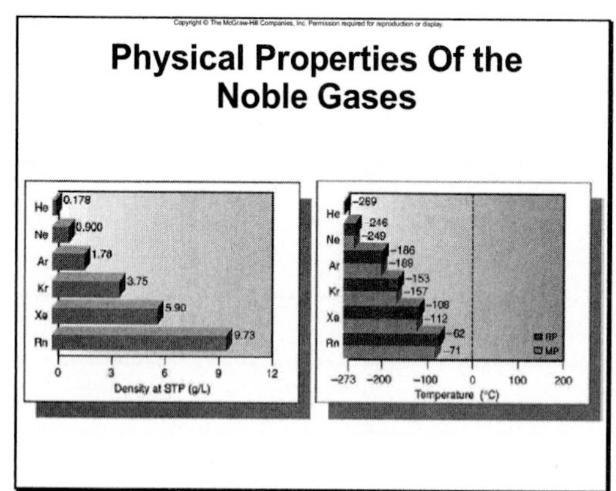
Physical Properties Of the Noble Gases
0.178
0.900
1.78
3.75
5.90
9.73
Density at STP (g/L)
−269
−246
−249
−186
−189
−153
−157
−108
−112
−62
−71
BP
MP
Temperature (°C)

Chapter 15

Chemistry: The Molecular Nature of Matter and Change

Third Edition

Martin S. Silberberg

The Chemical Diversity of Organic Compounds

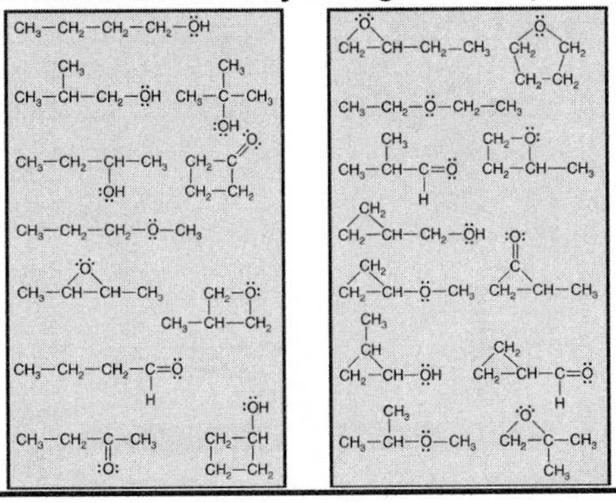

Four-Carbon Arrangements

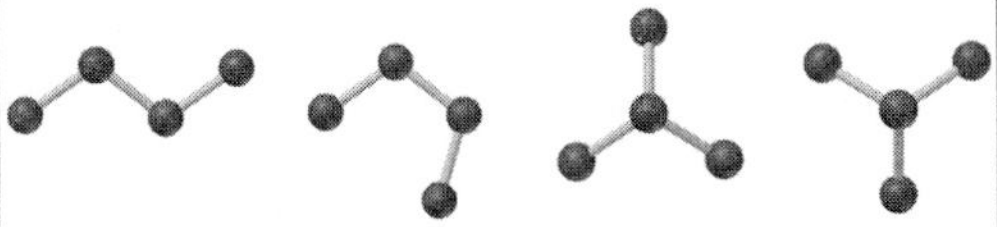

Copyright © The McGraw-Hill Companies, Inc. Permission required for reproduction or display.

Some Five-Carbon Skeletons

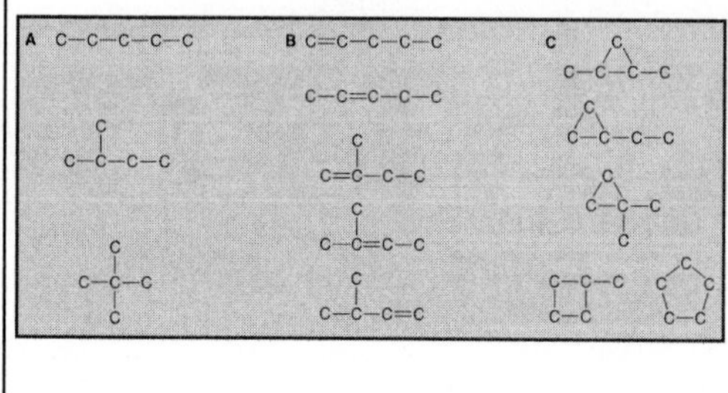

Copyright © The McGraw-Hill Companies, Inc. Permission required for reproduction or display.

Adding the H-Atom Skin to the C-Atom Skeleton

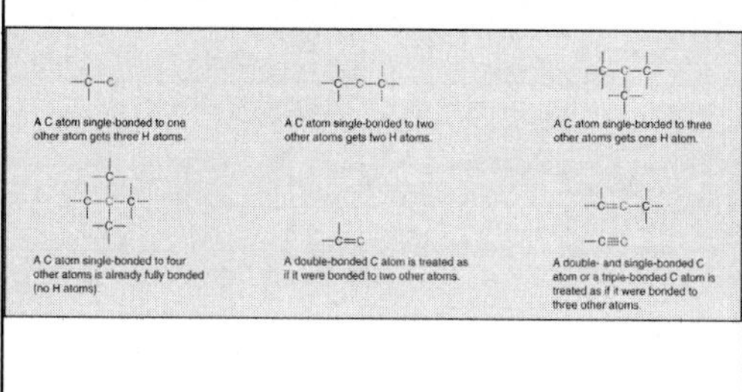

Copyright © The McGraw-Hill Companies, Inc. Permission required for reproduction or display.

Table 15.1 Numerical Roots for Carbon Chains and Branches

Roots	Number of C Atoms
meth-	1
eth-	
prop-	
but-	
pent-	
hex-	
hept-	
oct-	
non-	
dec-	

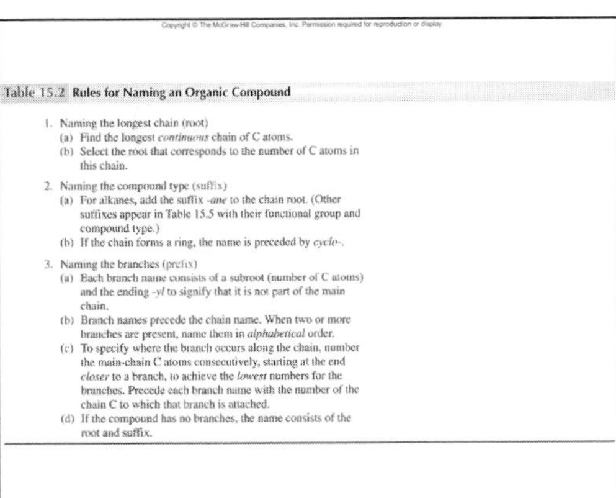

Table 15.2 Rules for Naming an Organic Compound

1. Naming the longest chain (root)
   (a) Find the longest *continuous* chain of C atoms.
   (b) Select the root that corresponds to the number of C atoms in this chain.
2. Naming the compound type (suffix)
   (a) For alkanes, add the suffix *-ane* to the chain root. (Other suffixes appear in Table 15.5 with their functional group and compound type.)
   (b) If the chain forms a ring, the name is preceded by *cyclo-*.
3. Naming the branches (prefix)
   (a) Each branch name consists of a subroot (number of C atoms) and the ending *-yl* to signify that it is not part of the main chain.
   (b) Branch names precede the chain name. When two or more branches are present, name them in *alphabetical* order.
   (c) To specify where the branch occurs along the chain, number the main-chain C atoms consecutively, starting at the end *closer* to a branch, to achieve the *lowest* numbers for the branches. Precede each branch name with the number of the chain C to which that branch is attached.
   (d) If the compound has no branches, the name consists of the root and suffix.

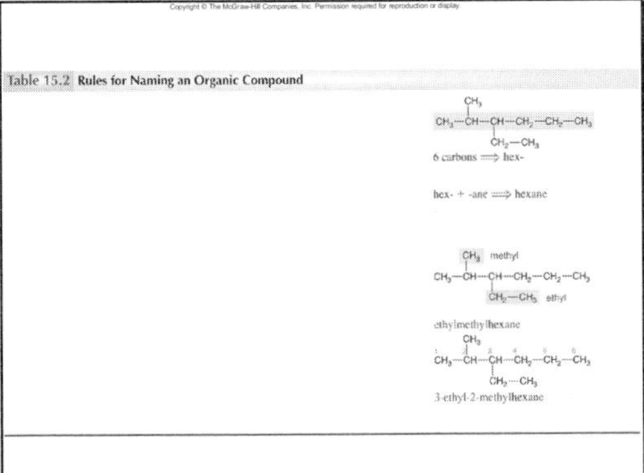

Table 15.2 Rules for Naming an Organic Compound

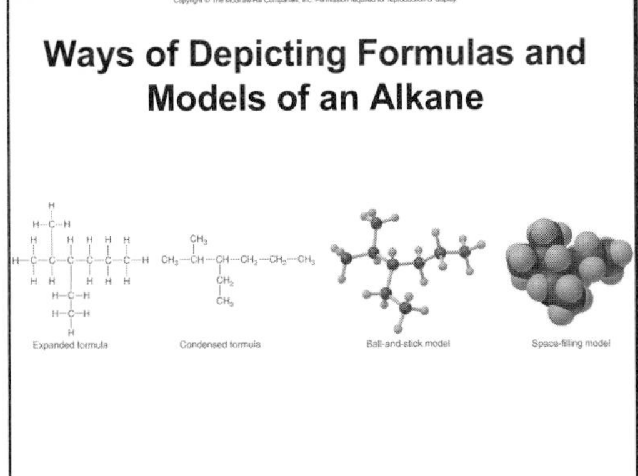

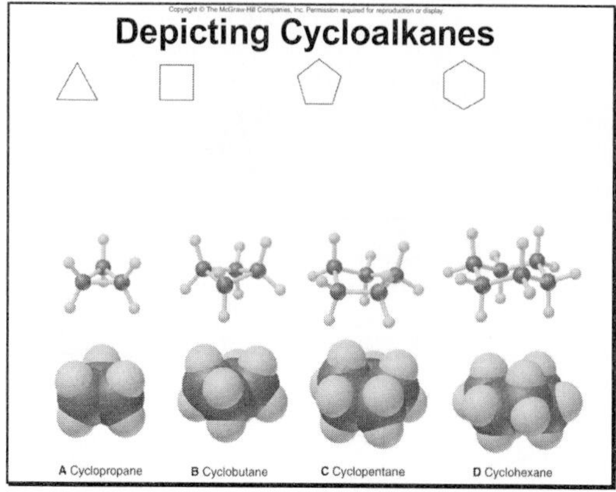

Table 15.3 The Constitutional Isomers of C_4H_{10} and C_5H_{12}

Systematic Name (Common Name)	Condensed Formula	Expanded Formula	Space-filling Model	Density (g/mL)	Boiling Point (°C)
Butane (*n*-butane)				0.579	−0.5
2-Methylpropane (isobutane)				0.549	−11.
Pentane (*n*-pentane)				0.626	36.1
2-Methylbutane (isopentane)				0.620	27.8
2,2-Dimethylpropane (neopentane)				0.614	9.5

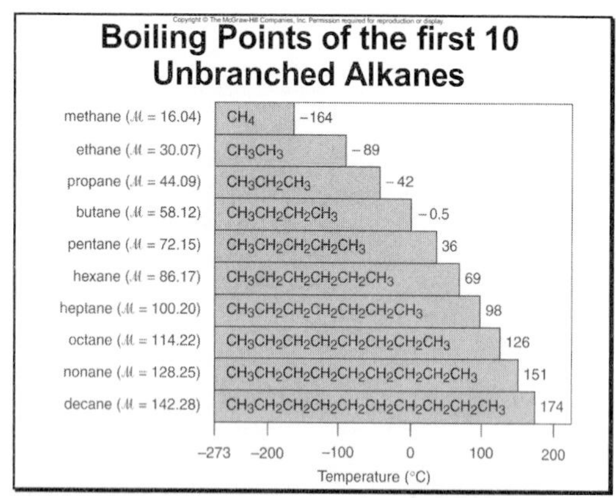

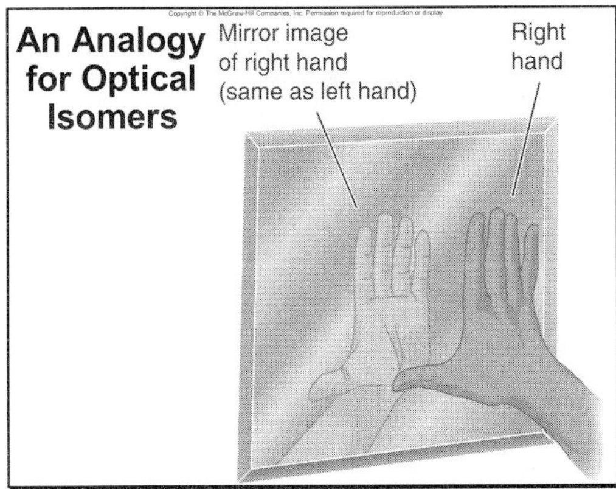
An Analogy for Optical Isomers
Mirror image of right hand (same as left hand)
Right hand

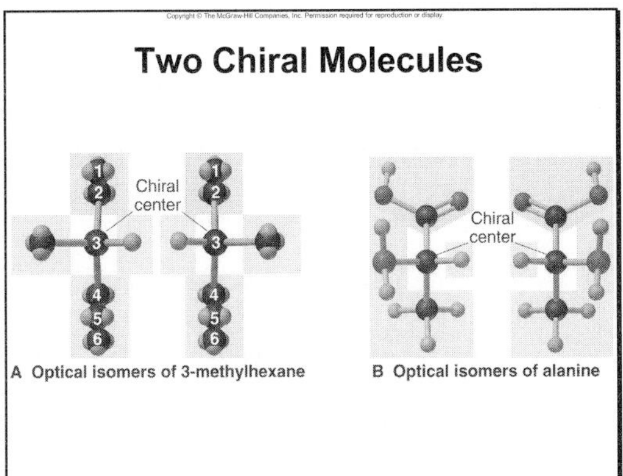
Two Chiral Molecules
Chiral center
Chiral center
A Optical isomers of 3-methylhexane
B Optical isomers of alanine

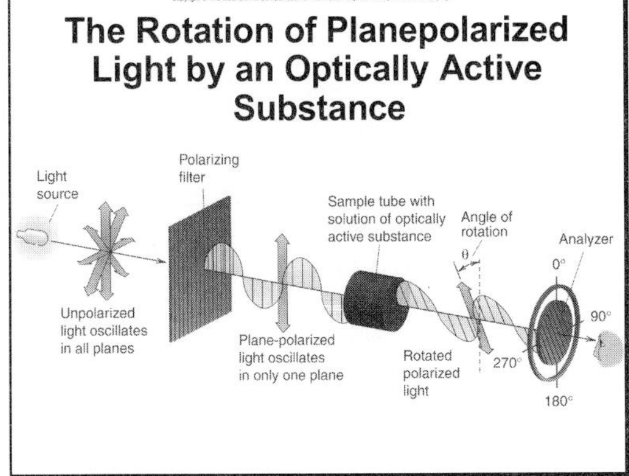
The Rotation of Planepolarized Light by an Optically Active Substance
Light source
Polarizing filter
Sample tube with solution of optically active substance
Angle of rotation
Analyzer
0°
90°
270°
180°
Unpolarized light oscillates in all planes
Plane-polarized light oscillates in only one plane
Rotated polarized light

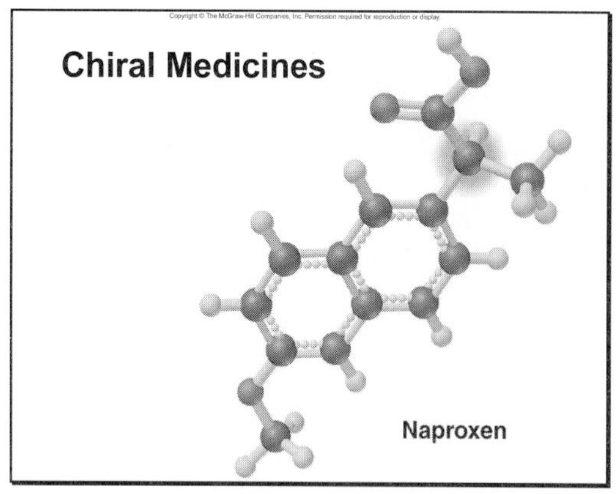

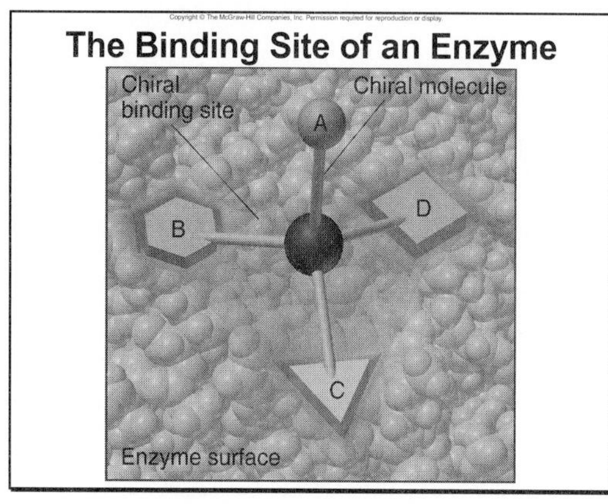

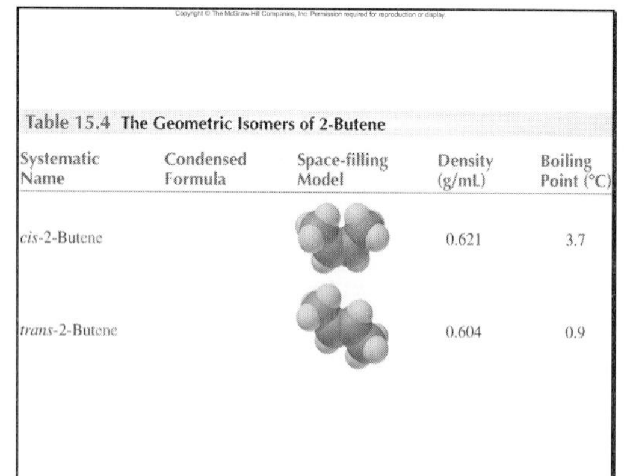

Table 15.4 The Geometric Isomers of 2-Butene

Systematic Name	Condensed Formula	Space-filling Model	Density (g/mL)	Boiling Point (°C)
cis-2-Butene			0.621	3.7
trans-2-Butene			0.604	0.9

The Initial Chemical Event in Vision

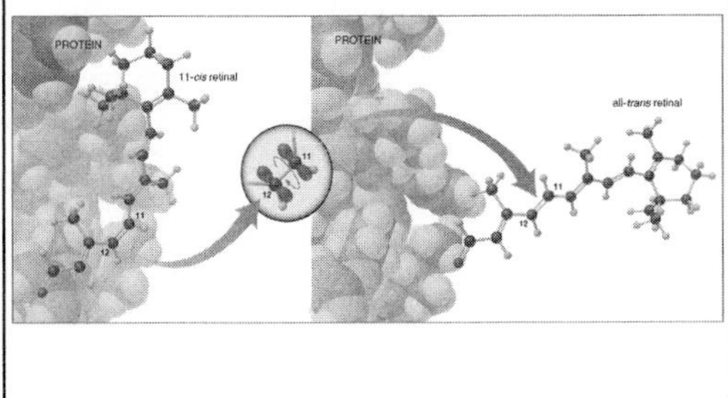

Representations of Benzene

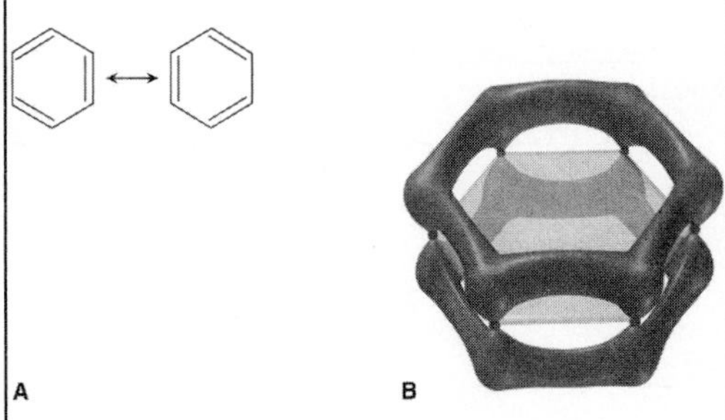

A B

Toluene and Isomers with 2 Methyl Groups

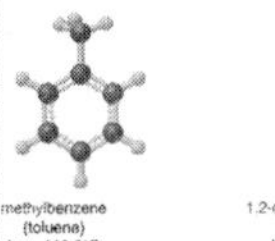

methylbenzene (toluene) bo = 110.6°C

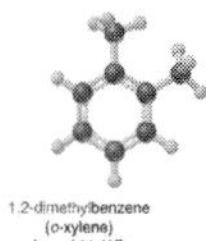

1,2-dimethylbenzene (*o*-xylene) bo = 144.4°C

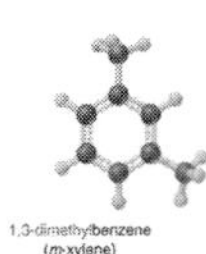

1,3-dimethylbenzene (*m*-xylene) bo = 139.1°C

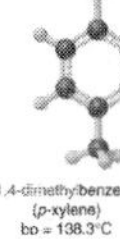

1,4-dimethylbenzene (*p*-xylene) bo = 138.3°C

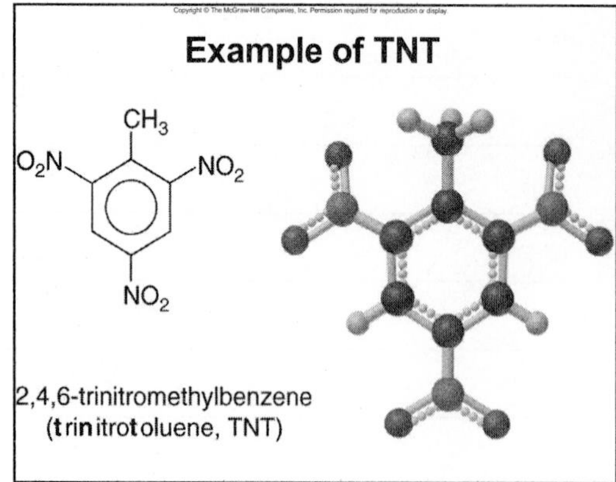
Copyright © The McGraw-Hill Companies, Inc. Permission required for reproduction or display.
Example of TNT
CH_3
O_2N
NO_2
NO_2
2,4,6-trinitromethylbenzene
(trinitrotoluene, TNT)

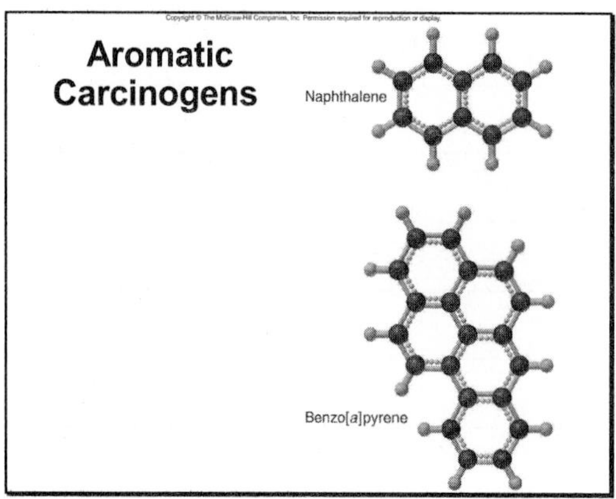
Copyright © The McGraw-Hill Companies, Inc. Permission required for reproduction or display.
Aromatic Carcinogens
Naphthalene
Benzo[a]pyrene

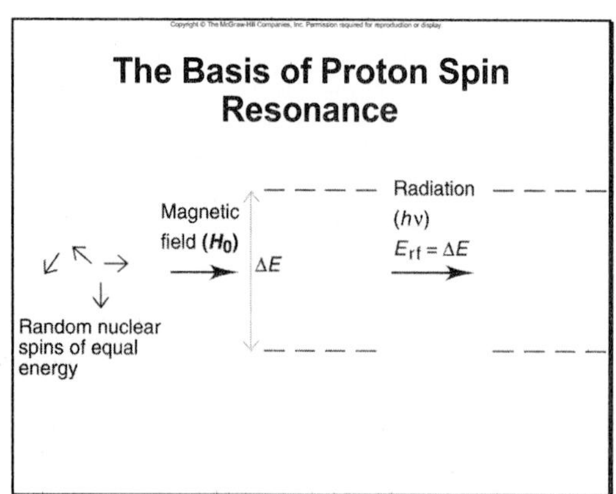
Copyright © The McGraw-Hill Companies, Inc. Permission required for reproduction or display.
The Basis of Proton Spin Resonance
Magnetic field (H_0)
ΔE
Radiation (hν)
$E_{rf} = \Delta E$
Random nuclear spins of equal energy

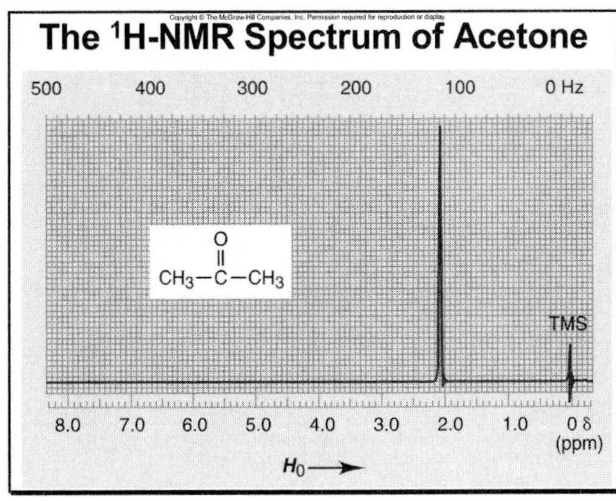
The ¹H-NMR Spectrum of Acetone
500
400
300
200
100
0 Hz
O
CH3—C—CH3
TMS
8.0
7.0
6.0
5.0
4.0
3.0
2.0
1.0
0 δ (ppm)
H0

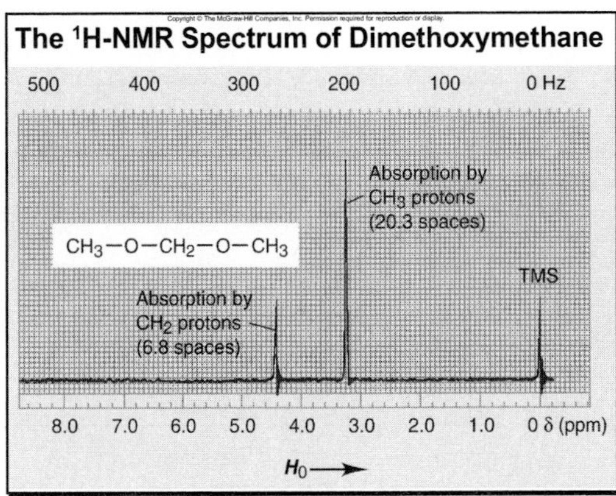
The ¹H-NMR Spectrum of Dimethoxymethane
500
400
300
200
100
0 Hz
Absorption by CH3 protons (20.3 spaces)
CH3—O—CH2—O—CH3
TMS
Absorption by CH2 protons (6.8 spaces)
8.0
7.0
6.0
5.0
4.0
3.0
2.0
1.0
0 δ (ppm)
H0

A Color Test for C=C Bonds
A
B

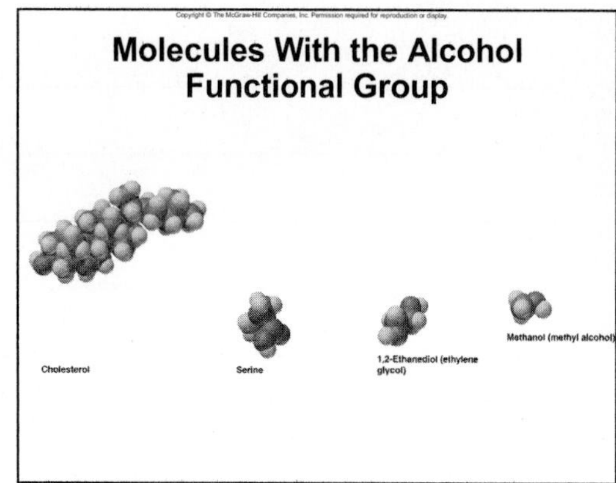

Table 15.5 Important Functional Groups in Organic Compounds – Part 1

Functional Group	Compound Type	Suffix or Prefix of Name	Example	Systematic Name (Common Name)
>C=C<	alkene			
—C≡C—	alkyne			
—C—Ö—H	alcohol			
—C—X: (X=halogen)	haloalkane			
—C—N—	amine			
:O: ‖ —C—H	aldehyde			

Table 15.5 Important Functional Groups in Organic Compounds – Part 2

Functional Group	Compound Type	Suffix or Prefix of Name	Example	Systematic Name (Common Name)
:O: ‖ —C—C—C—	ketone			
:O: ‖ —C—Ö—H	carboxylic acid			
:O: ‖ —C—Ö—C—	ester			
:O: ‖ —C—N—	amide			
—C≡N:	nitrile			

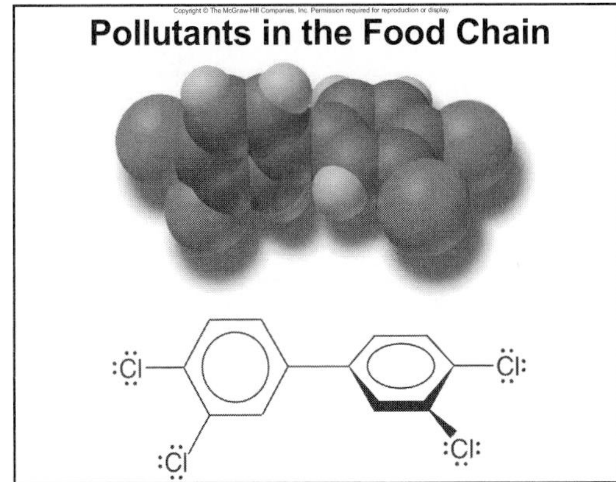
Copyright © The McGraw-Hill Companies, Inc. Permission required for reproduction or display
Pollutants in the Food Chain
:Cl
:Cl
Cl:
:Cl:

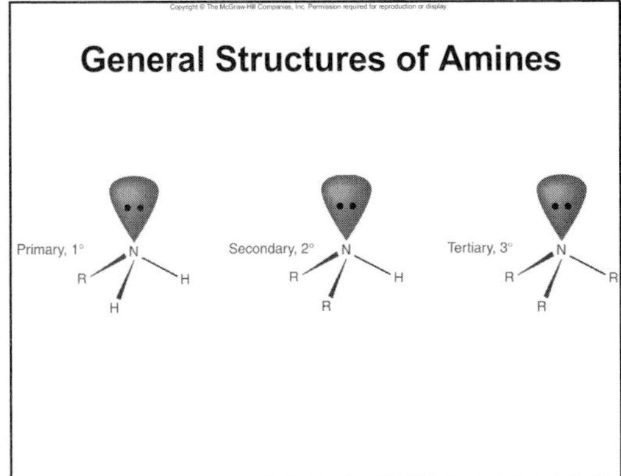
Copyright © The McGraw-Hill Companies, Inc. Permission required for reproduction or display
General Structures of Amines
Primary, 1°
Secondary, 2°
Tertiary, 3°
N
R
H
R

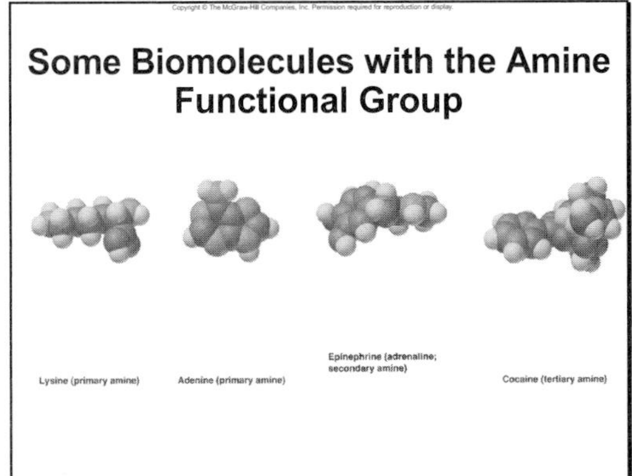
Copyright © The McGraw-Hill Companies, Inc. Permission required for reproduction or display
Some Biomolecules with the Amine Functional Group
Lysine (primary amine)
Adenine (primary amine)
Epinephrine (adrenaline; secondary amine)
Cocaine (tertiary amine)

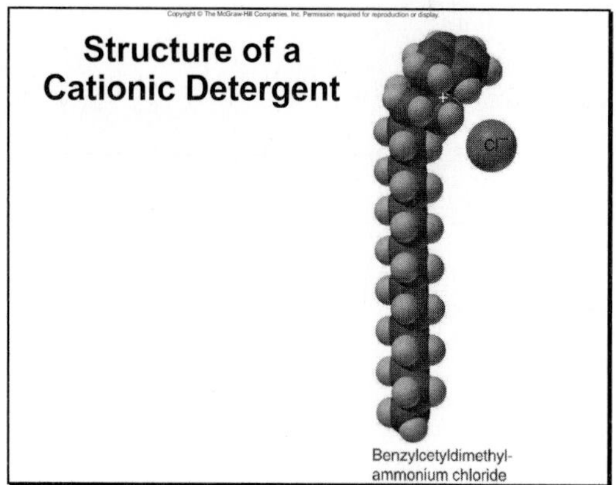
Structure of a Cationic Detergent
+
Cl⁻
Benzylcetyldimethyl-ammonium chloride

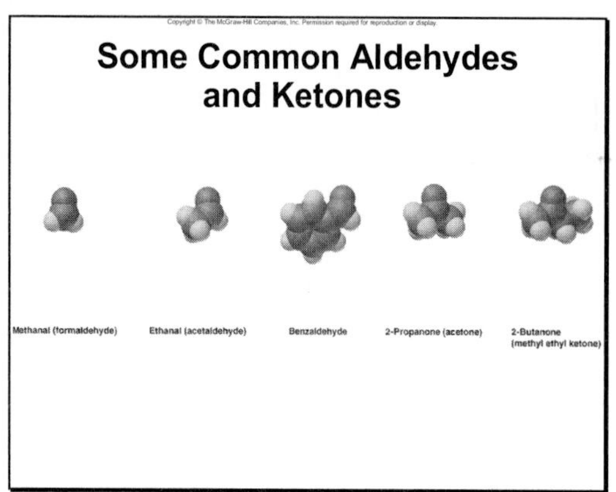
Some Common Aldehydes and Ketones
Methanal (formaldehyde)
Ethanal (acetaldehyde)
Benzaldehyde
2-Propanone (acetone)
2-Butanone (methyl ethyl ketone)

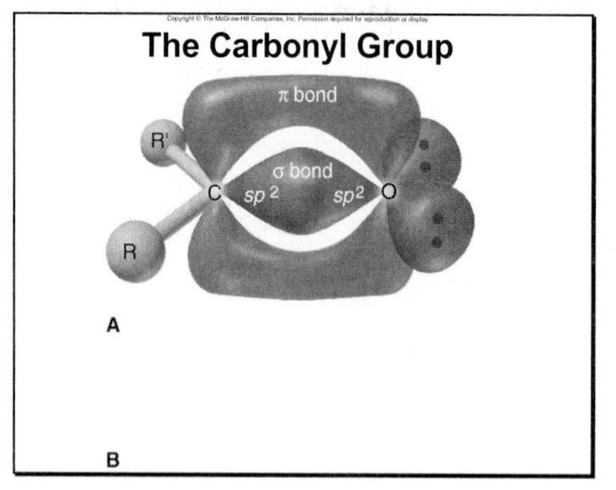
The Carbonyl Group
π bond
σ bond
R'
R
C
O
sp 2
sp2
A
B

Some Molecules with the Carboxylic Acid Functional Group

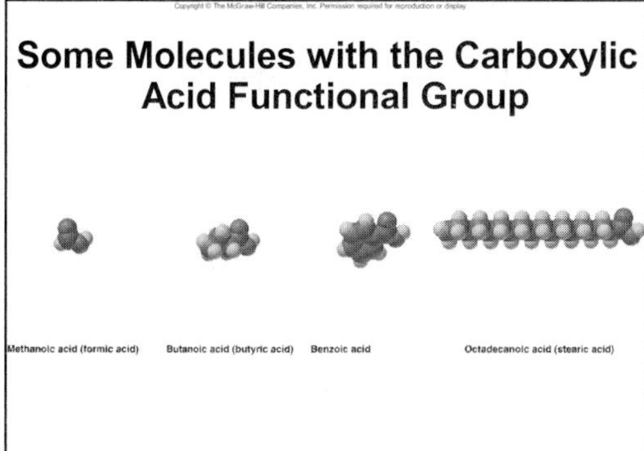

Some Lipid Molecules with the Ester Functional Group

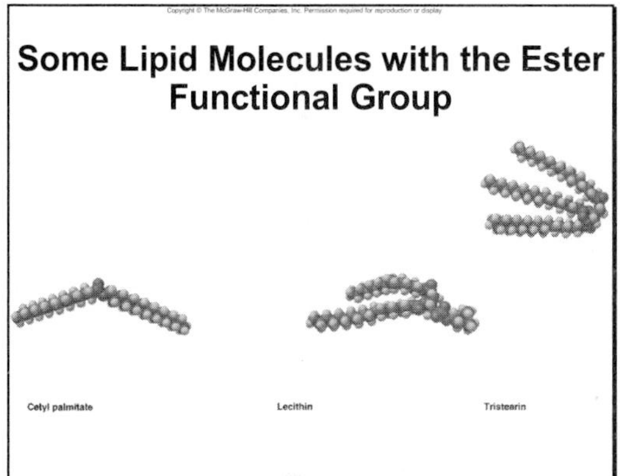

Which Reactant Contributes Which Group to the Ester?

A $$R{-}C({=}O){-}OH + R'{-}^{18}OH \rightleftharpoons R{-}C({=}O){-}^{18}O{-}R' + H{-}O{-}H$$

B $$R{-}C({=}O){-}^{18}OH + R'{-}OH \rightleftharpoons R{-}C({=}O){-}O{-}R' + H{-}^{18}O{-}H$$

Some Molecules with the Amide Functional Group

Acetaminophen

N,N-Dimethylmethanamide (dimethylformamide)

Lysergic acid diethylamide (LSD-25)

The Formation of Carboxylic, Phosphoric, and Sulfuric Acid Anhydrides

Acid		Anhydride
$2\ R{-}C({=}O){-}OH$	$\xrightarrow{-H_2O}$	$R{-}C({=}O){-}O{-}C({=}O){-}R$
$2\ HO{-}P({=}O)(OH){-}OH$	$\xrightarrow{-H_2O}$	$HO{-}P({=}O)(OH){-}O{-}P({=}O)(OH){-}OH$
$2\ HO{-}S({=}O)_2{-}OH$	$\xrightarrow{-H_2O}$	$HO{-}S({=}O)_2{-}O{-}S({=}O)_2{-}OH$

An Ester and an Amide of Other Nonmetals

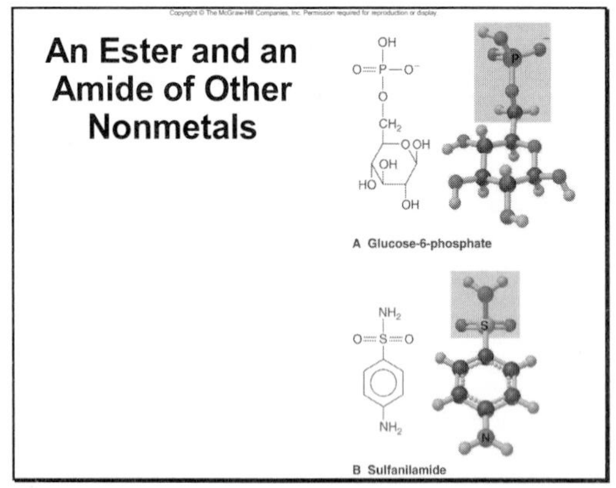

A Glucose-6-phosphate

B Sulfanilamide

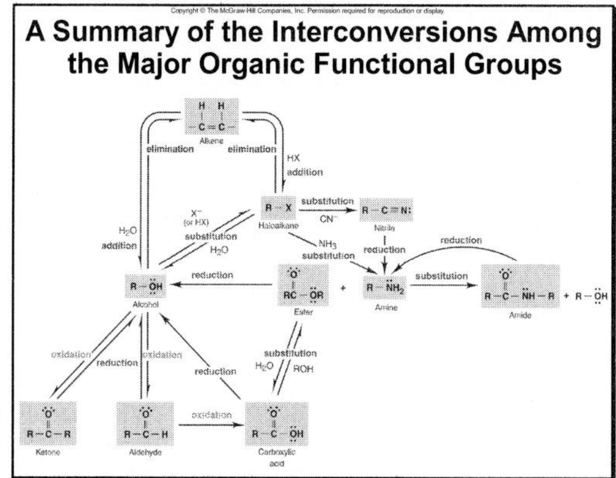

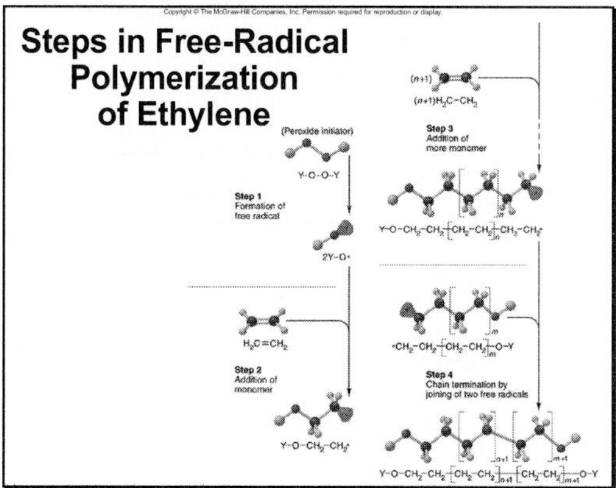

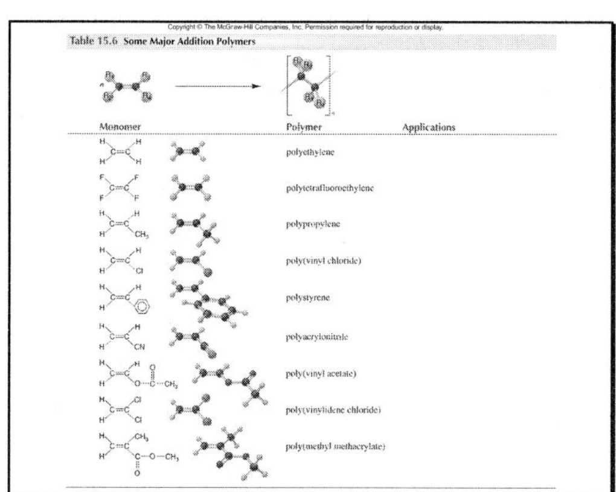

Table 15.6 Some Major Addition Polymers

Monomer	Polymer	Applications
$H_2C{=}CH_2$	polyethylene	
$F_2C{=}CF_2$	polytetrafluoroethylene	
$H_2C{=}CH{-}CH_3$	polypropylene	
$H_2C{=}CH{-}Cl$	poly(vinyl chloride)	
$H_2C{=}CH{-}C_6H_5$	polystyrene	
$H_2C{=}CH{-}CN$	polyacrylonitrile	
$H_2C{=}CH{-}O{-}C({=}O){-}CH_3$	poly(vinyl acetate)	
$H_2C{=}CCl_2$	poly(vinylidene chloride)	
$H_2C{=}C(CH_3){-}C({=}O){-}O{-}CH_3$	poly(methyl methacrylate)	

Condensation Polymers

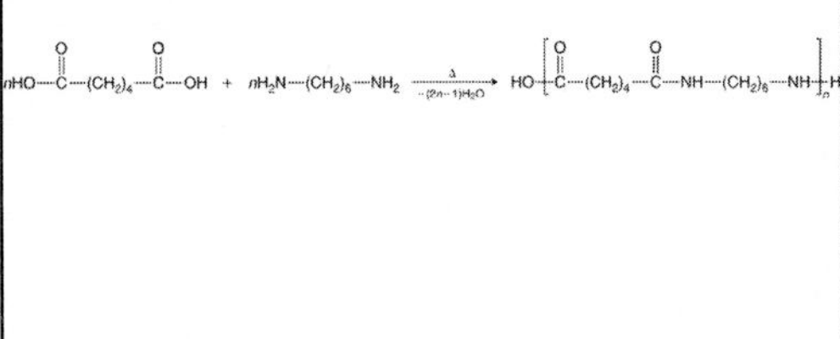

The Structure of Glucose in Aqueous Solution and the Formation of a Disaccharide

A

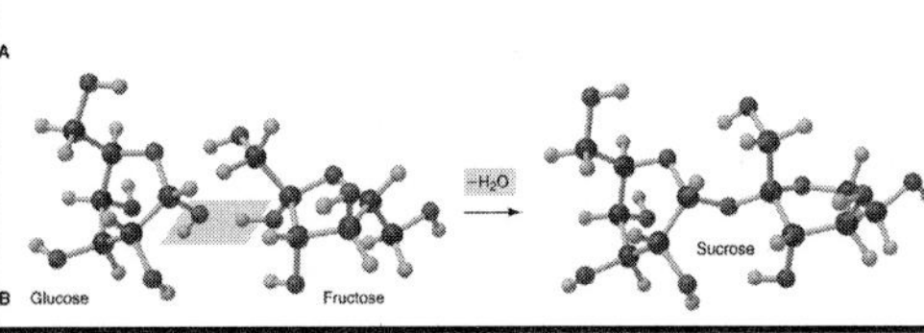

The Common Amino Acids

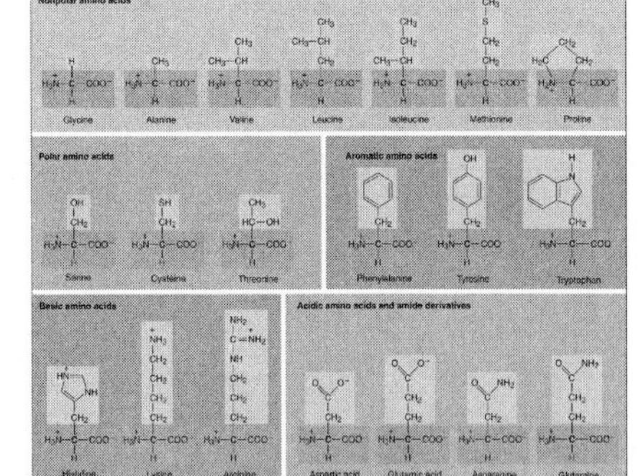

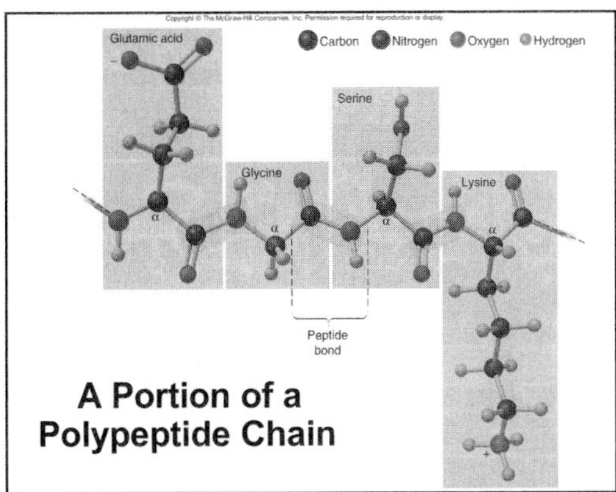
Copyright © The McGraw-Hill Companies, Inc. Permission required for reproduction or display.
Glutamic acid
Carbon
Nitrogen
Oxygen
Hydrogen
Serine
Glycine
Lysine
Peptide bond
A Portion of a Polypeptide Chain

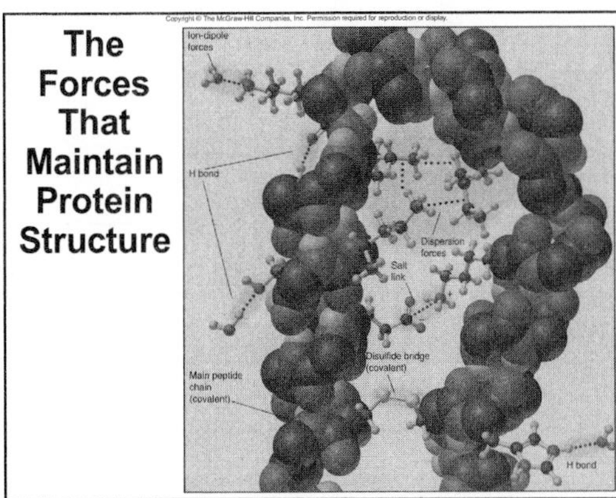
The Forces That Maintain Protein Structure
Copyright © The McGraw-Hill Companies, Inc. Permission required for reproduction or display.
Ion-dipole forces
H bond
Dispersion forces
Salt link
Disulfide bridge (covalent)
Main peptide chain (covalent)
H bond

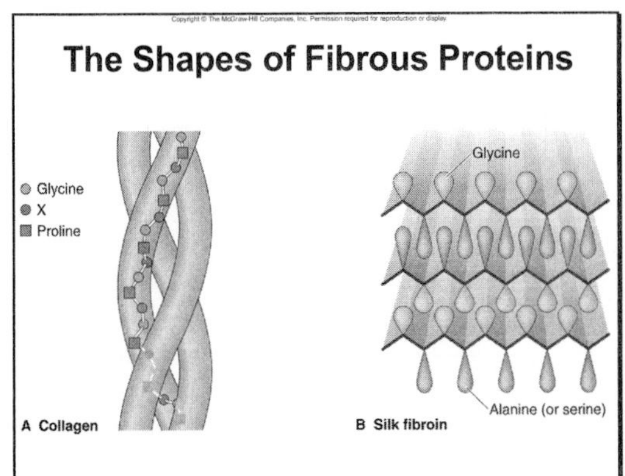
Copyright © The McGraw-Hill Companies, Inc. Permission required for reproduction or display.
The Shapes of Fibrous Proteins
Glycine
X
Proline
A Collagen
Glycine
Alanine (or serine)
B Silk fibroin

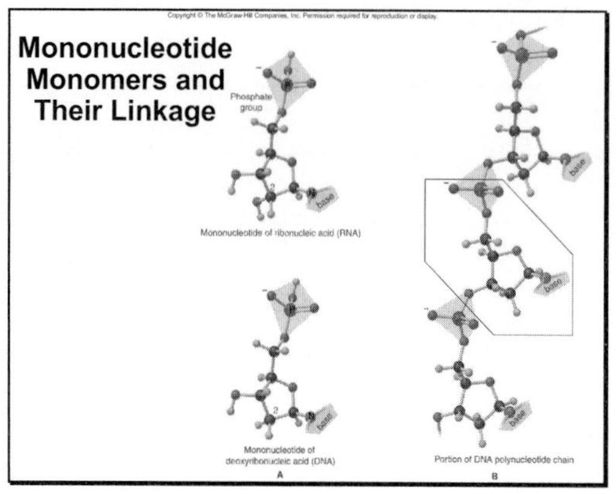
Copyright © The McGraw-Hill Companies, Inc. Permission required for reproduction or display.
Mononucleotide Monomers and Their Linkage
Phosphate group
base
Mononucleotide of ribonucleic acid (RNA)
Mononucleotide of deoxyribonucleic acid (DNA)
A
Portion of DNA polynucleotide chain
B

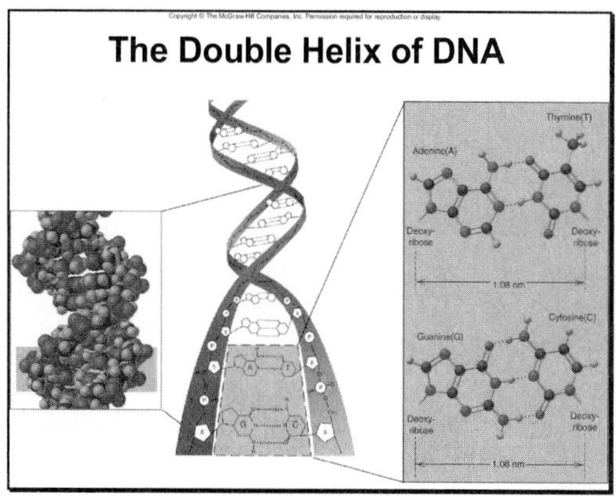
Copyright © The McGraw-Hill Companies, Inc. Permission required for reproduction or display.
The Double Helix of DNA
Thymine(T)
Adenine(A)
Deoxy-ribose
Deoxy-ribose
1.08 nm
Cytosine(C)
Guanine(G)
Deoxy-ribose
Deoxy-ribose
1.08 nm

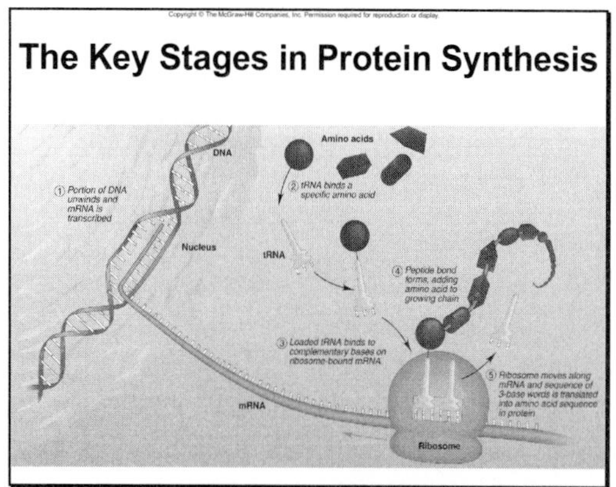
Copyright © The McGraw-Hill Companies, Inc. Permission required for reproduction or display.
The Key Stages in Protein Synthesis
DNA
Amino acids
① Portion of DNA unwinds and mRNA is transcribed
② tRNA binds a specific amino acid
Nucleus
tRNA
④ Peptide bond forms, adding amino acid to growing chain
③ Loaded tRNA binds to complementary bases on ribosome-bound mRNA
⑤ Ribosome moves along mRNA and sequence of 3-base words is translated into amino acid sequence in protein
mRNA
Ribosome

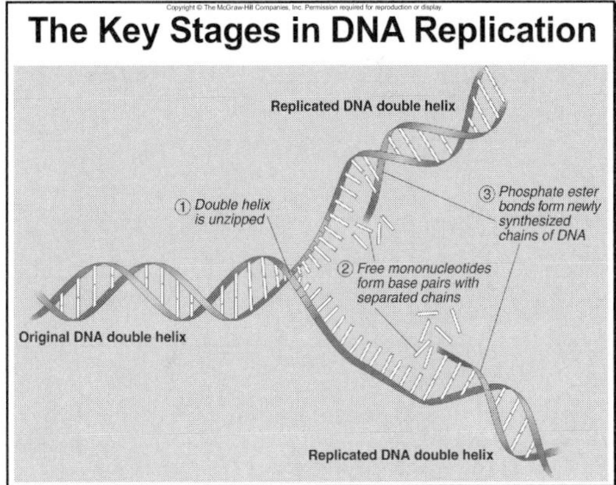
Copyright © The McGraw-Hill Companies, Inc. Permission required for reproduction or display.
The Key Stages in DNA Replication
Replicated DNA double helix
① Double helix is unzipped
③ Phosphate ester bonds form newly synthesized chains of DNA
② Free mononucleotides form base pairs with separated chains
Original DNA double helix
Replicated DNA double helix

Chapter 16

Chemistry: The Molecular Nature of Matter and Change

Third Edition

Martin S. Silberberg

Reaction Rate: The Central Focus of Chemical Kinetics

Reaction:

The Effect of Surface Area on Reaction Rate

A

B

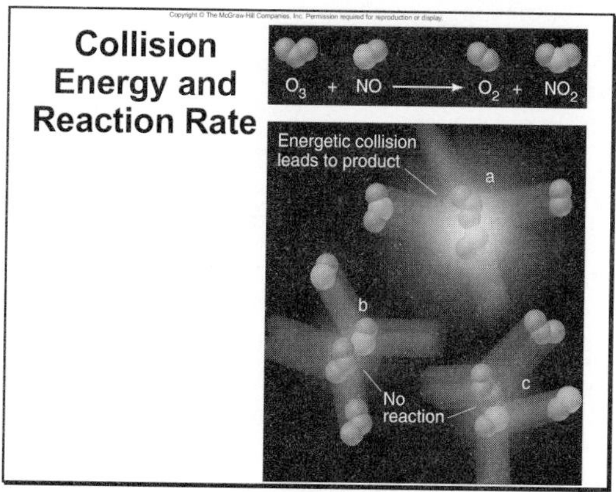

Table 16.1 Concentration of O_3 at Various Times in Its Reaction with C_2H_4 at 303 K

Time (s)	Concentration of O_3 (mol/L)
0.0	3.20×10^{-5}
10.0	2.42×10^{-5}
20.0	1.95×10^{-5}
30.0	1.63×10^{-5}
40.0	1.40×10^{-5}
50.0	1.23×10^{-5}
60.0	1.10×10^{-5}

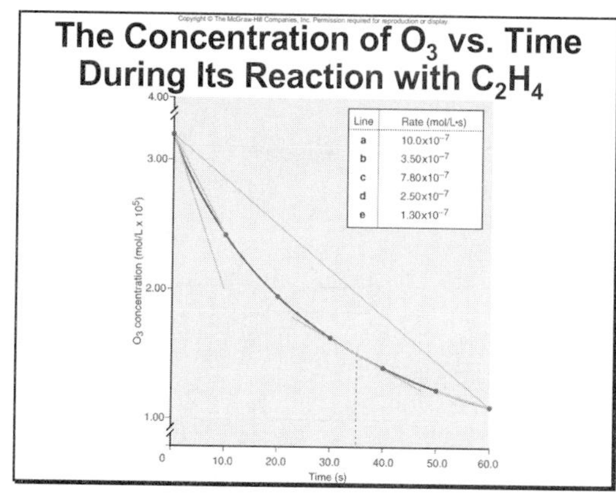

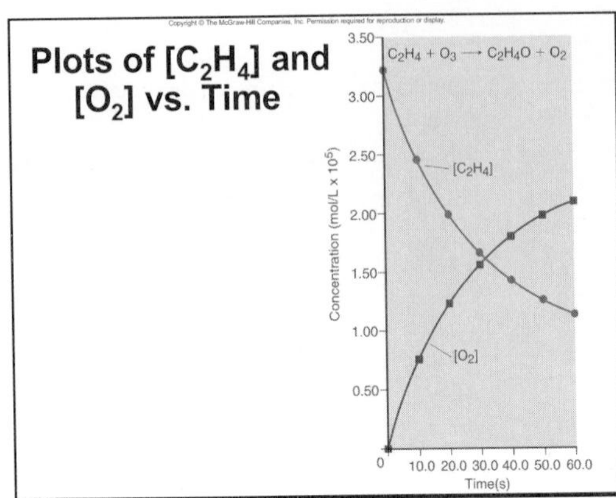
Plots of $[C_2H_4]$ and $[O_2]$ vs. Time
$C_2H_4 + O_3 \longrightarrow C_2H_4O + O_2$
$[C_2H_4]$
$[O_2]$
Concentration (mol/L x 10^5)
3.50
3.00
2.50
2.00
1.50
1.00
0.50
0
10.0 20.0 30.0 40.0 50.0 60.0
Time(s)

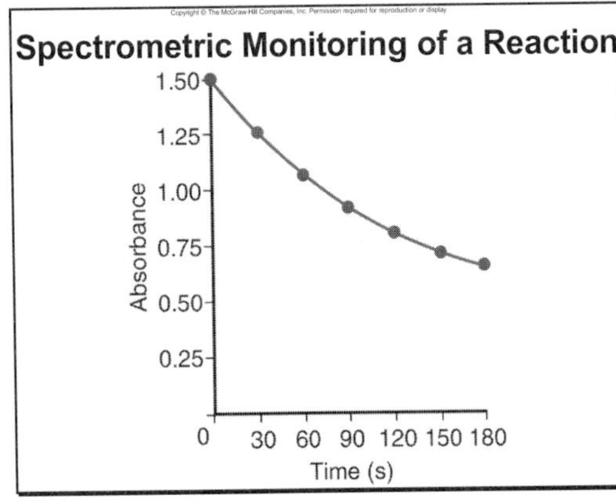
Spectrometric Monitoring of a Reaction
Absorbance
1.50
1.25
1.00
0.75
0.50
0.25
0
30 60 90 120 150 180
Time (s)

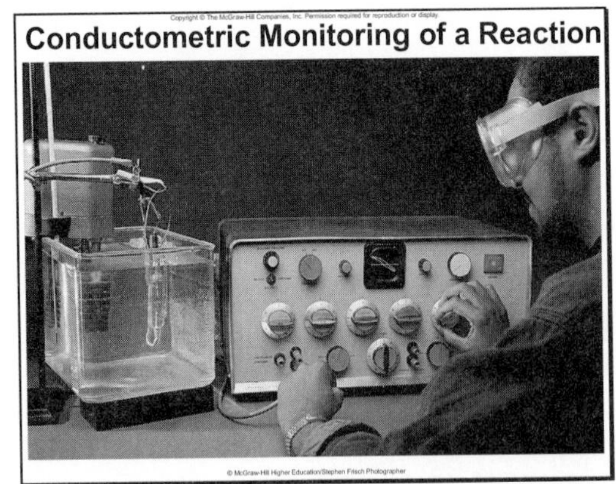
Conductometric Monitoring of a Reaction

Manometric Monitoring of a Reaction

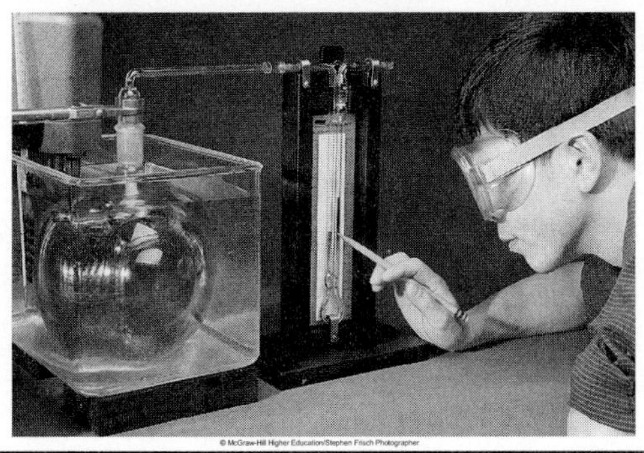

Table 16.2 Initial Rates for a Series of Experiments in the Reaction Between O_2 and NO

Experiment	Initial Reactant Concentrations (mol/L) O_2	NO	Initial Rate (mol/L·s)
1	1.10×10^{-2}	1.30×10^{-2}	3.21×10^{-3}
2	2.20×10^{-2}	1.30×10^{-2}	6.40×10^{-3}
3	1.10×10^{-2}	2.60×10^{-2}	12.8×10^{-3}
4	3.30×10^{-2}	1.30×10^{-2}	9.60×10^{-3}
5	1.10×10^{-2}	3.90×10^{-2}	28.8×10^{-3}

Table 16.3 Units of the Rate Constant k for Several Overall Reaction Orders

Overall Reaction Order	Units of k (t in seconds)
0	mol/L·s (or mol L^{-1} s^{-1})
1	1/s (or s^{-1})
2	L/mol·s (or L mol^{-1} s^{-1})
3	L^2/mol^2·s (or L^2 mol^{-1} s^{-1})

General formula:

$$\text{Units of } k = \frac{\left(\frac{L}{mol}\right)^{\text{order}-1}}{\text{unit of } t}$$

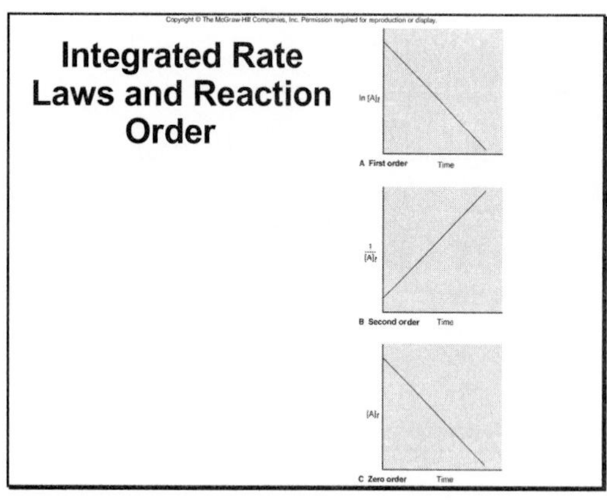

Reaction Order for the Decomposition of N_2O_5 — Part 1

Time (min)	$[N_2O_5]$	ln $[N_2O_5]$	$1/[N_2O_5]$
0	0.0165	−4.104	60.6
10	0.0124	−4.390	80.6
20	0.0093	−4.68	1.1×10^2
30	0.0071	−4.95	1.4×10^2
40	0.0053	−5.24	1.9×10^2
50	0.0039	−5.55	2.6×10^2
60	0.0029	−5.84	3.4×10^2

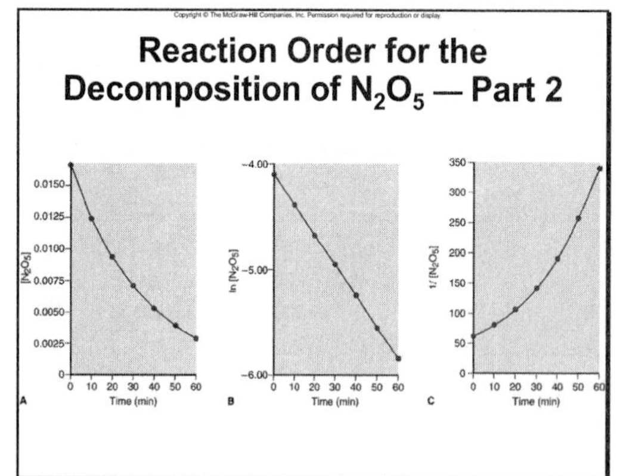

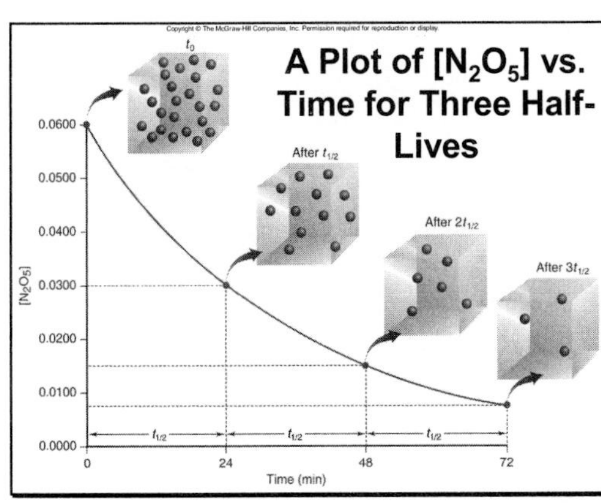

Table 16.4 An Overview of Zero-Order, First-Order, and Simple Second-Order Reactions

	Zero Order	First Order	Second Order
Rate law			
Units for k			
Integrated rate law in straight-line form			
Plot for straight line			
Slope, y intercept			
Half-life			

Dependence of the Rate Constant on Temperature

A

Exp't	[Ester]	$[H_2O]$	T (K)	Rate (mol/L·s)	k (L/mol·s)
1	0.100	0.200	288	1.04×10^{-3}	0.0521
2	0.100	0.200	298	2.02×10^{-3}	0.101
3	0.100	0.200	308	3.68×10^{-3}	0.184
4	0.100	0.200	318	6.64×10^{-3}	0.332

B

k (L/mol·s): 0.400, 0.300, 0.200, 0.100

Temperature (K): 288, 298, 308, 318

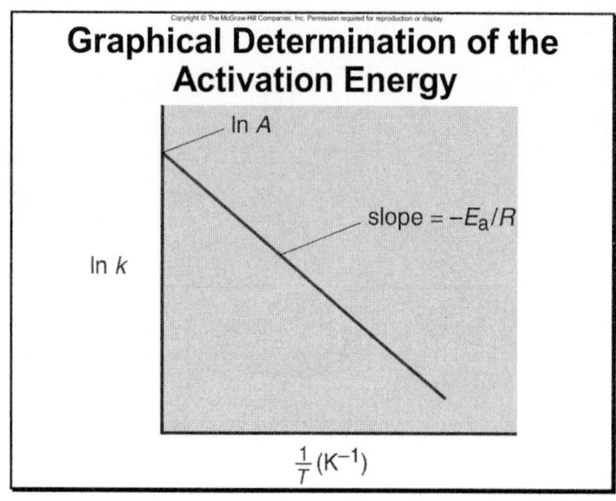
Graphical Determination of the Activation Energy
ln A
slope = $-E_a/R$
ln k
$\frac{1}{T}$ (K^{-1})

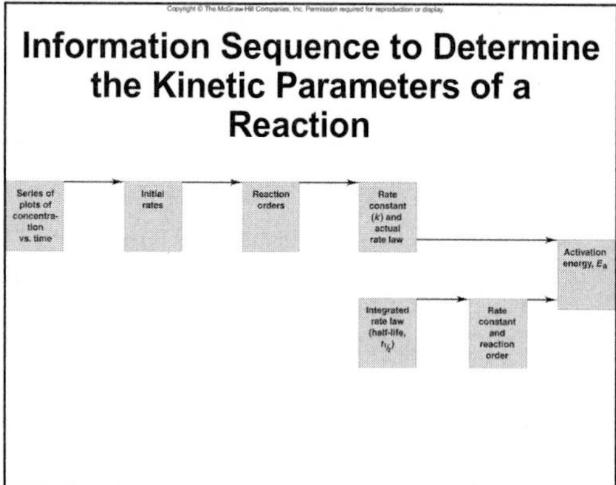
Information Sequence to Determine the Kinetic Parameters of a Reaction
Series of plots of concentration vs. time
Initial rates
Reaction orders
Rate constant (k) and actual rate law
Activation energy, E_a
Integrated rate law (half-life, $t_{1/2}$)
Rate constant and reaction order

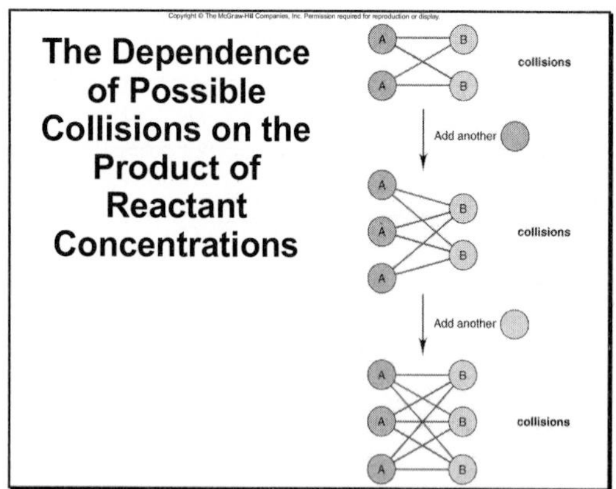
The Dependence of Possible Collisions on the Product of Reactant Concentrations
collisions
Add another
collisions
Add another
collisions

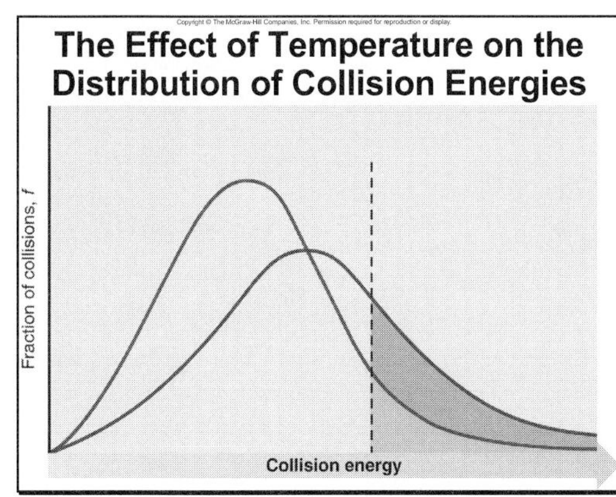

Table 16.5 The Effect of E_a and T on the Fraction (f) of Collisions with Sufficient Energy to Allow Reaction

E_a (kJ/mol)	f (at T = 298 K)
50	1.70×10^{-9}
75	7.03×10^{-14}
100	2.90×10^{-18}
T	f (at E_a = 50 kJ/mol)
25°C (298 K)	1.70×10^{-9}
35°C (308 K)	3.29×10^{-9}
45°C (318 K)	6.12×10^{-9}

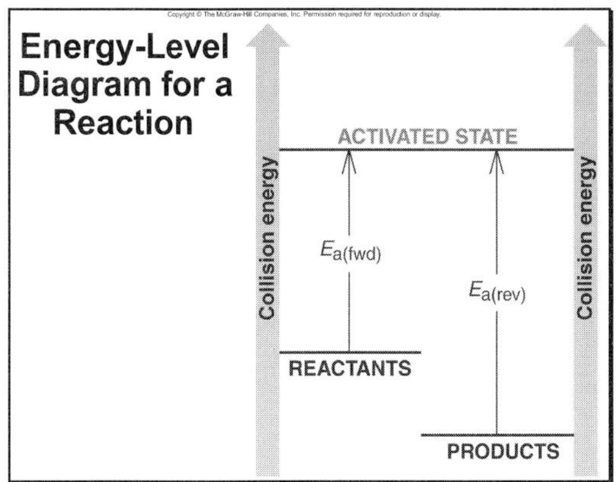

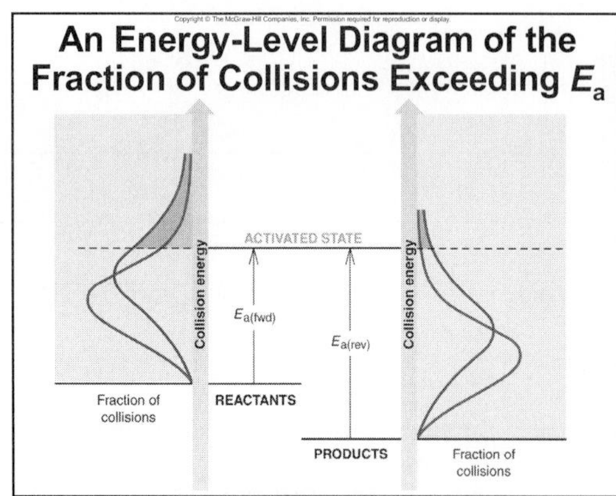

The Importance of Molecular Orientation to an Effective Collision

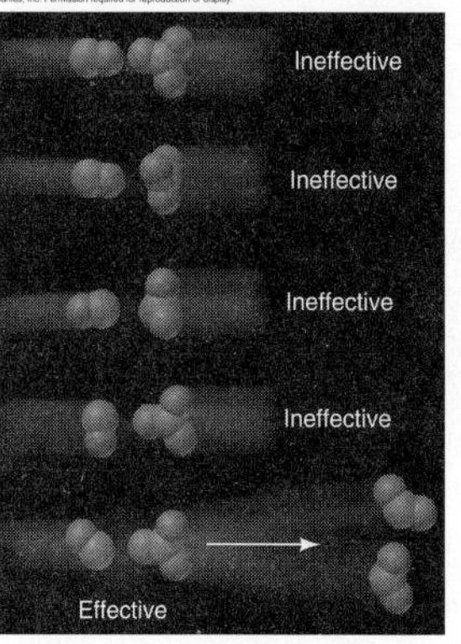

Nature of the Transition State in the Reaction Between CH_3Br and OH^-

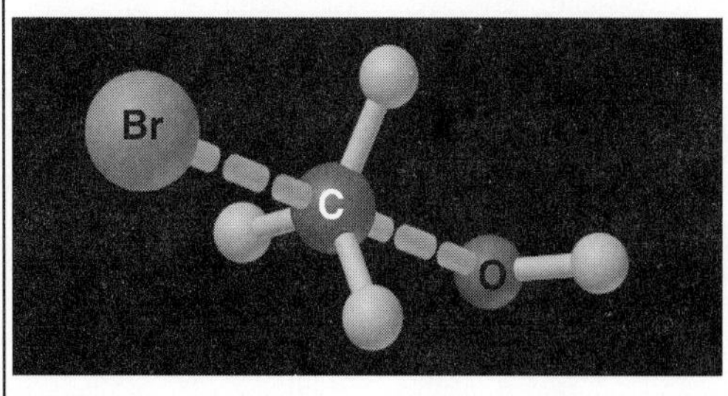

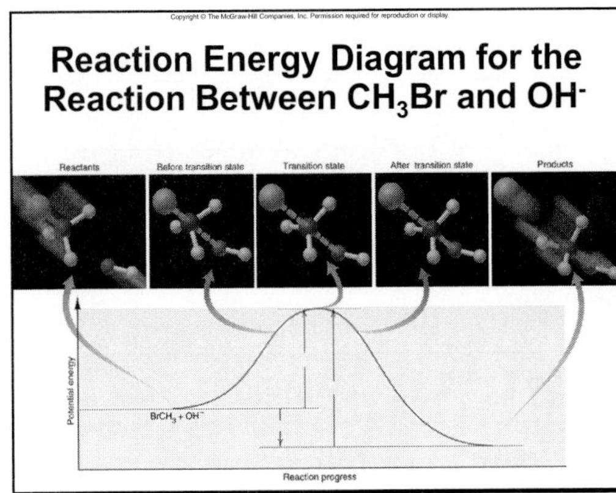

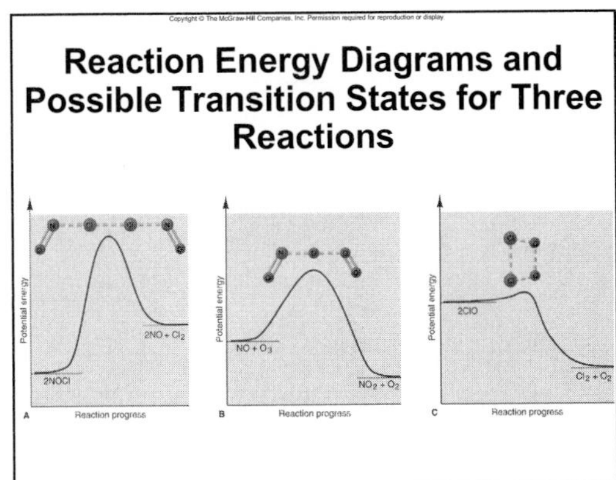

Table 16.6 Rate Laws for General Elementary Steps

Elementary Step	Molecularity	Rate Law
A $\longrightarrow$ product		
2A $\longrightarrow$ product		
A + B $\longrightarrow$ product		
2A + B $\longrightarrow$ product		

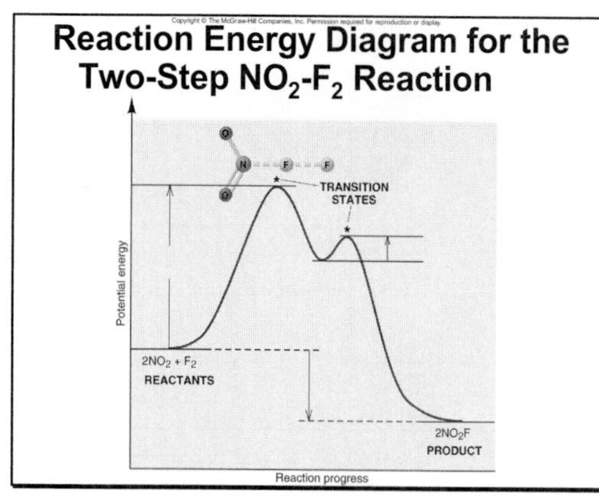

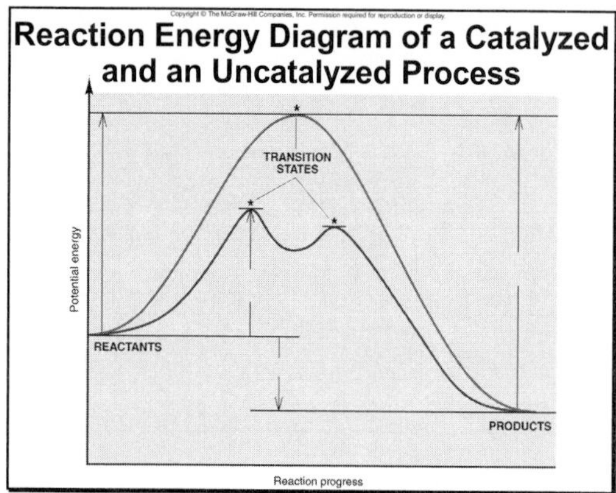

Mechanism for the Catalyzed Hydrolysis of an Organic Ester — Part 1

Step 1

fast

Resonance forms

Resonance hybrid

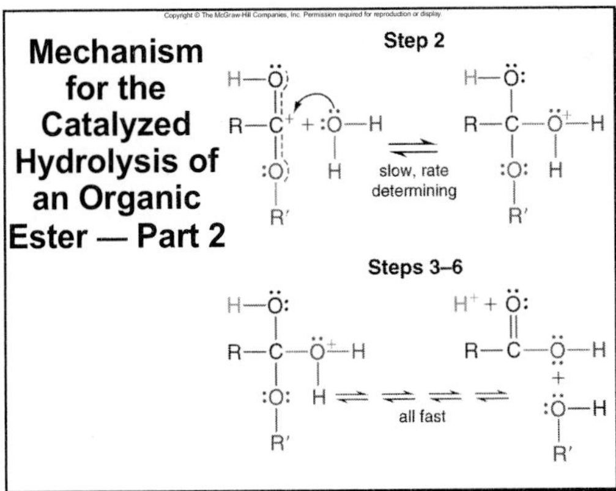

Table 16.7 Some Modern Processes Based on Catalysis

Reactants	Catalyst	Product	Use
Homogeneous			
Propylene, oxidizer	Mo(VI) complexes	Propylene oxide	Polyurethane foams; polyesters
Methanol, CO	$[Rh(CO)_2I_2]^-$	Acetic acid	Poly(vinyl acetate) coatings; poly(vinyl alcohol)
Butadiene, HCN	Ni/P compounds	Adiponitrile	Nylons (fibers, plastics)
α-Olefins, CO, H_2	Rh/P compounds	Aldehydes	Plasticizers, lubricants
Heterogeneous			
Ethylene, O_2	Silver, cesium chloride on alumina	Ethylene oxide	Polyesters, ethylene glycol, lubricants
Propylene, NH_3, O_2	Bismuth molybdates	Acrylonitrile	Plastics, fibers, resins
Ethylene	Organochromium and titanium halides on silica	High-density polyethylene	Molded products

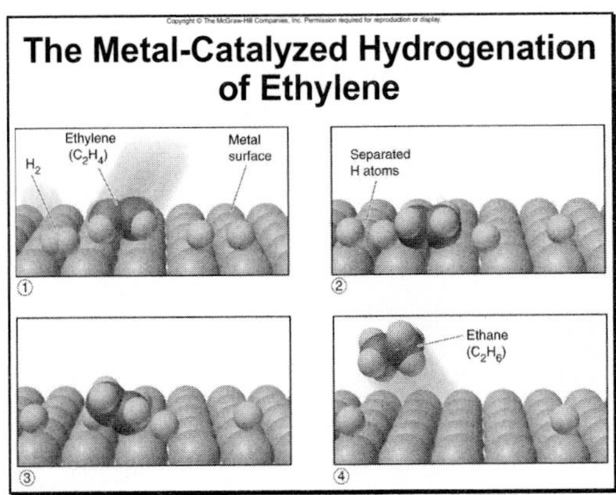

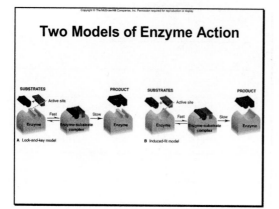

Two Models of Enzyme Action

SUBSTRATES
Active site
Fast
Slow
PRODUCT
Enzyme
Enzyme-substrate complex
Enzyme

A Lock-and-key model

SUBSTRATES
Active site
Fast
Slow
PRODUCT
Enzyme
Enzyme-substrate complex
Enzyme

B Induced-fit model

Chapter 17

Chemistry: The Molecular Nature of Matter and Change

Third Edition

Martin S. Silberberg

Reaching Equilibrium on the Macroscopic and Molecular Levels

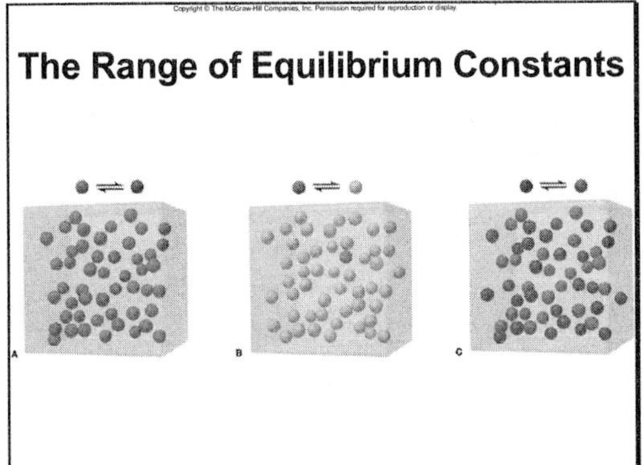

The Range of Equilibrium Constants

A

B

C

Table 17.1 Initial and Equilibrium Concentration Ratios for the N_2O_4-NO_2 System at 100°C

	Initial		Ratio (Q)	Equilibrium		Ratio (K)
Exp't	$[N_2O_4]$	$[NO_2]$	$[NO_2]^2/[N_2O_4]$	$[N_2O_4]_{eq}$	$[NO_2]_{eq}$	$[NO_2]^2_{eq}/[N_2O_4]_{eq}$
1	0.1000	0.0000	0.0000	0.0491	0.1018	0.211
2	0.0000	0.1000	∞	0.0185	0.0627	0.212
3	0.0500	0.0500	0.0500	0.0332	0.0837	0.211
4	0.0750	0.0250	0.00833	0.0411	0.0930	0.210

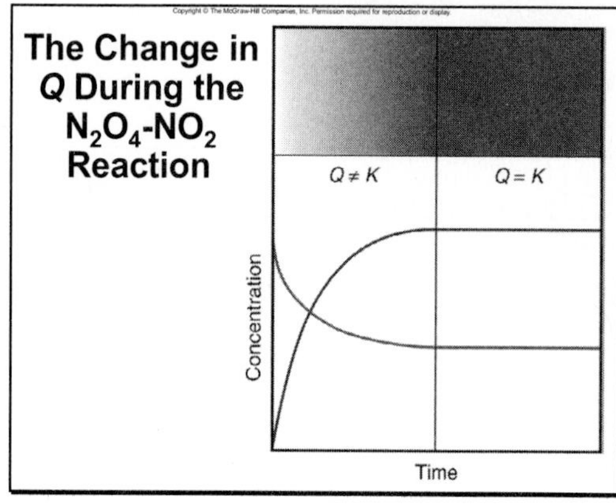

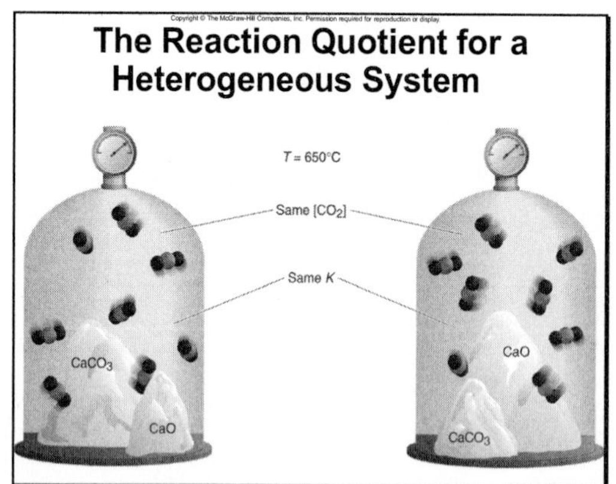

Table 17.2 Ways of Expressing Q and Calculating K

Form of Chemical Equation	Form of Q	Value of K
Reference reaction: $A \rightleftharpoons B$	$Q_{(ref)} = \frac{[B]}{[A]}$	$K_{(ref)} = \frac{[B]_{eq}}{[A]_{eq}}$
Reverse reaction: $B \rightleftharpoons A$	$Q = \frac{1}{Q_{(ref)}} = \frac{[A]}{[B]}$	$K = \frac{1}{K_{(ref)}}$
Reaction as sum of two steps: (1) $A \rightleftharpoons C$	$Q_1 = \frac{[C]}{[A]}; Q_2 = \frac{[B]}{[C]}$	
(2) $C \rightleftharpoons B$	$Q_{overall} = Q_1 \times Q_2 = Q_{(ref)} = \frac{\cancel{[C]}}{[A]} \times \frac{[B]}{\cancel{[C]}} = \frac{[B]}{[A]}$	$K_{overall} = K_1 \times K_2 = K_{(ref)}$
Coefficients multiplied by n	$Q = Q^n_{(ref)}$	$K = K^n_{(ref)}$
Reaction with pure solid or liquid component, such as $A(s)$	$Q = Q_{(ref)}[A] = [B]$	$K = K_{(ref)}[A] = [B]$

Reaction Direction and the Relative Sizes of Q and K

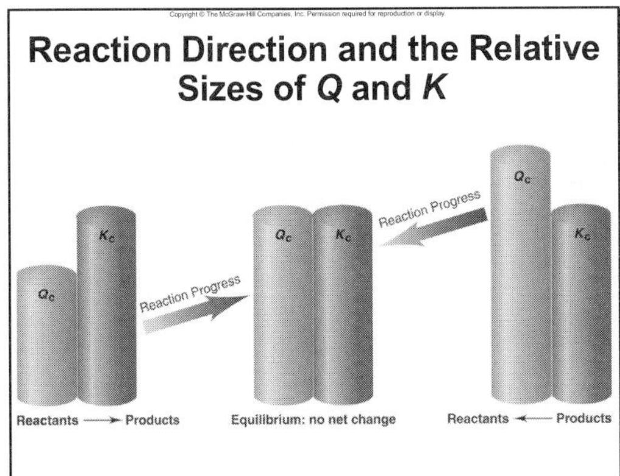

Steps in Solving Equilibrium Problems Part 1

SOLVING EQUILIBRIUM PROBLEMS

PRELIMINARY SETTING UP

1. Write the balanced equation
2. Write the reaction quotient, Q
3. Convert all amounts into the correct units (M or atm)

WORKING ON THE REACTION TABLE

4. When reaction direction is not known, compare Q with K
5. Construct a reaction table

✓Check the sign of x, the change in the quantity

Steps in Solving Equilibrium Problems Part 2

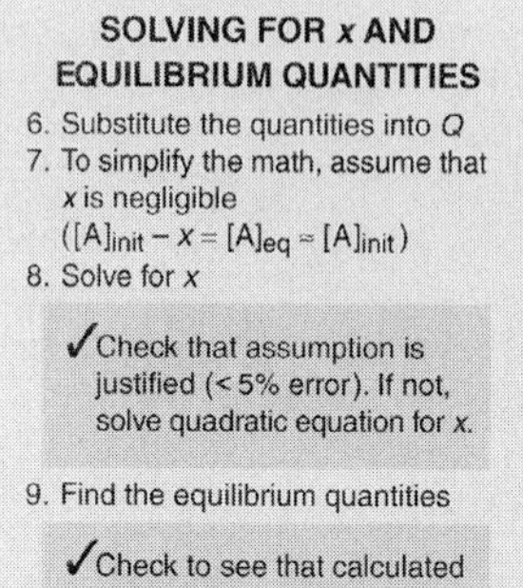
SOLVING FOR x AND EQUILIBRIUM QUANTITIES
6. Substitute the quantities into Q
7. To simplify the math, assume that x is negligible
([A]init − x = [A]eq ≈ [A]init)
8. Solve for x
✓Check that assumption is justified (< 5% error). If not, solve quadratic equation for x.
9. Find the equilibrium quantities
✓Check to see that calculated values give the known K

Table 17.3 The Effect of Added Cl_2 on the PCl_3-Cl_2-PCl_5 System

Concentration (M)	$PCl_3(g)$	+	$Cl_2(g)$	⇌	$PCl_5(g)$
Original equilibrium	0.200		0.125		0.600
Disturbance			+0.075		
New initial	0.200		0.200		0.600
Change	$-x$		$-x$		$+x$
New equilibrium	$0.200 - x$		$0.200 - x$		$0.600 + x$ (0.637)*

*Experimentally determined value.

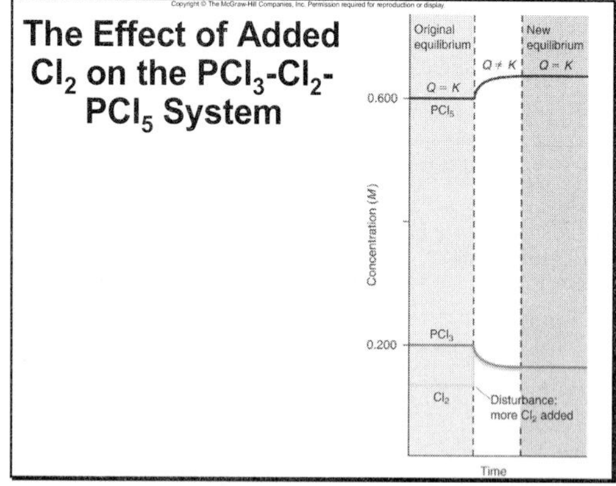
The Effect of Added Cl2 on the PCl3-Cl2-PCl5 System
Original equilibrium
New equilibrium
Q ≠ K
Q = K
Q = K
0.600
PCl5
Concentration (M)
PCl3
0.200
Cl2
Disturbance: more Cl2 added
Time

Effect of Pressure (Volume) On an Equilibrium System

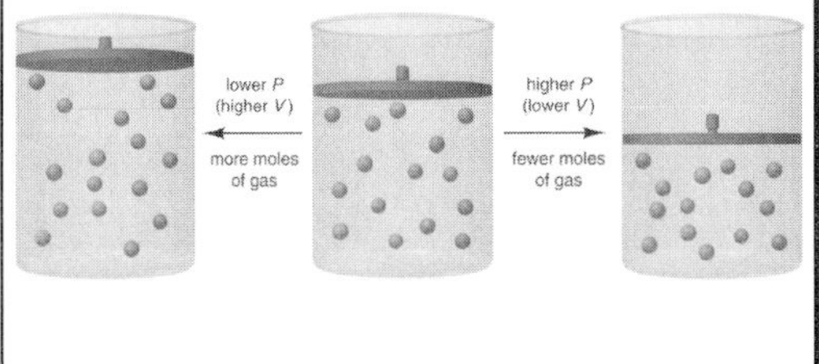

Temperature-Dependent Systems

$$\ln \frac{K_2}{K_1} = -\frac{\Delta H^0_{rxn}}{R}\left(\frac{1}{T_2} - \frac{1}{T_1}\right)$$

$$\ln \frac{k_2}{k_1} = -\frac{E_a}{R}\left(\frac{1}{T_2} - \frac{1}{T_1}\right)$$

$$\ln \frac{P_2}{P_1} = -\frac{\Delta H_{vap}}{R}\left(\frac{1}{T_2} - \frac{1}{T_1}\right)$$

Catalyzed Perpetual Motion?

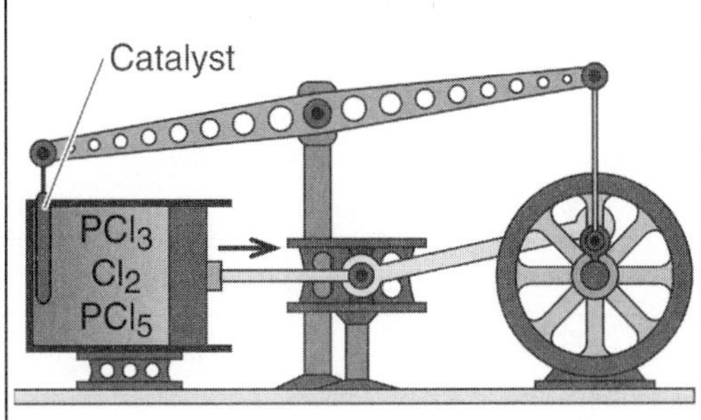

Table 17.4 Effect of Various Disturbances on an Equilibrium System

Disturbance	Net Direction of Reaction	Effect on Value of K
Concentration		
Increase [reactant]		
Decrease [reactant]		
Increase [product]		
Decrease [product]		
Pressure		
Increase P (decrease V)		
Decrease P (increase V)		
Increase P (add inert gas, no change in V)		
Temperature		
Increase T		
Decrease T		
Catalyst added		

Table B17.1 Effect of Temperature on K_c for Ammonia Synthesis

T (K)	K_c
200.	7.17×10^{15}
300.	2.69×10^{8}
400.	3.94×10^{4}
500.	1.72×10^{2}
600.	4.53×10^{0}
700.	2.96×10^{-1}
800.	3.96×10^{-2}

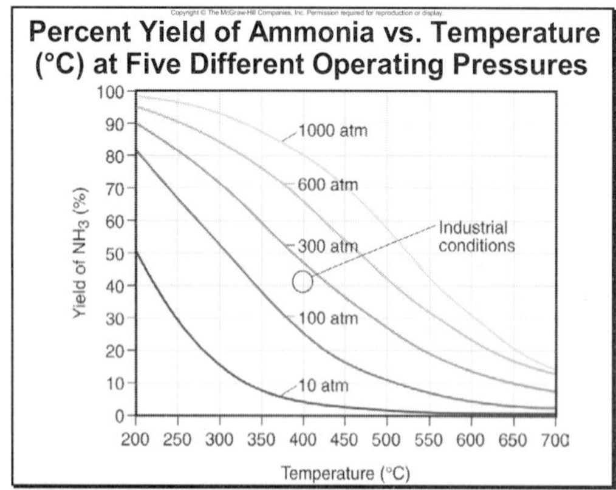

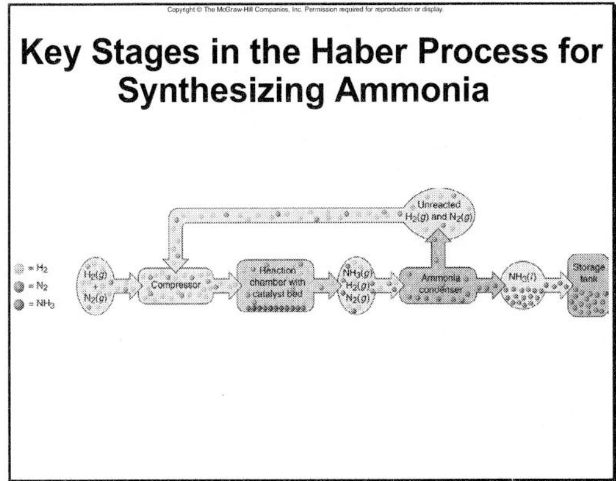
Key Stages in the Haber Process for Synthesizing Ammonia
Unreacted $H_2(g)$ and $N_2(g)$
$= H_2$
$= N_2$
$= NH_3$
$H_2(g)$ + $N_2(g)$
Compressor
Reaction chamber with catalyst bed
$NH_3(g)$ $H_2(g)$ $N_2(g)$
Ammonia condenser
$NH_3(l)$
Storage tank

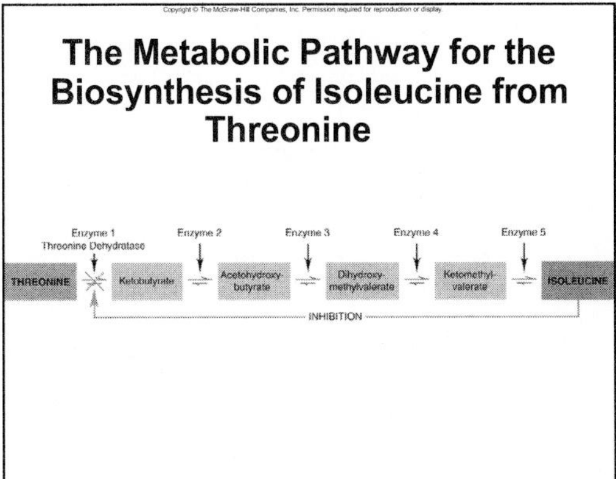
The Metabolic Pathway for the Biosynthesis of Isoleucine from Threonine
Enzyme 1
Threonine Dehydratase
Enzyme 2
Enzyme 3
Enzyme 4
Enzyme 5
THREONINE
Ketobutyrate
Acetohydroxy-butyrate
Dihydroxy-methylvalerate
Ketomethyl-valerate
ISOLEUCINE
INHIBITION

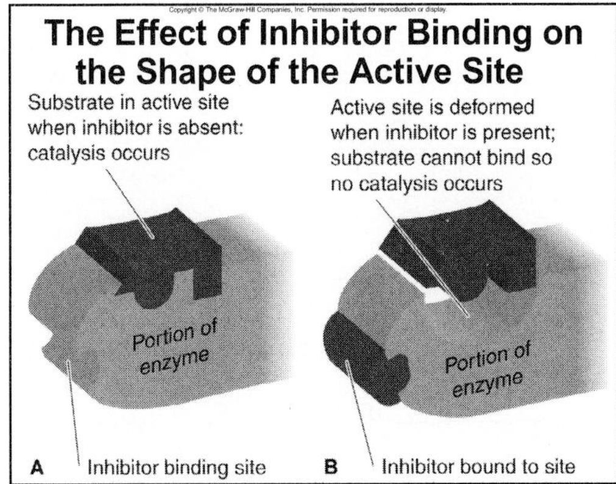
The Effect of Inhibitor Binding on the Shape of the Active Site
Substrate in active site when inhibitor is absent: catalysis occurs
Active site is deformed when inhibitor is present; substrate cannot bind so no catalysis occurs
Portion of enzyme
Portion of enzyme
A
Inhibitor binding site
B
Inhibitor bound to site

Chapter 18

Chemistry: The Molecular Nature of Matter and Change

Third Edition

Martin S. Silberberg

Table 18.1 Some Common Acids and Bases and Their Household Uses

Substance	Use
Acids	
Acetic acid, CH_3COOH	
Citric acid, $H_3C_6H_5O_7$	
Phosphoric acid, H_3PO_4	
Boric acid, H_3BO_3	
Aluminum salts, $NaAl(SO_4)_2 \cdot 12H_2O$	
Hydrochloric acid (muriatic acid), HCl	
Bases	
Sodium hydroxide (lye), NaOH	
Ammonia, NH_3	
Sodium carbonate, Na_2CO_3	
Sodium hydrogen carbonate, $NaHCO_3$	
Sodium phosphate, Na_3PO_4	

The Nature of the Hydrated Proton

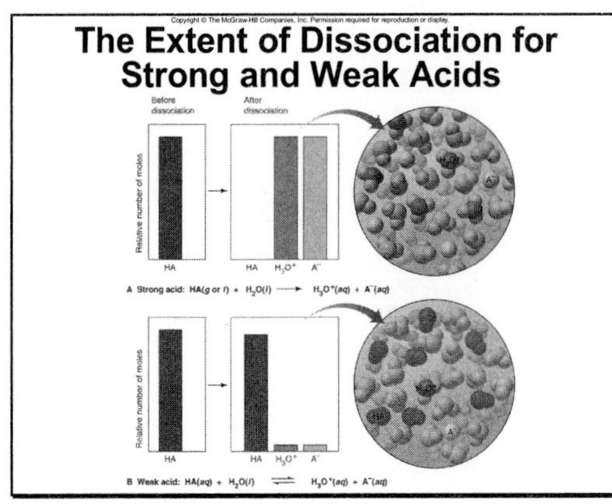

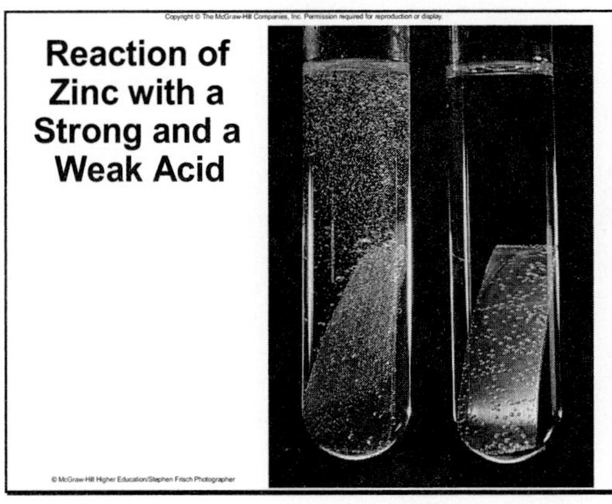

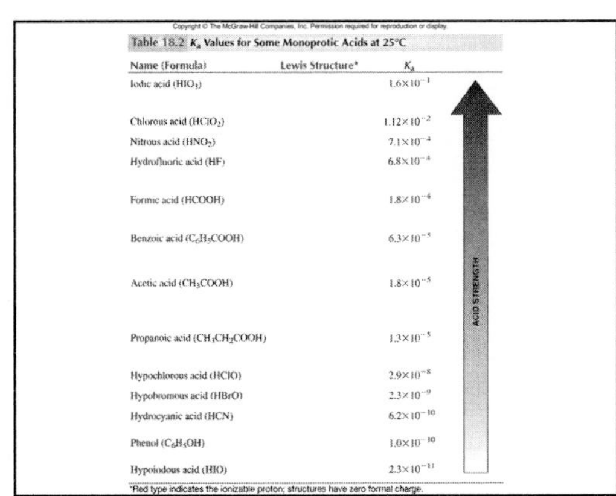

Table 18.2 K_a Values for Some Monoprotic Acids at 25°C

Name (Formula)	Lewis Structure*	K_a
Iodic acid (HIO_3)		1.6×10^{-1}
Chlorous acid ($HClO_2$)		1.12×10^{-2}
Nitrous acid (HNO_2)		7.1×10^{-4}
Hydrofluoric acid (HF)		6.8×10^{-4}
Formic acid (HCOOH)		1.8×10^{-4}
Benzoic acid (C_6H_5COOH)		6.3×10^{-5}
Acetic acid (CH_3COOH)		1.8×10^{-5}
Propanoic acid (CH_3CH_2COOH)		1.3×10^{-5}
Hypochlorous acid (HClO)		2.9×10^{-8}
Hypobromous acid (HBrO)		2.3×10^{-9}
Hydrocyanic acid (HCN)		6.2×10^{-10}
Phenol (C_6H_5OH)		1.0×10^{-10}
Hypoiodous acid (HIO)		2.3×10^{-11}

*Red type indicates the ionizable proton; structures have zero formal charge.

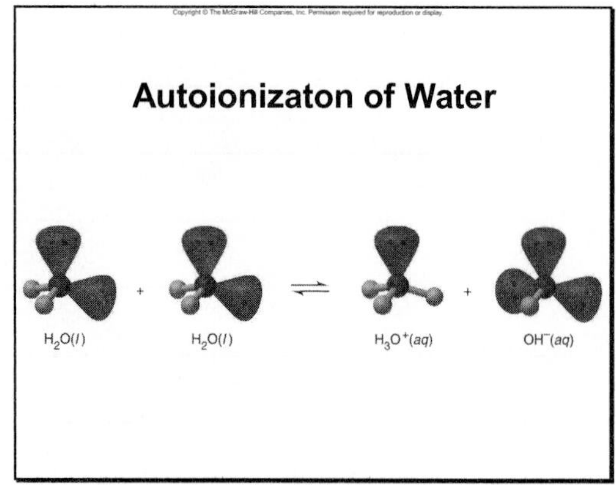
Copyright © The McGraw-Hill Companies, Inc. Permission required for reproduction or display.
Autoionizaton of Water
$H_2O(l)$
$H_2O(l)$
$H_3O^+(aq)$
$OH^-(aq)$

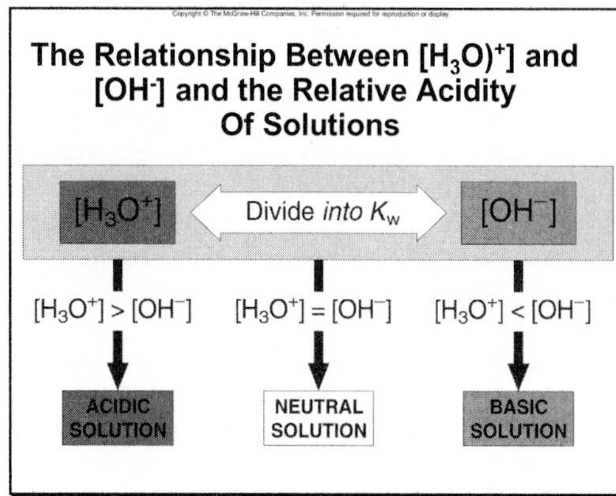
Copyright © The McGraw-Hill Companies, Inc. Permission required for reproduction or display.
The Relationship Between $[H_3O)^+]$ and $[OH^-]$ and the Relative Acidity Of Solutions
$[H_3O^+]$
Divide *into* K_w
$[OH^-]$
$[H_3O^+] > [OH^-]$
$[H_3O^+] = [OH^-]$
$[H_3O^+] < [OH^-]$
ACIDIC SOLUTION
NEUTRAL SOLUTION
BASIC SOLUTION

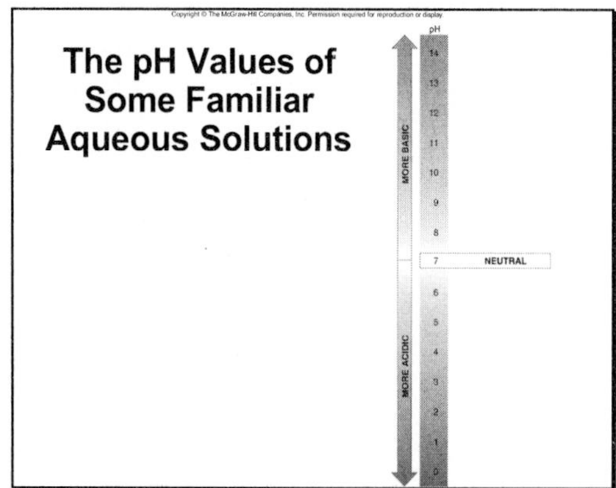
Copyright © The McGraw-Hill Companies, Inc. Permission required for reproduction or display.
The pH Values of Some Familiar Aqueous Solutions
pH
14
13
12
11
10
9
8
7
NEUTRAL
6
5
4
3
2
1
0
MORE BASIC
MORE ACIDIC

Table 18.3 The Relationship Between K_a and pK_a

Acid Name (Formula)	K_a at 25°C	pK_a
Hydrogen sulfate ion (HSO_4^-)	1.02×10^{-2}	1.991
Nitrous acid (HNO_2)	7.1×10^{-4}	3.15
Acetic acid (CH_3COOH)	1.8×10^{-5}	4.74
Hypobromous acid (HBrO)	2.3×10^{-9}	8.64
Phenol (C_6H_5OH)	1.0×10^{-10}	10.00

The Relations Among $[H_3O^+]$, pH, $[OH^-]$, and pOH

		$[H_3O^+]$	pH	$[OH^-]$	pOH
MORE BASIC		1.0×10^{-15}	15.00	1.0×10^{1}	−1.00
		1.0×10^{-14}	14.00	1.0×10^{0}	0.00
		1.0×10^{-13}	13.00	1.0×10^{-1}	1.00
	BASIC	1.0×10^{-12}	12.00	1.0×10^{-2}	2.00
		1.0×10^{-11}	11.00	1.0×10^{-3}	3.00
		1.0×10^{-10}	10.00	1.0×10^{-4}	4.00
		1.0×10^{-9}	9.00	1.0×10^{-5}	5.00
		1.0×10^{-8}	8.00	1.0×10^{-6}	6.00
	NEUTRAL	1.0×10^{-7}	7.00	1.0×10^{-7}	7.00
MORE ACIDIC		1.0×10^{-6}	6.00	1.0×10^{-8}	8.00
		1.0×10^{-5}	5.00	1.0×10^{-9}	9.00
		1.0×10^{-4}	4.00	1.0×10^{-10}	10.00
	ACIDIC	1.0×10^{-3}	3.00	1.0×10^{-11}	11.00
		1.0×10^{-2}	2.00	1.0×10^{-12}	12.00
		1.0×10^{-1}	1.00	1.0×10^{-13}	13.00
		1.0×10^{0}	0.00	1.0×10^{-14}	14.00
		1.0×10^{1}	−1.00	1.0×10^{-15}	15.00

Methods for Measuring the pH of an Aqueous Solution

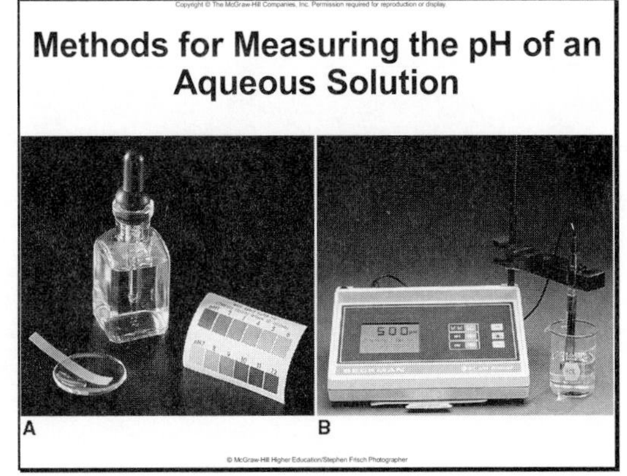

A B

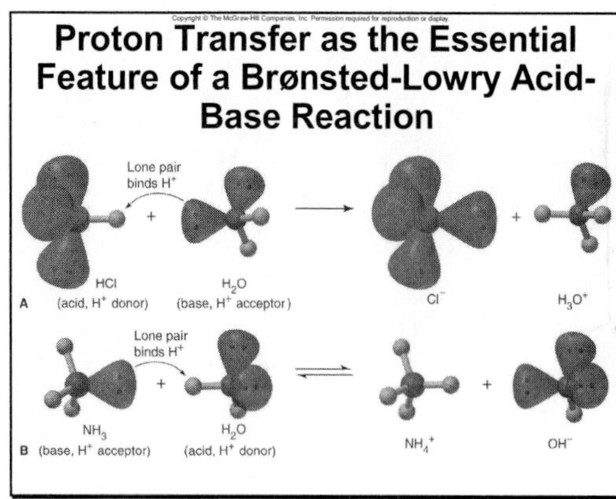

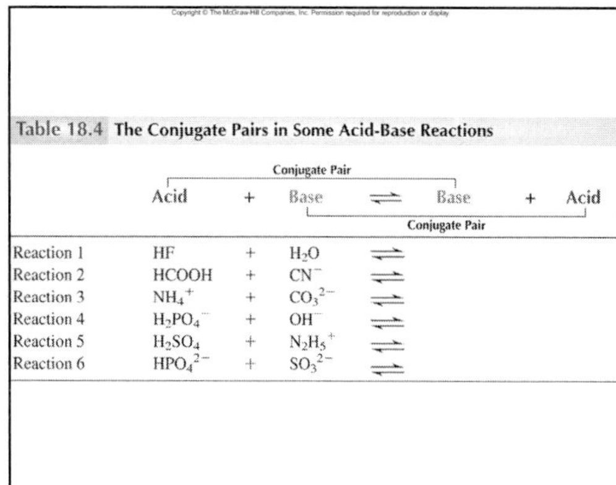

Table 18.4 The Conjugate Pairs in Some Acid-Base Reactions

	Acid	+	Base	⇌	Base	+	Acid
Reaction 1	HF	+	H_2O	⇌			
Reaction 2	HCOOH	+	CN^-	⇌			
Reaction 3	NH_4^+	+	CO_3^{2-}	⇌			
Reaction 4	$H_2PO_4^-$	+	OH^-	⇌			
Reaction 5	H_2SO_4	+	$N_2H_5^+$	⇌			
Reaction 6	HPO_4^{2-}	+	SO_3^{2-}	⇌			

(Conjugate Pair: Acid ↔ Base on the right; Conjugate Pair: Base ↔ Acid on the right)

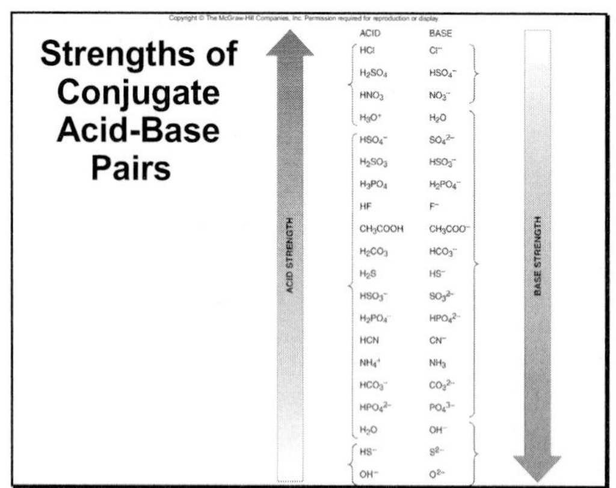

ACID	BASE
HCl	Cl^-
H_2SO_4	HSO_4^-
HNO_3	NO_3^-
H_3O^+	H_2O
HSO_4^-	SO_4^{2-}
H_2SO_3	HSO_3^-
H_3PO_4	$H_2PO_4^-$
HF	F^-
CH_3COOH	CH_3COO^-
H_2CO_3	HCO_3^-
H_2S	HS^-
HSO_3^-	SO_3^{2-}
$H_2PO_4^-$	HPO_4^{2-}
HCN	CN^-
NH_4^+	NH_3
HCO_3^-	CO_3^{2-}
HPO_4^{2-}	PO_4^{3-}
H_2O	OH^-
HS^-	S^{2-}
OH^-	O^{2-}

Table 18.5 Successive K_a Values for Some Polyprotic Acids at 25°C

Name (Formula)	Lewis Structure*	K_{a1}	K_{a2}	K_{a3}
Oxalic acid ($H_2C_2O_4$)	H—O—C(=O)—C(=O)—O—H	5.6×10^{-2}	5.4×10^{-5}	
Phosphorous acid (H_3PO_3)	H—O—P(=O)(H)—O—H	3×10^{-2}	1.7×10^{-7}	
Sulfurous acid (H_2SO_3)	H—O—S(=O)—O—H	1.4×10^{-2}	6.5×10^{-8}	
Phosphoric acid (H_3PO_4)	H—O—P(=O)(O—H)—O—H	7.2×10^{-3}	6.3×10^{-8}	4.2×10^{-13}
Arsenic acid (H_3AsO_4)	H—O—As(=O)(O—H)—O—H	6×10^{-3}	1.1×10^{-7}	3×10^{-12}
Citric acid ($H_3C_6H_5O_7$)	H—O—C(=O)—CH₂—C(OH)(COOH)—CH₂—C(=O)—O—H	7.5×10^{-4}	1.7×10^{-5}	4.0×10^{-7}
Carbonic acid (H_2CO_3)	H—O—C(=O)—O—H	4.5×10^{-7}	4.7×10^{-11}	
Hydrosulfuric acid (H_2S)	H—S—H	9×10^{-8}	1×10^{-17}	

ACID STRENGTH

*Red type indicates the ionizable protons.

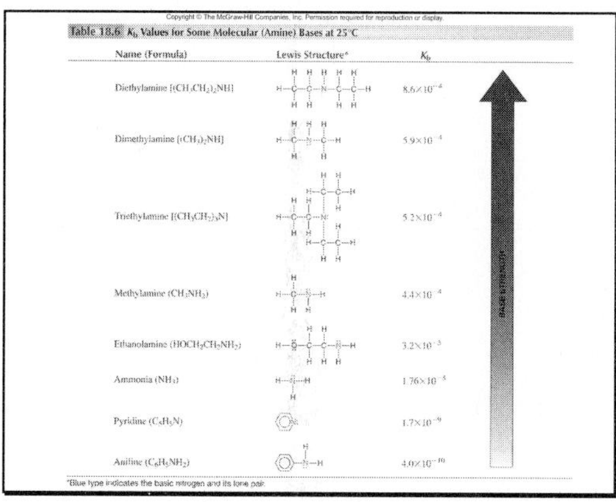

Table 18.6 K_b Values for Some Molecular (Amine) Bases at 25°C

Name (Formula)	Lewis Structure*	K_b
Diethylamine [$(CH_3CH_2)_2NH$]	H—C—C—N—C—C—H	8.6×10^{-4}
Dimethylamine [$(CH_3)_2NH$]	H—C—N—C—H	5.9×10^{-4}
Triethylamine [$(CH_3CH_2)_3N$]	H—C—C—N	5.2×10^{-4}
Methylamine (CH_3NH_2)	H—C—N—H	4.4×10^{-4}
Ethanolamine ($HOCH_2CH_2NH_2$)	H—O—C—C—N—H	3.2×10^{-5}
Ammonia (NH_3)	H—N—H	1.76×10^{-5}
Pyridine (C_5H_5N)		1.7×10^{-9}
Aniline ($C_6H_5NH_2$)	—N—H	4.0×10^{-10}

BASE STRENGTH

*Blue type indicates the basic nitrogen and its lone pair.

Abstraction of a Proton from Water by Methylamine

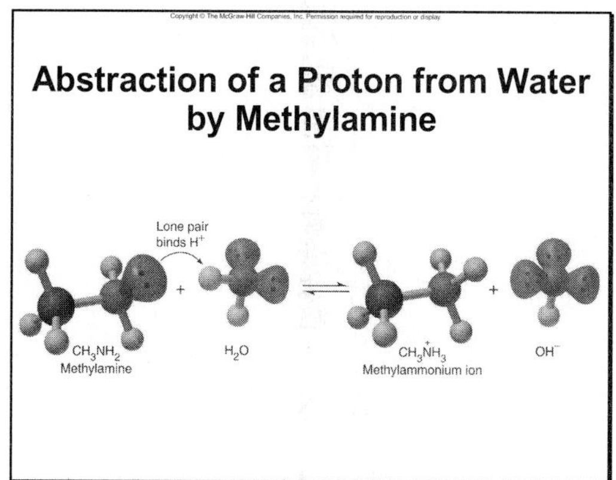

The Effect of Atomic and Molecular Properties on Nonmetal Hydride Acidity

Electronegativity increases, acidity increases →

Bond strength decreases, acidity increases ↓

6A(16)	7A(17)
H_2O	HF
H_2S	HCl
H_2Se	HBr
H_2Te	HI

The Relative Strengths of Oxoacids

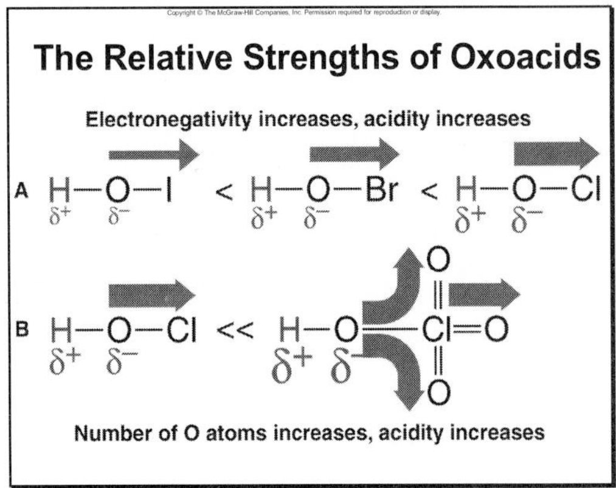

Table 18.7 K_a Values of Some Hydrated Metal Ions at 25°C

Free Ion	Hydrated Ion	K_a
Fe^{3+}	$Fe(H_2O)_6^{3+}(aq)$	6×10^{-3}
Sn^{2+}	$Sn(H_2O)_6^{2+}(aq)$	4×10^{-4}
Cr^{3+}	$Cr(H_2O)_6^{3+}(aq)$	1×10^{-4}
Al^{3+}	$Al(H_2O)_6^{3+}(aq)$	1×10^{-5}
Be^{2+}	$Be(H_2O)_4^{2+}(aq)$	4×10^{-6}
Cu^{2+}	$Cu(H_2O)_6^{2+}(aq)$	3×10^{-8}
Pb^{2+}	$Pb(H_2O)_6^{2+}(aq)$	3×10^{-8}
Zn^{2+}	$Zn(H_2O)_6^{2+}(aq)$	1×10^{-9}
Co^{2+}	$Co(H_2O)_6^{2+}(aq)$	2×10^{-10}
Ni^{2+}	$Ni(H_2O)_6^{2+}(aq)$	1×10^{-10}

ACID STRENGTH ↑

The Acidic Behavior of the Hydrated Al^{3+} Ion

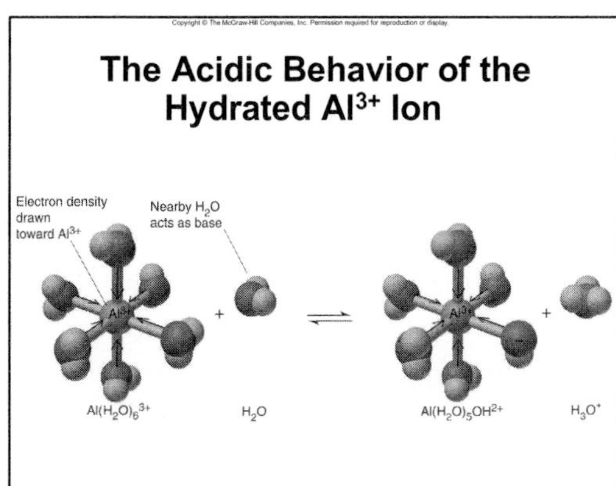

Table 18.8 The Behavior of Salts in Water

Salt Solution (Examples)	pH	Nature of Ions	Ion That Reacts with Water
Neutral [NaCl, KBr, $Ba(NO_3)_2$]	7.0	Cation of strong base; Anion of strong acid	
Acidic (NH_4Cl, NH_4NO_3, CH_3NH_3Br)	<7.0	Cation of weak base; Anion of strong acid	
Acidic [$Al(NO_3)_3$, $CrCl_3$, $FeBr_3$]	<7.0	Small, highly charged cation; Anion of strong acid	
Acidic (NaH_2PO_4, $KHSO_4$, $NaHSO_3$)	<7.0	Cation of strong base; First anion of polyprotic acid	
Basic (CH_3COONa, KF, Na_2CO_3)	>7.0	Cation of strong base; Anion of weak acid	

Metal Cations as Lewis Acids

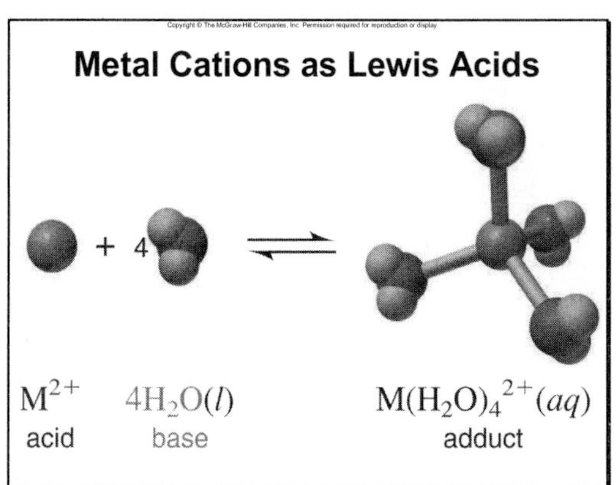

M^{2+} acid $4H_2O(l)$ base $M(H_2O)_4^{2+}(aq)$ adduct

The Mg^{2+} Ion as a Lewis Acid in the Chlorophyll Molecule

Chapter 19

Chemistry: The Molecular Nature of Matter and Change

Third Edition

Martin S. Silberberg

The Effect of Addition of Acid or Base to an Unbuffered or Buffered Solution

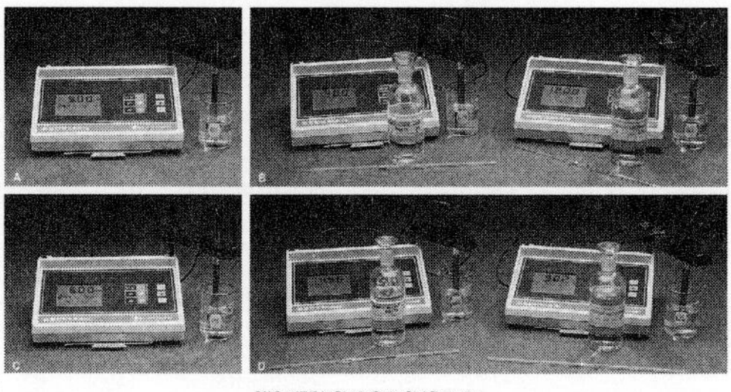

Table 19.1 The Effect of Added Acetate Ion on the Dissociation of Acetic Acid

$[CH_3COOH]_{init}$	$[CH_3COO^-]_{added}$	% Dissociation*	pH
0.10	0.00	1.3	2.89
0.10	0.050	0.036	4.44
0.10	0.10	0.018	4.74
0.10	0.15	0.012	4.92

*% Dissociation $= \frac{[CH_3COOH]_{dissoc}}{[CH_3COOH]_{init}} \times 100$

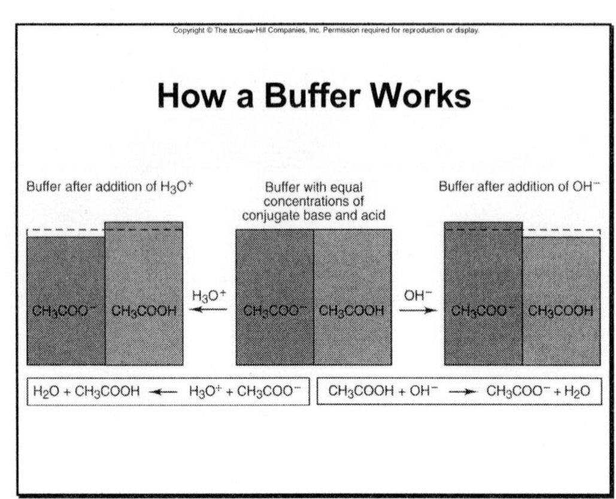
Copyright © The McGraw-Hill Companies, Inc. Permission required for reproduction or display.
How a Buffer Works
Buffer after addition of H_3O^+
Buffer with equal concentrations of conjugate base and acid
Buffer after addition of OH^-
CH_3COO^-
CH_3COOH
H_3O^+
OH^-
$H_2O + CH_3COOH \leftarrow H_3O^+ + CH_3COO^-$
$CH_3COOH + OH^- \rightarrow CH_3COO^- + H_2O$

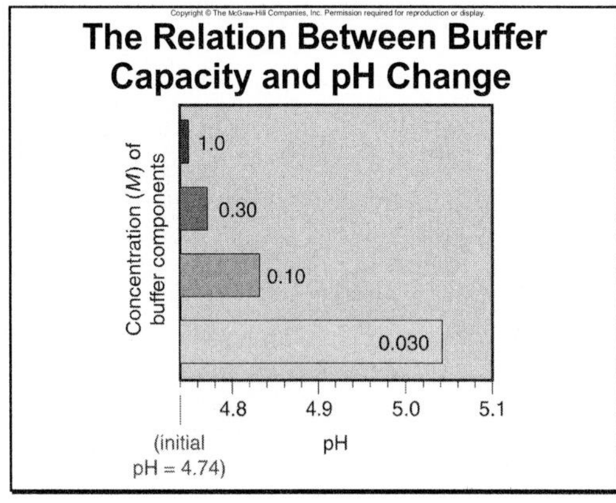
Copyright © The McGraw-Hill Companies, Inc. Permission required for reproduction or display.
The Relation Between Buffer Capacity and pH Change
Concentration (M) of buffer components
1.0
0.30
0.10
0.030
4.8
4.9
5.0
5.1
(initial pH = 4.74)
pH

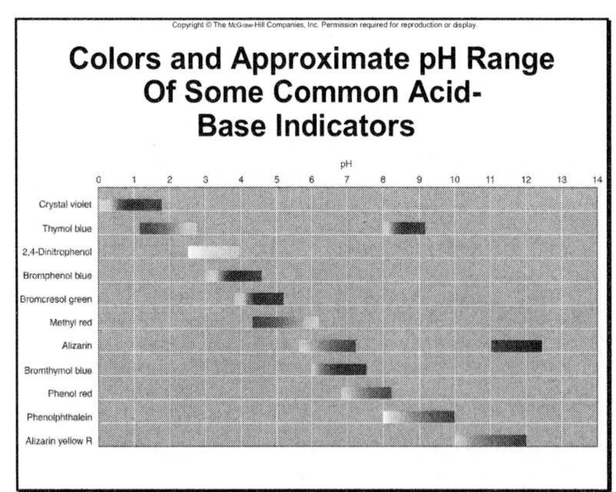
Copyright © The McGraw-Hill Companies, Inc. Permission required for reproduction or display.
Colors and Approximate pH Range Of Some Common Acid-Base Indicators
pH
0 1 2 3 4 5 6 7 8 9 10 11 12 13 14
Crystal violet
Thymol blue
2,4-Dinitrophenol
Bromphenol blue
Bromcresol green
Methyl red
Alizarin
Bromthymol blue
Phenol red
Phenolphthalein
Alizarin yellow R

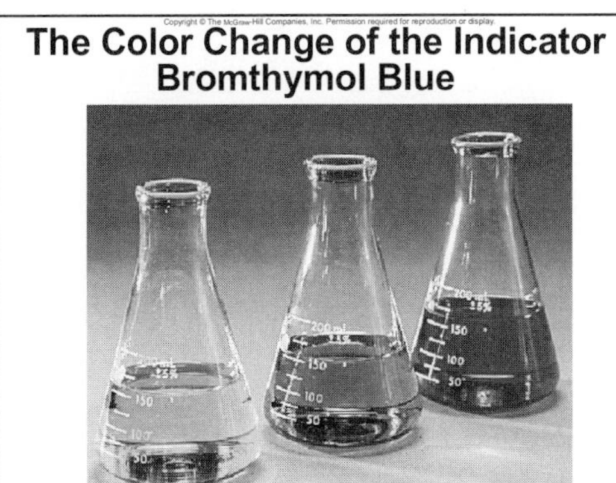

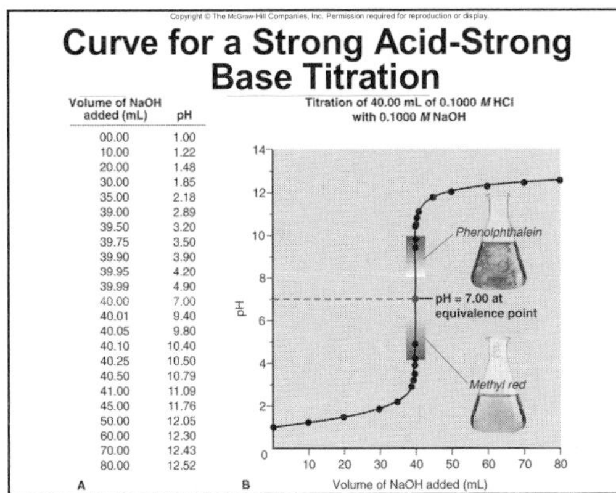

Volume of NaOH added (mL)	pH
00.00	1.00
10.00	1.22
20.00	1.48
30.00	1.85
35.00	2.18
39.00	2.89
39.50	3.20
39.75	3.50
39.90	3.90
39.95	4.20
39.99	4.90
40.00	7.00
40.01	9.40
40.05	9.80
40.10	10.40
40.25	10.50
40.50	10.79
41.00	11.09
45.00	11.76
50.00	12.05
60.00	12.30
70.00	12.43
80.00	12.52

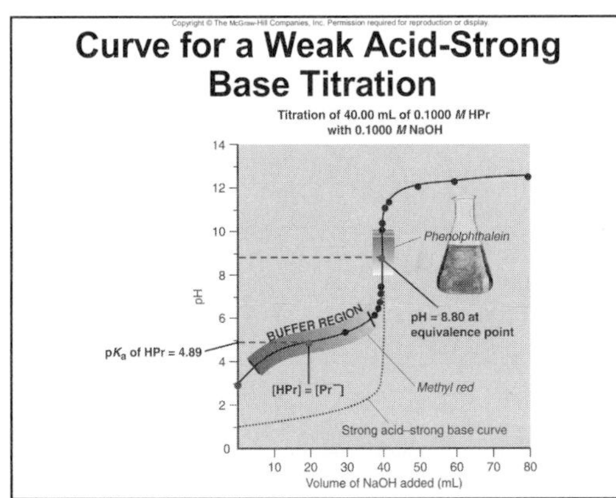

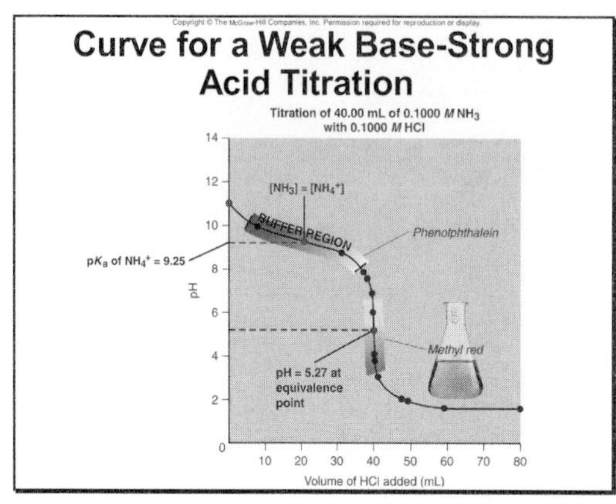
Curve for a Weak Base-Strong Acid Titration
Titration of 40.00 mL of 0.1000 M NH3 with 0.1000 M HCl
[NH3] = [NH4+]
BUFFER REGION
Phenolphthalein
pKa of NH4+ = 9.25
Methyl red
pH = 5.27 at equivalence point
pH
Volume of HCl added (mL)

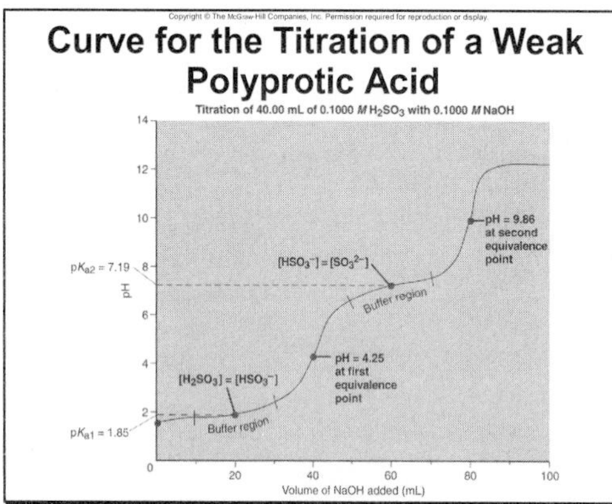
Curve for the Titration of a Weak Polyprotic Acid
Titration of 40.00 mL of 0.1000 M H2SO3 with 0.1000 M NaOH
pH = 9.86 at second equivalence point
[HSO3−] = [SO32−]
pKa2 = 7.19
Buffer region
pH = 4.25 at first equivalence point
[H2SO3] = [HSO3−]
pKa1 = 1.85
Buffer region
pH
Volume of NaOH added (mL)

PbCl2, a Slightly Soluble Ionic Compound

Table 19.2 Solubility-Product Constants (K_{sp}) of Selected Ionic Compounds at 25°C

Name, Formula	K_{sp}
Aluminum hydroxide, $Al(OH)_3$	3×10^{-34}
Cobalt(II) carbonate, $CoCO_3$	1.0×10^{-10}
Iron(II) hydroxide, $Fe(OH)_2$	4.1×10^{-15}
Lead(II) fluoride, PbF_2	3.6×10^{-8}
Lead(II) sulfate, $PbSO_4$	1.6×10^{-8}
Mercury(I) iodide, Hg_2I_2	4.7×10^{-29}
Silver sulfide, Ag_2S	8×10^{-48}
Zinc iodate, $Zn(IO_3)_2$	3.9×10^{-6}

Table 19.3 Relationship Between K_{sp} and Solubility at 25°C

No. of Ions	Formula	Cation:Anion	K_{sp}	Solubility (M)
2	$MgCO_3$	1:1	3.5×10^{-8}	1.9×10^{-4}
2	$PbSO_4$	1:1	1.6×10^{-8}	1.3×10^{-4}
2	$BaCrO_4$	1:1	2.1×10^{-10}	1.4×10^{-5}
3	$Ca(OH)_2$	1:2	6.5×10^{-6}	1.2×10^{-2}
3	BaF_2	1:2	1.5×10^{-6}	7.2×10^{-3}
3	CaF_2	1:2	3.2×10^{-11}	2.0×10^{-4}
3	Ag_2CrO_4	2:1	2.6×10^{-12}	8.7×10^{-5}

The Effect of a Common Ion on Solubility

$PbCrO_4(s) \rightleftharpoons Pb^{2+}(aq) + CrO_4^{2-}(aq)$

A

$PbCrO_4(s) \leftleftharpoons Pb^{2+}(aq) + CrO_4^{2-}(aq; \text{added})$

B

Copyright © The McGraw-Hill Companies, Inc. Permission required for reproduction or display.
Test for the Presence of a Carbonate
© McGraw-Hill Higher Education/Stephen Frisch Photographer

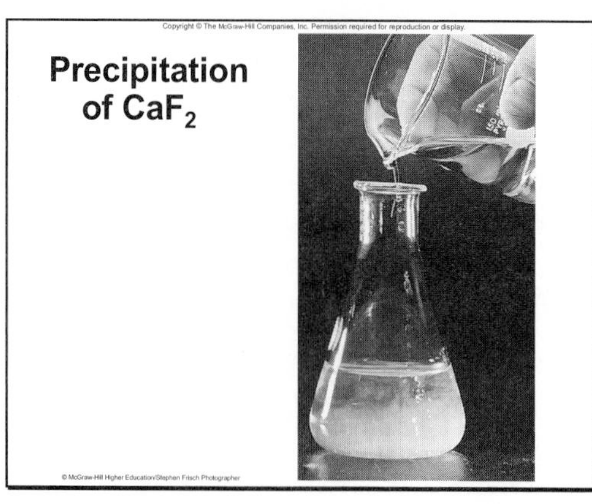
Copyright © The McGraw-Hill Companies, Inc. Permission required for reproduction or display.
Precipitation of CaF_2
© McGraw-Hill Higher Education/Stephen Frisch Photographer

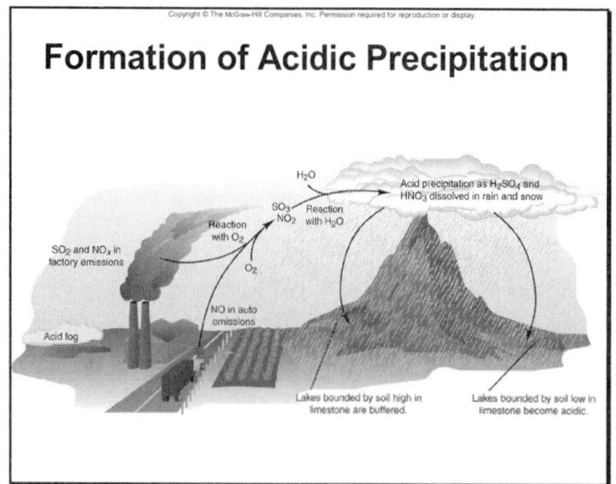
Copyright © The McGraw-Hill Companies, Inc. Permission required for reproduction or display.
Formation of Acidic Precipitation
H_2O
Acid precipitation as H_2SO_4 and HNO_3 dissolved in rain and snow
SO_3
NO_2
Reaction with H_2O
Reaction with O_2
SO_2 and NO_x in factory emissions
O_2
NO in auto emissions
Acid fog
Lakes bounded by soil high in limestone are buffered.
Lakes bounded by soil low in limestone become acidic.

$Cr(NH_3)_6^{3+}$, a Typical Complex Ion

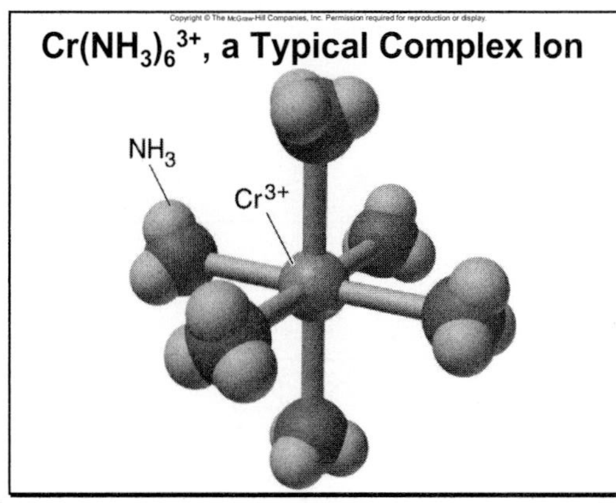

Table 19.4 Formation Constants (K_f) of Some Complex Ions at 25°C

Complex Ion	K_f
$Ag(CN)_2^-$	3.0×10^{20}
$Ag(NH_3)_2^+$	1.7×10^{7}
$Ag(S_2O_3)_2^{3-}$	4.7×10^{13}
AlF_6^{3-}	4×10^{19}
$Al(OH)_4^-$	3×10^{33}
$Be(OH)_4^{2-}$	4×10^{18}
CdI_4^{2-}	1×10^{6}
$Co(OH)_4^{2-}$	5×10^{9}
$Cr(OH)_4^-$	8.0×10^{29}
$Cu(NH_3)_4^{2+}$	5.6×10^{11}
$Fe(CN)_6^{4-}$	3×10^{35}
$Fe(CN)_6^{3-}$	4.0×10^{43}
$Hg(CN)_4^{2-}$	9.3×10^{38}
$Ni(NH_3)_6^{2+}$	2.0×10^{8}
$Pb(OH)_3^-$	8×10^{13}
$Sn(OH)_3^-$	3×10^{25}
$Zn(CN)_4^{2-}$	4.2×10^{19}
$Zn(NH_3)_4^{2+}$	7.8×10^{8}
$Zn(OH)_4^{2-}$	3×10^{15}

The Stepwise Exchange of NH_3 for H_2O in $M(H_2O)_4^{2+}$

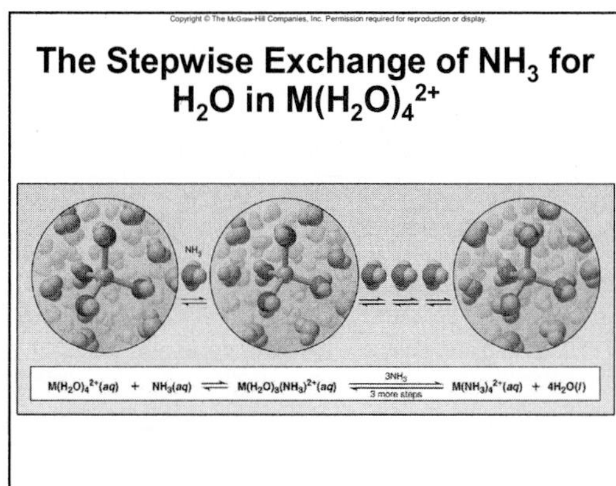

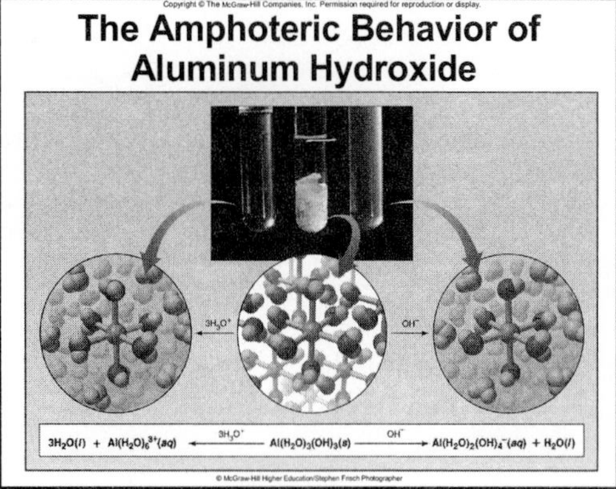
Copyright © The McGraw-Hill Companies, Inc. Permission required for reproduction or display.
The Amphoteric Behavior of Aluminum Hydroxide
$3H_3O^+$
OH^-
$3H_2O(l) + Al(H_2O)_6^{3+}(aq) \xleftarrow{3H_3O^+} Al(H_2O)_3(OH)_3(s) \xrightarrow{OH^-} Al(H_2O)_2(OH)_4^-(aq) + H_2O(l)$

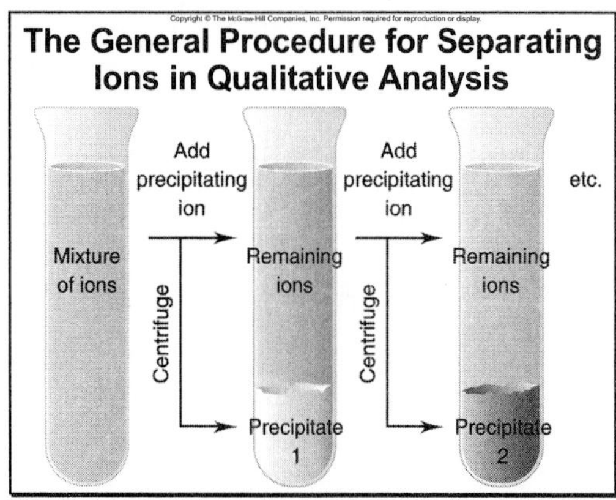
Copyright © The McGraw-Hill Companies, Inc. Permission required for reproduction or display.
The General Procedure for Separating Ions in Qualitative Analysis
Add precipitating ion
Add precipitating ion
etc.
Mixture of ions
Remaining ions
Remaining ions
Centrifuge
Centrifuge
Precipitate 1
Precipitate 2

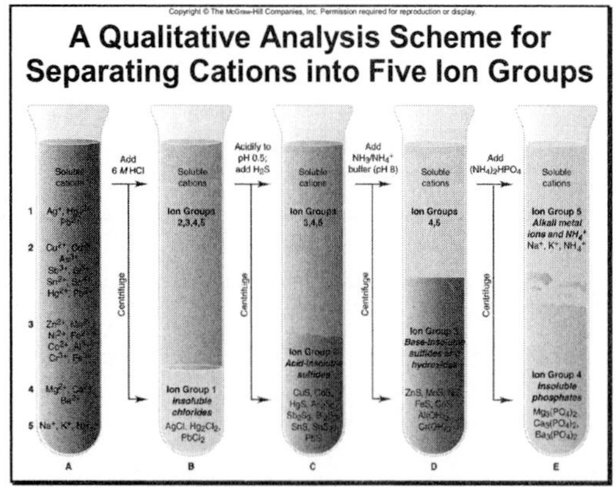
Copyright © The McGraw-Hill Companies, Inc. Permission required for reproduction or display.
A Qualitative Analysis Scheme for Separating Cations into Five Ion Groups
Add 6 M HCl
Acidify to pH 0.5; add H_2S
Add NH_3/NH_4^+ buffer (pH 8)
Add $(NH_4)_2HPO_4$
Soluble cations
Centrifuge
Ion Groups 2,3,4,5
Ion Groups 3,4,5
Ion Groups 4,5
Ion Group 1 Insoluble chlorides
AgCl, Hg_2Cl_2, $PbCl_2$
Ion Group 5 Alkali metal ions and NH_4^+
Na^+, K^+, NH_4^+
Ion Group 4 Insoluble phosphates
$Mg_3(PO_4)_2$, $Ca_3(PO_4)_2$, $Ba_3(PO_4)_2$
A
B
C
D
E

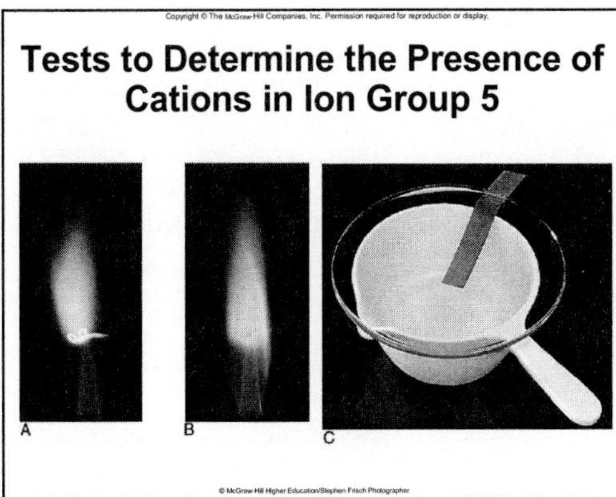
Copyright © The McGraw-Hill Companies, Inc. Permission required for reproduction or display.
Tests to Determine the Presence of Cations in Ion Group 5
A
B
C
© McGraw-Hill Higher Education/Stephen Frisch Photographer

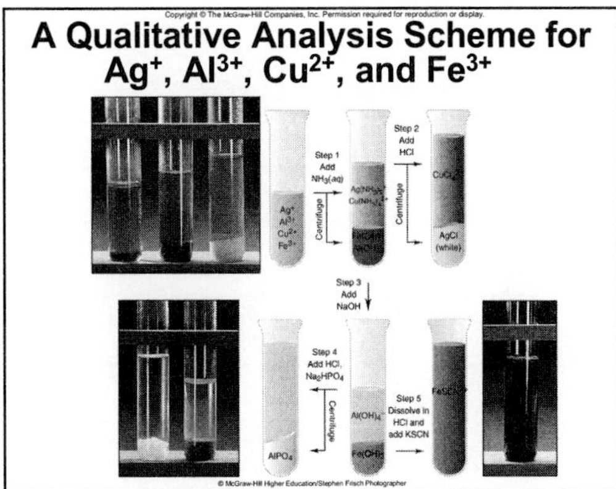
Copyright © The McGraw-Hill Companies, Inc. Permission required for reproduction or display.
A Qualitative Analysis Scheme for Ag^+, Al^{3+}, Cu^{2+}, and Fe^{3+}
Ag^+ Al^{3+} Cu^{2+} Fe^{3+}
Step 1 Add $NH_3(aq)$
Centrifuge
Step 2 Add HCl
Centrifuge
AgCl (white)
Step 3 Add NaOH
Step 4 Add HCl, Na_2HPO_4
Centrifuge
$AlPO_4$
Step 5 Dissolve in HCl and add KSCN
© McGraw-Hill Higher Education/Stephen Frisch Photographer

Chapter 20

Chemistry: The Molecular Nature of Matter and Change

Third Edition

Martin S. Silberberg

A Spontaneous, Endothermic Chemical Reaction

Spontaneous Expansion of a Gas

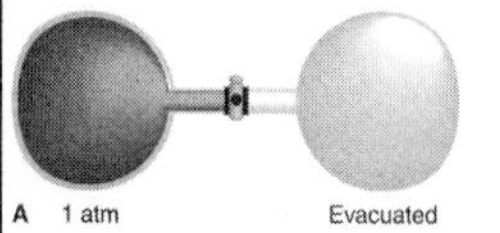

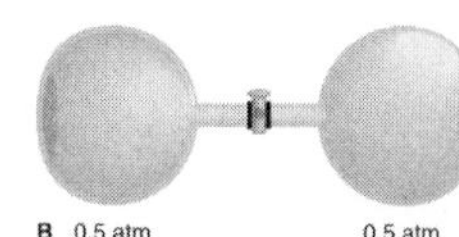

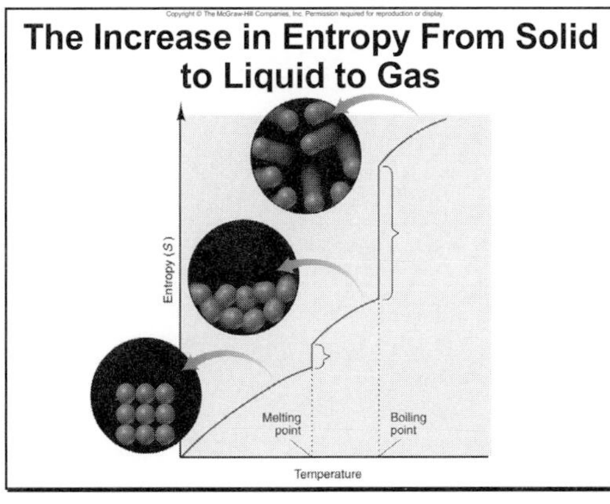
Copyright © The McGraw-Hill Companies, Inc. Permission required for reproduction or display.
The Increase in Entropy From Solid to Liquid to Gas
Entropy (S)
Melting point
Boiling point
Temperature

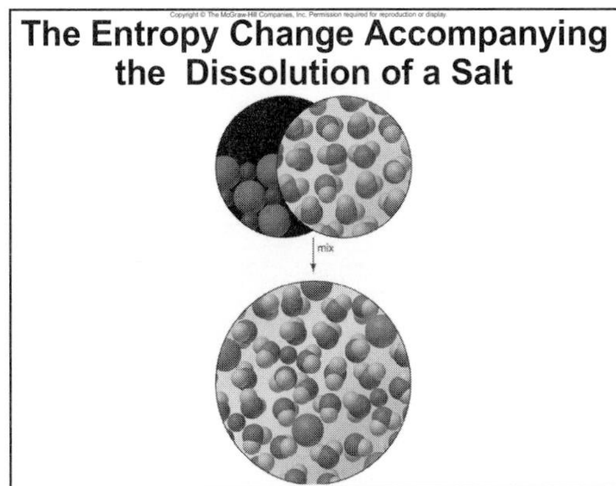
Copyright © The McGraw-Hill Companies, Inc. Permission required for reproduction or display.
The Entropy Change Accompanying the Dissolution of a Salt
mix

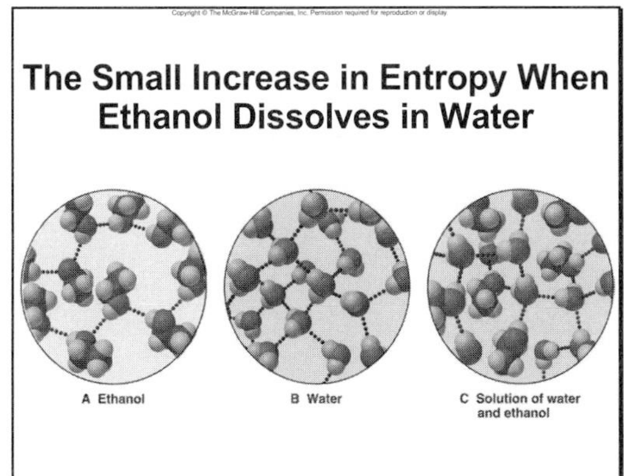
Copyright © The McGraw-Hill Companies, Inc. Permission required for reproduction or display.
The Small Increase in Entropy When Ethanol Dissolves in Water
A Ethanol
B Water
C Solution of water and ethanol

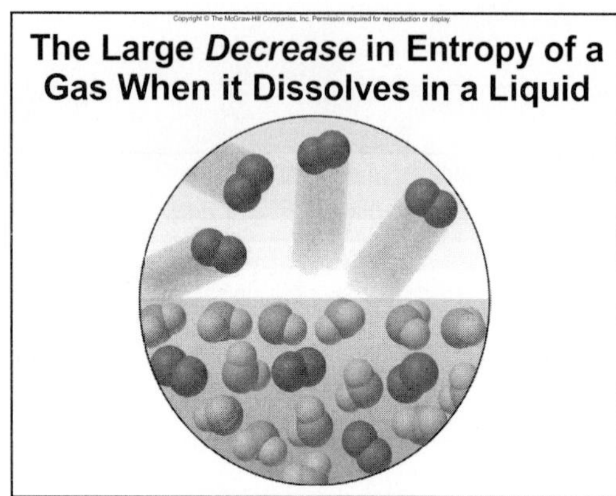

The Large *Decrease* in Entropy of a Gas When it Dissolves in a Liquid

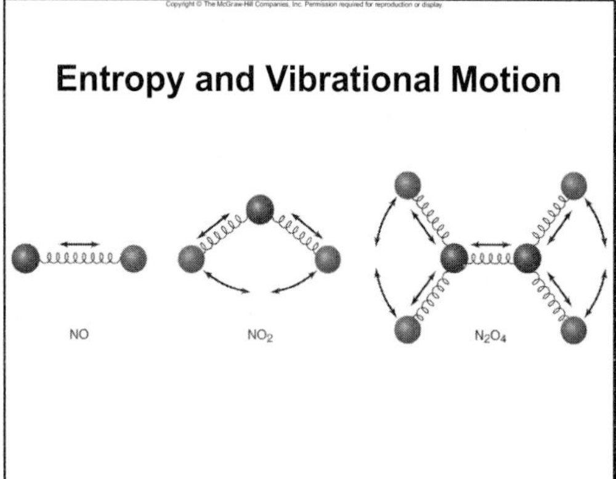

Entropy and Vibrational Motion
NO
NO2
N2O4

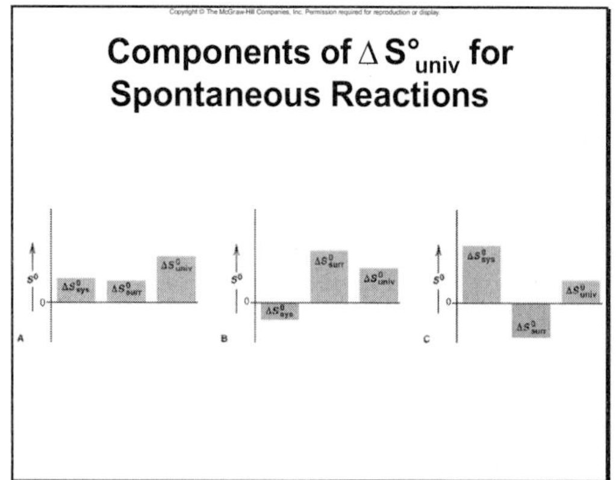

Components of ΔS°univ for Spontaneous Reactions

Table 20.1 Reaction Spontaneity and the Signs of ΔH^0, ΔS^0, and ΔG^0

ΔH^0	ΔS^0	$-T\Delta S^0$	ΔG^0	Description
−	+	−	−	
+	−	+	+	
+	+	−	+ or −	
−	−	+	+ or −	

The Effect of Temperature on Reaction Spontaneity

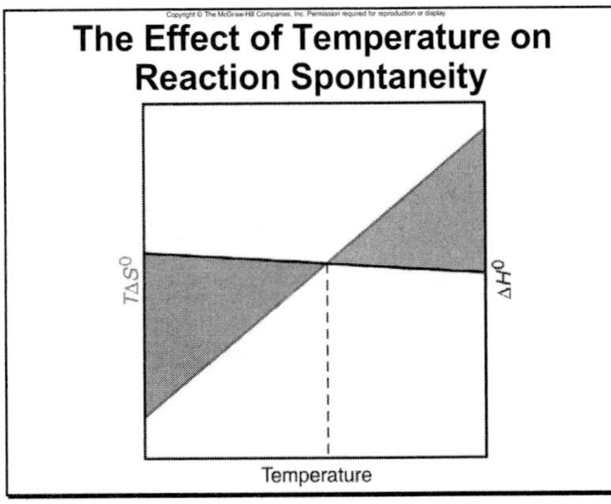

The Coupling of a Nonspontaneous Reaction to the Hydrolysis of ATP

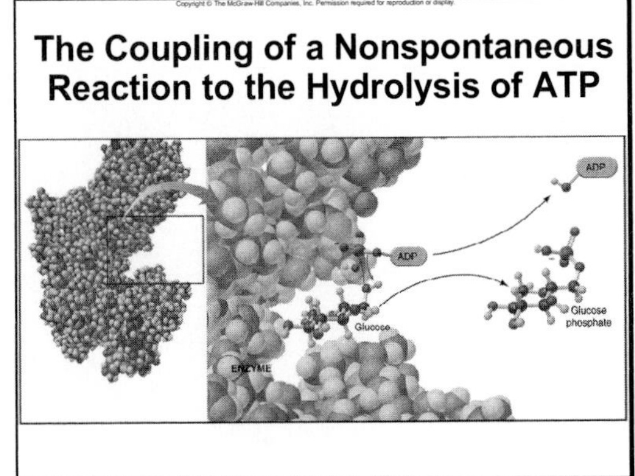

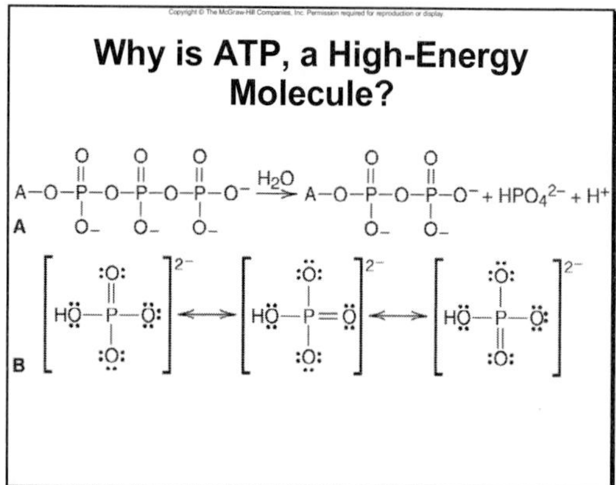

Table 20.2 The Relationship Between ΔG^0 and K at 298 K

ΔG^0 (kJ)	K	Significance
200	9×10^{-36}	Essentially no forward reaction; reverse reaction goes to completion
100	3×10^{-18}	
50	2×10^{-9}	
10	2×10^{-2}	
1	7×10^{-1}	
0	1	Forward and reverse reactions proceed to same extent
−1	1.5	
−10	5×10^{1}	
−50	6×10^{8}	
−100	3×10^{17}	
−200	1×10^{35}	Forward reaction goes to completion; essentially no reverse reaction

FORWARD REACTION
REVERSE REACTION

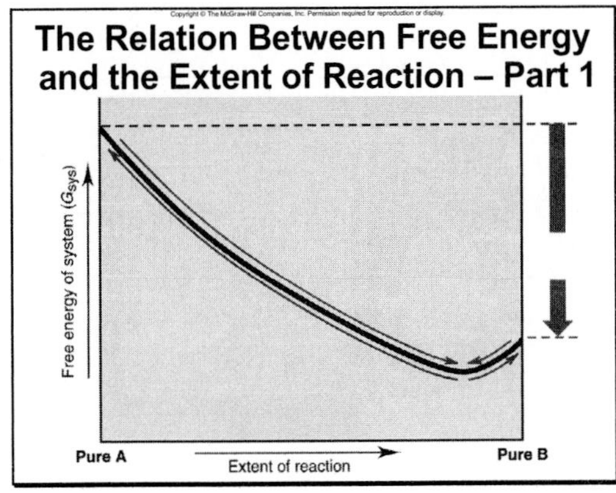
Copyright © The McGraw-Hill Companies, Inc. Permission required for reproduction or display.
The Relation Between Free Energy and the Extent of Reaction – Part 1
Free energy of system (G_{sys})
Pure A
Extent of reaction
Pure B

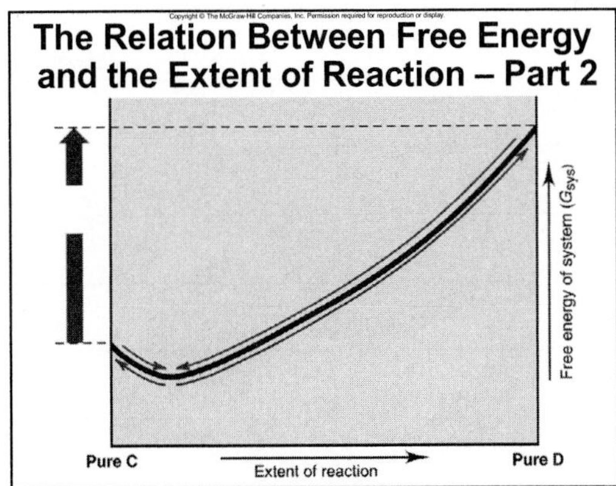
Copyright © The McGraw-Hill Companies, Inc. Permission required for reproduction or display.
The Relation Between Free Energy and the Extent of Reaction – Part 2
Free energy of system (G_{sys})
Pure C
Extent of reaction
Pure D

Chapter 21

Chemistry: The Molecular Nature of Matter and Change

Third Edition

Martin S. Silberberg

Copyright © The McGraw-Hill Companies, Inc. Permission required for reproduction or display.

A Summary of Redox Terminology

PROCESS	$Zn(s) + 2H^+(aq) \longrightarrow Zn^{2+}(aq) + H_2(g)$
OXIDATION • One reactant loses electrons. • Reducing agent is oxidized. • Oxidation number increases.	Zinc **loses** electrons. Zinc is the reducing agent and becomes **oxidized.** The oxidation number of Zn **increases** from 0 to +2.
REDUCTION • Other reactant gains electrons. • Oxidizing agent is reduced. • Oxidation number decreases.	Hydrogen ion **gains** electrons. Hydrogen ion is the oxidizing agent and becomes **reduced.** The oxidation number of H **decreases** from +1 to 0.

Copyright © The McGraw-Hill Companies, Inc. Permission required for reproduction or display.

The Redox Reaction Between Dichromate Ion and Iodide Ion

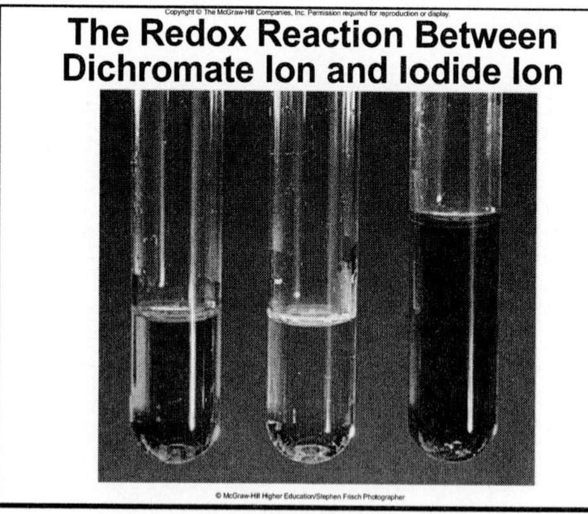

© McGraw-Hill Higher Education/Stephen Frisch Photographer

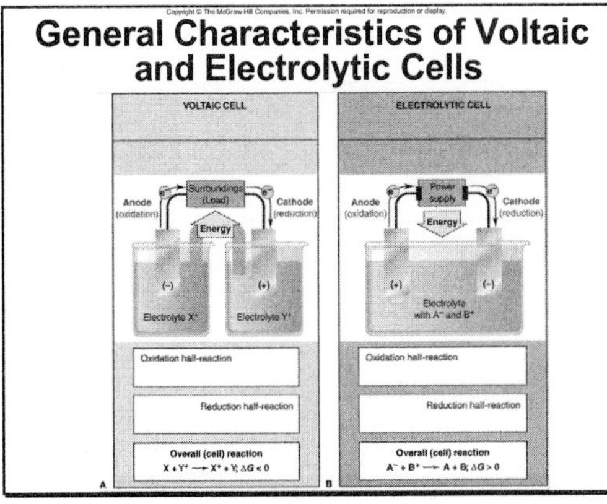
General Characteristics of Voltaic and Electrolytic Cells
VOLTAIC CELL
ELECTROLYTIC CELL
Surroundings (Load)
Power supply
Energy
Anode (oxidation)
Cathode (reduction)
Electrolyte X+
Electrolyte Y+
Electrolyte with A− and B+
Oxidation half-reaction
Reduction half-reaction
Overall (cell) reaction
X + Y+ ⟶ X+ + Y; ΔG < 0
A− + B+ ⟶ A + B; ΔG > 0

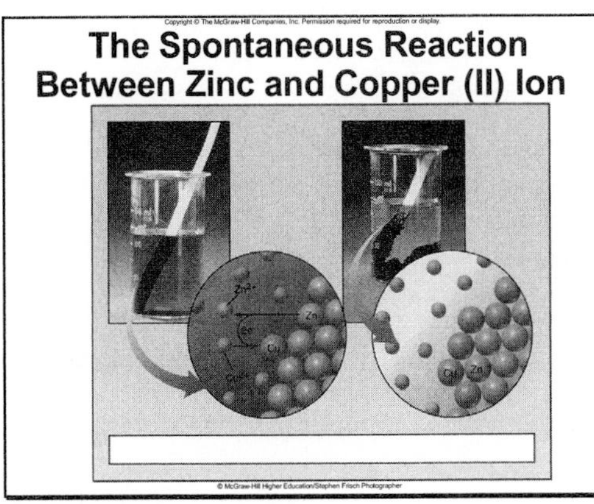
The Spontaneous Reaction Between Zinc and Copper (II) Ion

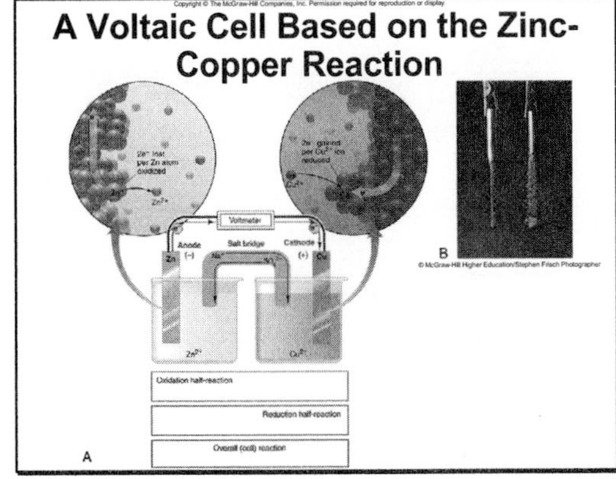
A Voltaic Cell Based on the Zinc-Copper Reaction
Voltmeter
Anode (−)
Salt bridge
Cathode (+)
Oxidation half-reaction
Reduction half-reaction
Overall (cell) reaction

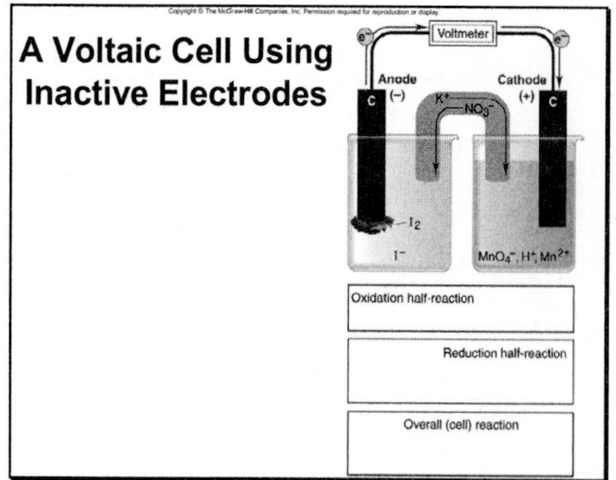

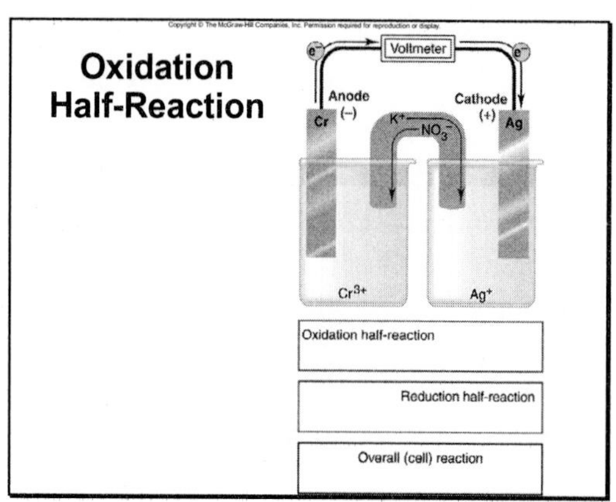

Table 21.1 Voltages of Some Voltaic Cells

Voltaic Cell	Voltage (V)
Common alkaline battery	1.5
Lead-acid car battery (6 cells = 12 V)	2.0
Calculator battery (mercury)	1.3
Electric eel (~5000 cells in 6-ft eel = 750 V)	0.15
Nerve of giant squid (across cell membrane)	0.070

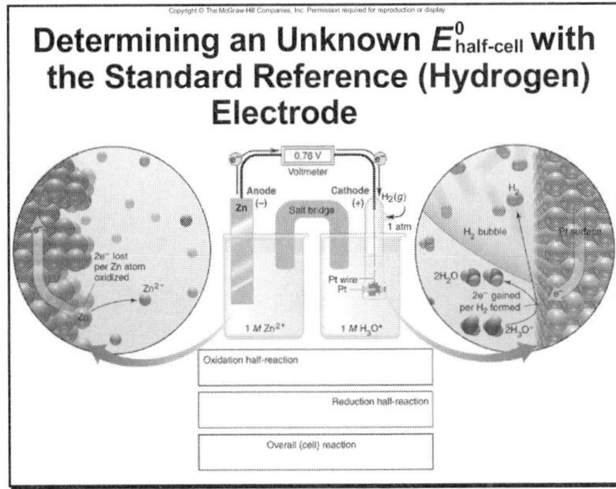

Table 21.2 Selected Standard Electrode Potentials (298 K)

Half-Reaction	E^0 (V)
$F_2(g) + 2e^- \rightleftharpoons 2F^-(aq)$	+2.87
$Cl_2(g) + 2e^- \rightleftharpoons 2Cl^-(aq)$	+1.36
$MnO_2(s) + 4H^+(aq) + 2e^- \rightleftharpoons Mn^{2+}(aq) + 2H_2O(l)$	+1.23
$NO_3^-(aq) + 4H^+(aq) + 3e^- \rightleftharpoons NO(g) + 2H_2O(l)$	+0.96
$Ag^+(aq) + e^- \rightleftharpoons Ag(s)$	+0.80
$Fe^{3+}(aq) + e^- \rightleftharpoons Fe^{2+}(aq)$	+0.77
$O_2(g) + 2H_2O(l) + 4e^- \rightleftharpoons 4OH^-(aq)$	+0.40
$Cu^{2+}(aq) + 2e^- \rightleftharpoons Cu(s)$	+0.34
$2H^+(aq) + 2e^- \rightleftharpoons H_2(g)$	0.00
$N_2(g) + 5H^+(aq) + 4e^- \rightleftharpoons N_2H_5^+(aq)$	−0.23
$Fe^{2+}(aq) + 2e^- \rightleftharpoons Fe(s)$	−0.44
$2H_2O(l) + 2e^- \rightleftharpoons H_2(g) + 2OH^-(aq)$	−0.83
$Na^+(aq) + e^- \rightleftharpoons Na(s)$	−2.71
$Li^+(aq) + e^- \rightleftharpoons Li(s)$	−3.05

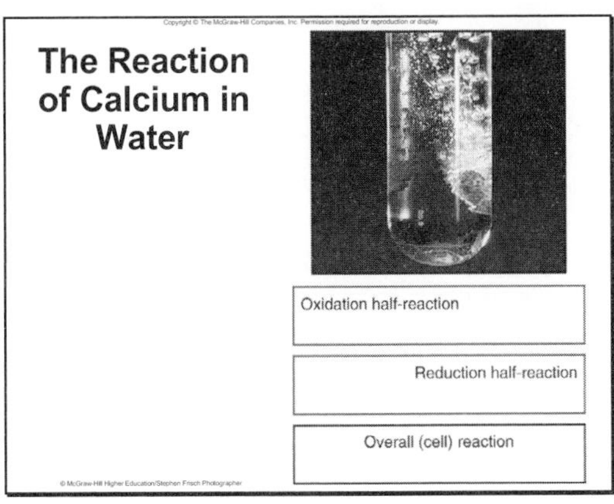

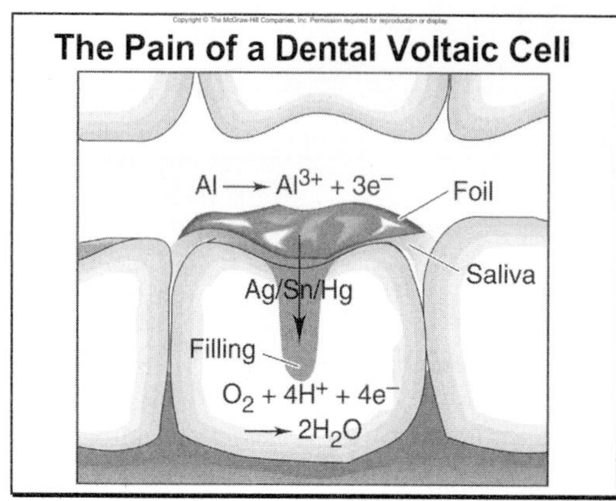
The Pain of a Dental Voltaic Cell
Al ⟶ Al3+ + 3e−
Foil
Saliva
Ag/Sn/Hg
Filling
O2 + 4H+ + 4e− ⟶ 2H2O

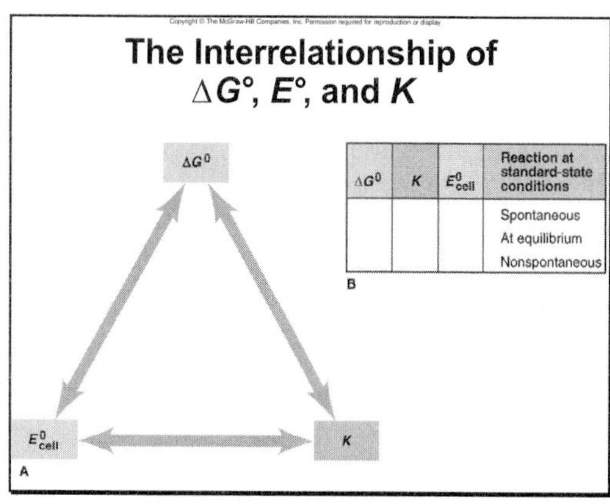
The Interrelationship of ΔG°, E°, and K
ΔG0
E0cell
K
A
ΔG0
K
E0cell
Reaction at standard-state conditions
Spontaneous
At equilibrium
Nonspontaneous
B

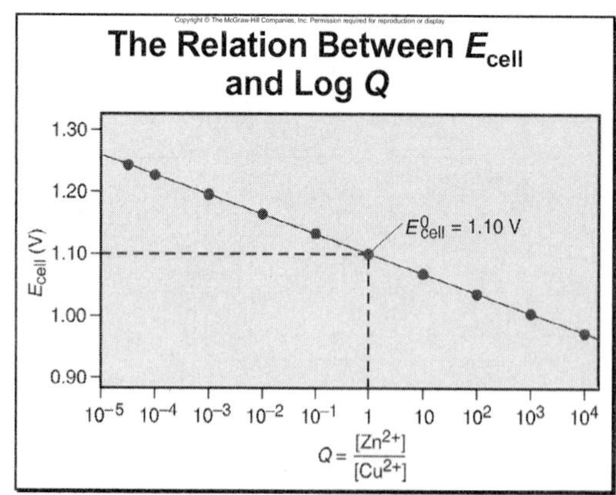
The Relation Between Ecell and Log Q
Ecell (V)
1.30
1.20
1.10
1.00
0.90
E0cell = 1.10 V
10−5 10−4 10−3 10−2 10−1 1 10 102 103 104
Q = [Zn2+]/[Cu2+]

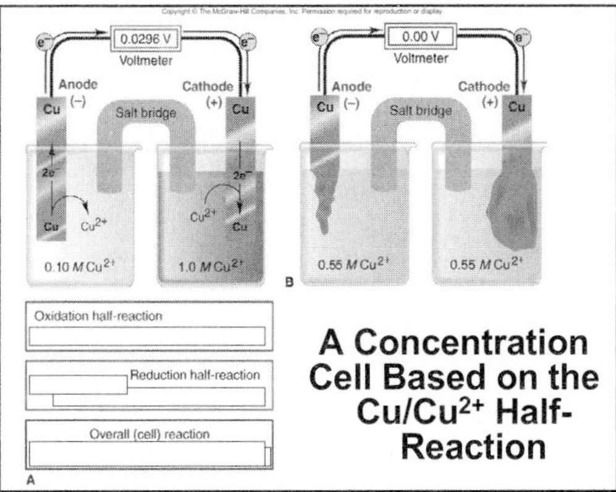

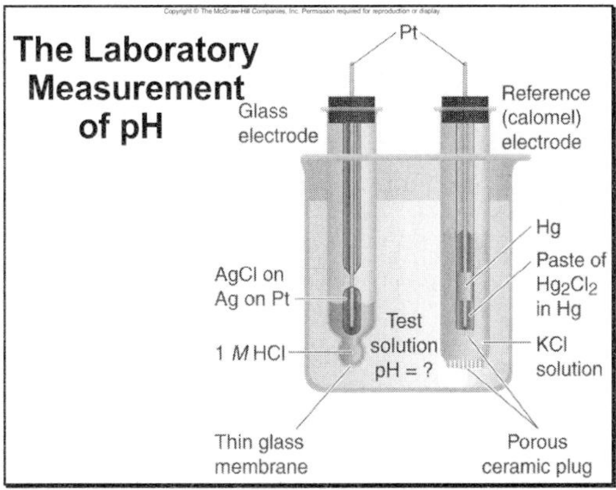

Table 21.3 Some Ions Measured with Ion-Specific Electrodes

Species Detected	Typical Sample
NH_3/NH_4^+	Industrial wastewater, seawater
CO_2/HCO_3^-	Blood, groundwater
F^-	Drinking water, urine, soil, industrial stack gases
Br^-	Grain, plant tissue
I^-	Milk, pharmaceuticals
NO_3^-	Soil, fertilizer, drinking water
K^+	Blood serum, soil, wine
H^+	Laboratory solutions, soil, natural waters

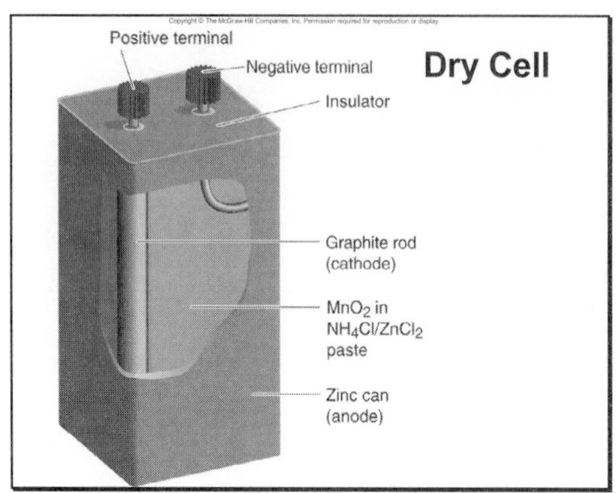
Dry Cell
Positive terminal
Negative terminal
Insulator
Graphite rod
(cathode)
MnO_2 in
$NH_4Cl/ZnCl_2$
paste
Zinc can
(anode)

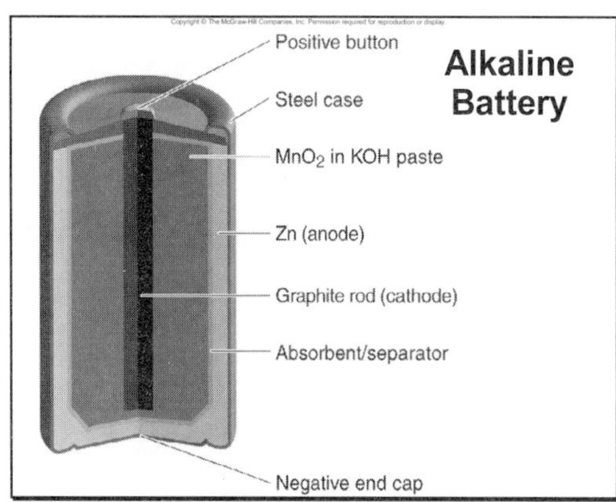
Alkaline
Battery
Positive button
Steel case
MnO_2 in KOH paste
Zn (anode)
Graphite rod (cathode)
Absorbent/separator
Negative end cap

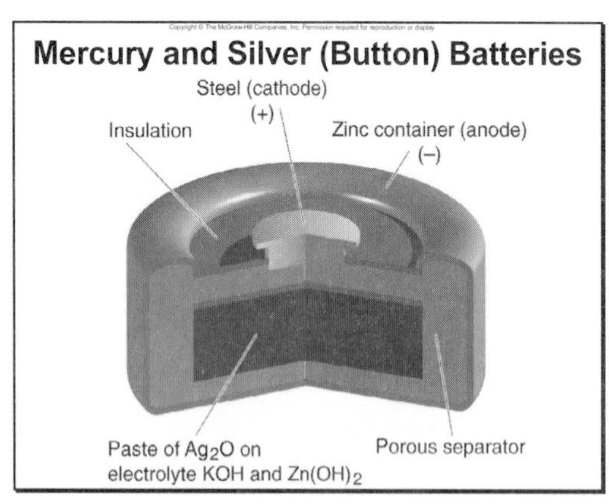
Mercury and Silver (Button) Batteries
Steel (cathode)
(+)
Insulation
Zinc container (anode)
(–)
Paste of Ag_2O on
electrolyte KOH and $Zn(OH)_2$
Porous separator

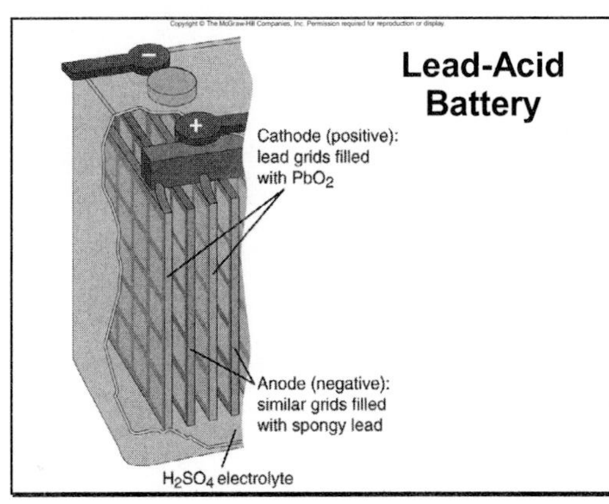
Lead-Acid Battery
Cathode (positive): lead grids filled with PbO_2
Anode (negative): similar grids filled with spongy lead
H_2SO_4 electrolyte

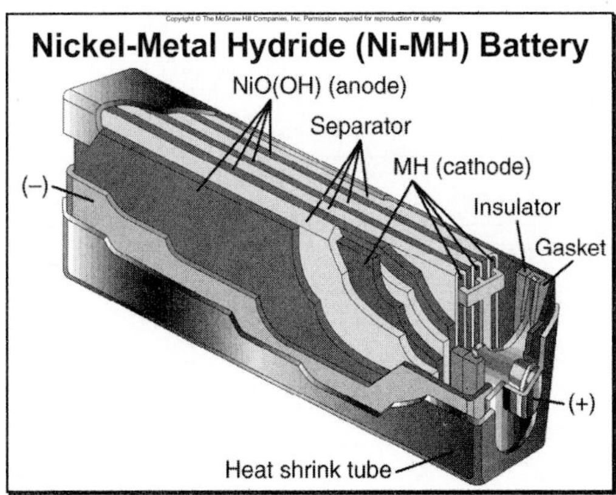
Nickel-Metal Hydride (Ni-MH) Battery
NiO(OH) (anode)
Separator
MH (cathode)
Insulator
Gasket
(−)
(+)
Heat shrink tube

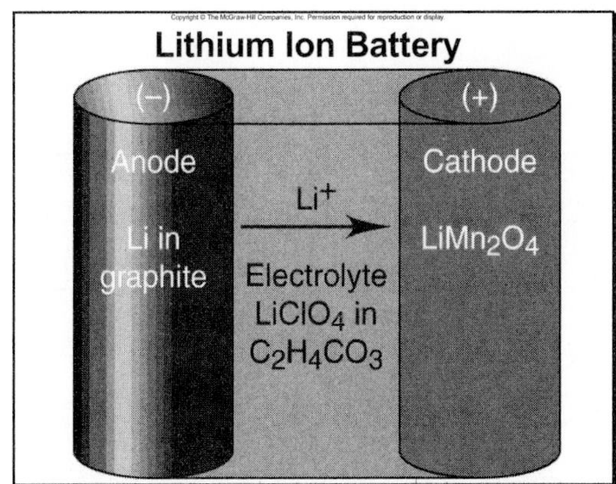
Lithium Ion Battery
(−)
(+)
Anode
Cathode
Li in graphite
Li^+
$LiMn_2O_4$
Electrolyte
$LiClO_4$ in $C_2H_4CO_3$

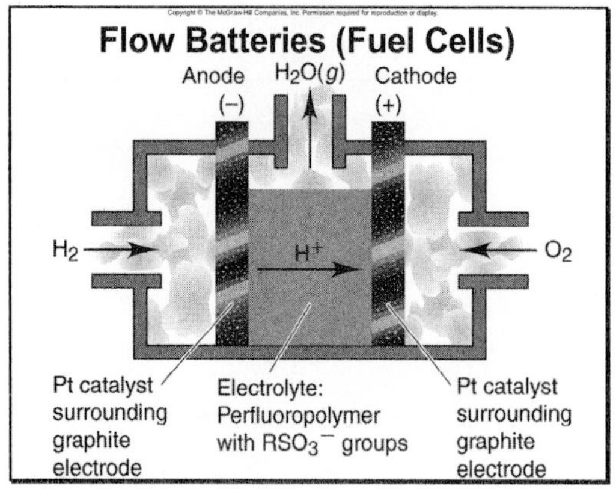
Copyright © The McGraw-Hill Companies, Inc. Permission required for reproduction or display.
Flow Batteries (Fuel Cells)
Anode (−)
$H_2O(g)$
Cathode (+)
H_2
H^+
O_2
Pt catalyst surrounding graphite electrode
Electrolyte: Perfluoropolymer with RSO_3^- groups
Pt catalyst surrounding graphite electrode

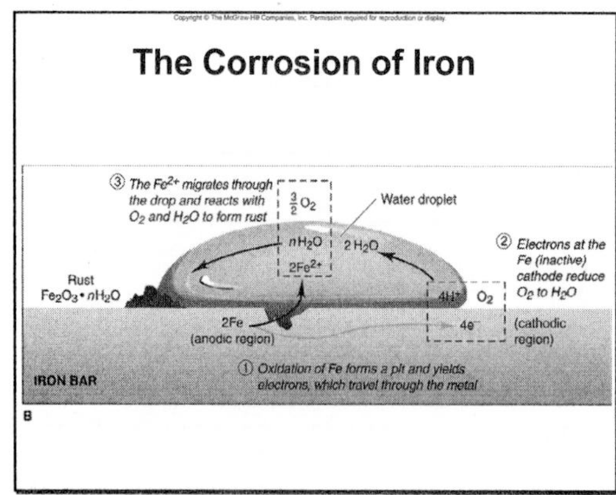
Copyright © The McGraw-Hill Companies, Inc. Permission required for reproduction or display.
The Corrosion of Iron
③ The Fe^{2+} migrates through the drop and reacts with O_2 and H_2O to form rust
$\frac{3}{2}O_2$
nH_2O
$2Fe^{2+}$
$2H_2O$
Water droplet
② Electrons at the Fe (inactive) cathode reduce O_2 to H_2O
Rust $Fe_2O_3 \cdot nH_2O$
$4H^+$
O_2
$4e^-$
2Fe (anodic region)
(cathodic region)
① Oxidation of Fe forms a pit and yields electrons, which travel through the metal
IRON BAR
B

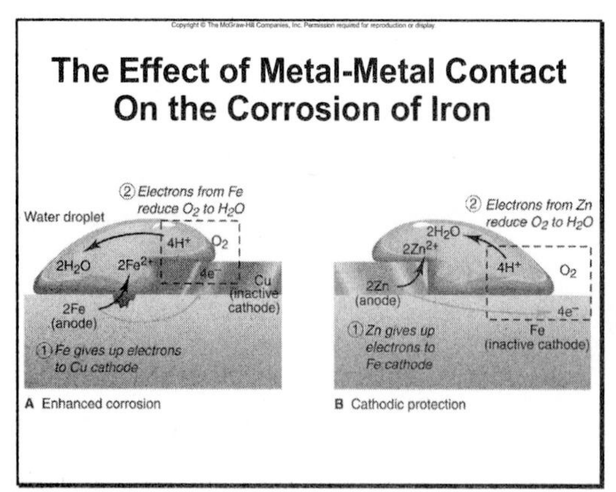
Copyright © The McGraw-Hill Companies, Inc. Permission required for reproduction or display.
The Effect of Metal-Metal Contact On the Corrosion of Iron
Water droplet
② Electrons from Fe reduce O_2 to H_2O
$4H^+$
O_2
$2H_2O$
$2Fe^{2+}$
$4e^-$
Cu (inactive cathode)
2Fe (anode)
① Fe gives up electrons to Cu cathode
A Enhanced corrosion
② Electrons from Zn reduce O_2 to H_2O
$2H_2O$
$2Zn^{2+}$
$4H^+$
O_2
2Zn (anode)
$4e^-$
① Zn gives up electrons to Fe cathode
Fe (inactive cathode)
B Cathodic protection

The Use of Sacrificial Anodes to Prevent Iron Corrosion

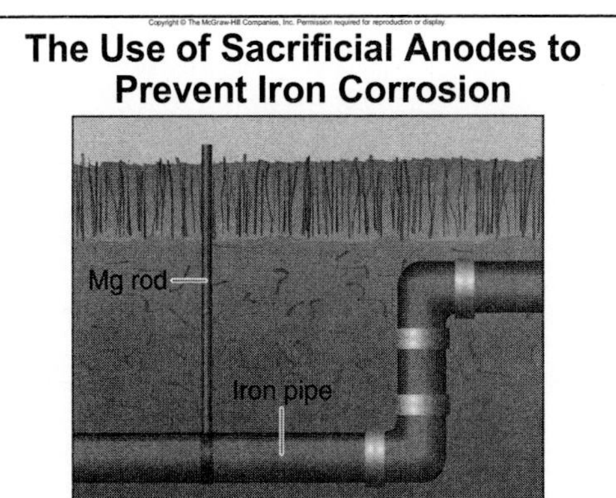

The Tin-Copper Reaction as the Basis of a Voltaic and an Electrolytic Cell

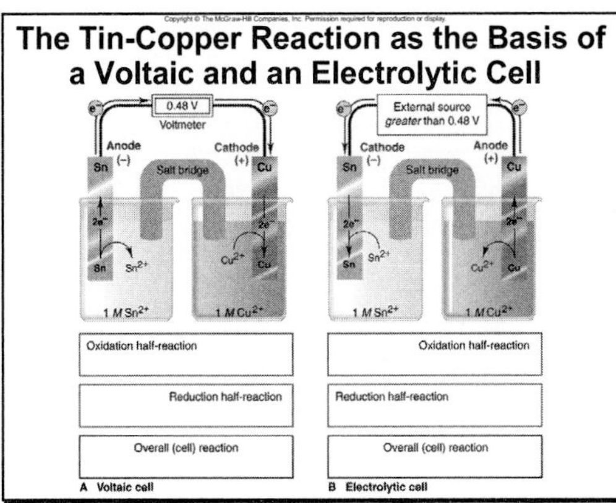

The Processes Occurring During the Discharge and Recharge of a Lead-Acid Battery

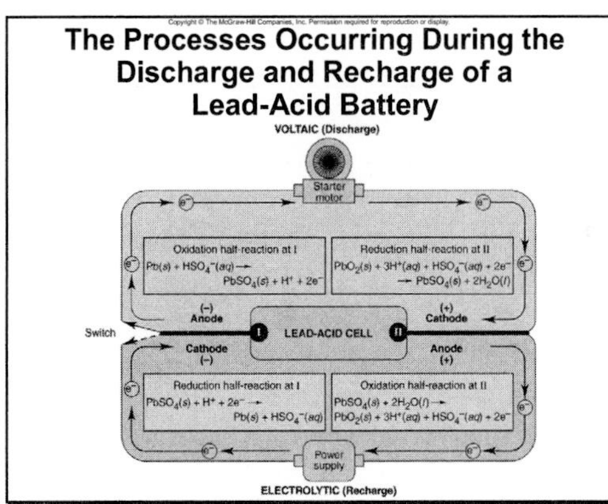

Table 21.4 Comparison of Voltaic and Electrolytic Cells

Cell Type	ΔG	E_{cell}	Electrode Name	Electrode Process	Electrode Sign
Voltaic					
Voltaic					
Electrolytic					
Electrolytic					

The Electrolysis Of Water

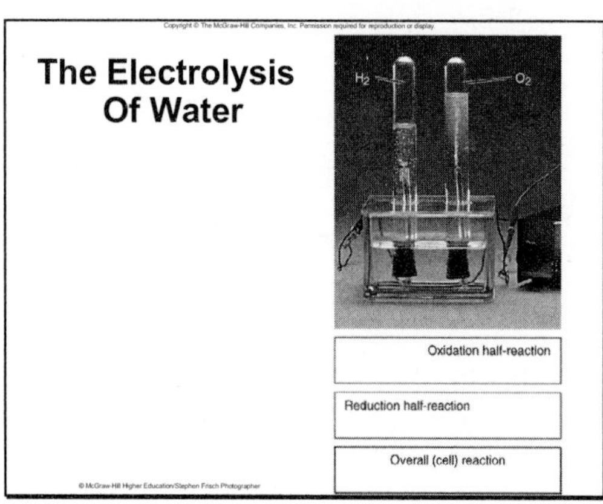

Oxidation half-reaction

Reduction half-reaction

Overall (cell) reaction

Electrolysis of Aqueous KBr

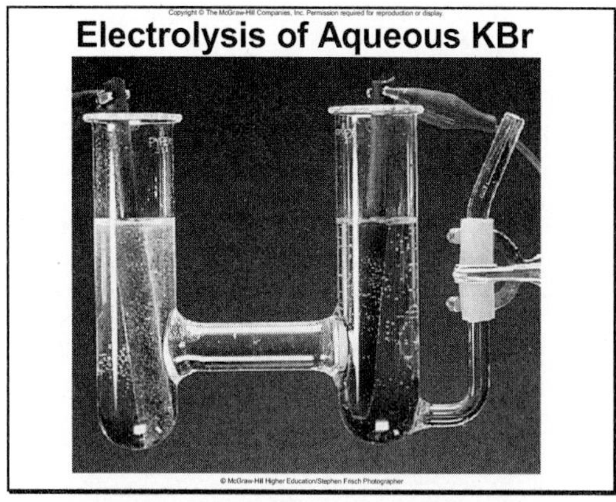

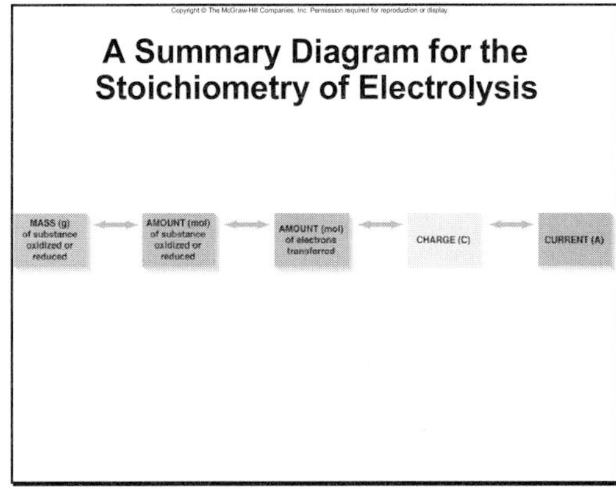
A Summary Diagram for the Stoichiometry of Electrolysis
MASS (g) of substance oxidized or reduced
AMOUNT (mol) of substance oxidized or reduced
AMOUNT (mol) of electrons transferred
CHARGE (C)
CURRENT (A)

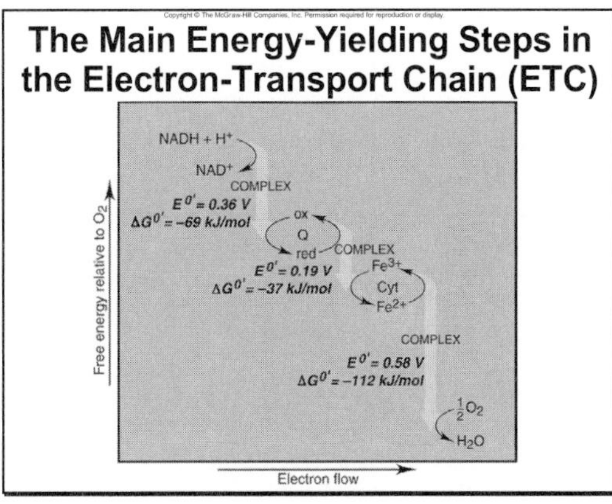
The Main Energy-Yielding Steps in the Electron-Transport Chain (ETC)
NADH + H+
NAD+
COMPLEX
E0' = 0.36 V
ΔG0' = −69 kJ/mol
ox
Q
red
COMPLEX
E0' = 0.19 V
ΔG0' = −37 kJ/mol
Fe3+
Cyt
Fe2+
COMPLEX
E0' = 0.58 V
ΔG0' = −112 kJ/mol
1/2 O2
H2O
Free energy relative to O2
Electron flow

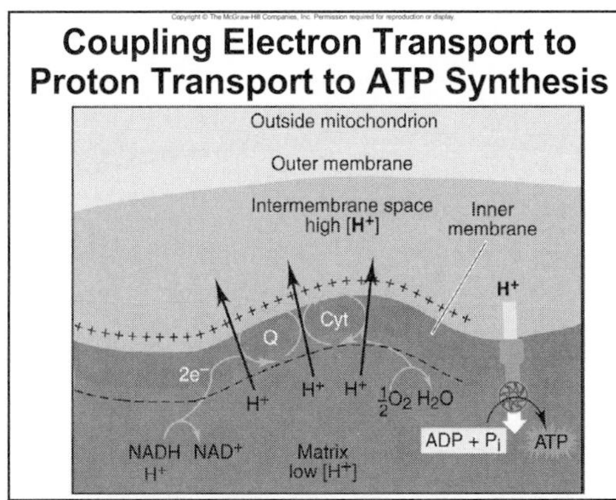
Coupling Electron Transport to Proton Transport to ATP Synthesis
Outside mitochondrion
Outer membrane
Intermembrane space high [H+]
Inner membrane
H+
Q
Cyt
2e−
H+
H+ H+
1/2 O2 H2O
ADP + Pi
ATP
NADH NAD+
H+
Matrix low [H+]

Chapter 22

Chemistry: The Molecular Nature of Matter and Change

Third Edition

Martin S. Silberberg

Cosmic and Terrestrial Abundances of Selected Elements (mass %)

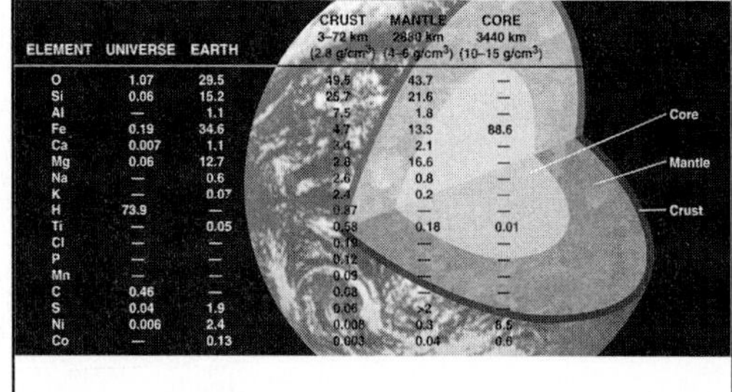

ELEMENT	UNIVERSE	EARTH	CRUST 3–72 km (2.8 g/cm³)	MANTLE 2880 km (4–6 g/cm³)	CORE 3440 km (10–15 g/cm³)
O	1.07	29.5	49.5	43.7	—
Si	0.06	15.2	25.7	21.6	—
Al	—	1.1	7.5	1.8	—
Fe	0.19	34.6	4.7	13.3	88.6
Ca	0.007	1.1	3.4	2.1	—
Mg	0.06	12.7	2.8	16.6	—
Na	—	0.6	2.6	0.8	—
K	—	0.07	2.4	0.2	—
H	73.9	—	0.87	—	—
Ti	—	0.05	0.58	0.18	0.01
Cl	—	—	0.19	—	—
P	—	—	0.12	—	—
Mn	—	—	0.09	—	—
C	0.46	—	0.08	—	—
S	0.04	1.9	0.06	>2	—
Ni	0.006	2.4	0.008	0.3	8.5
Co	—	0.13	0.003	0.04	0.6

Geochemical Differentiation of the Elements

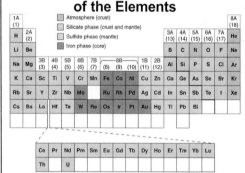

- Atmosphere (crust)
- Silicate phase (crust and mantle)
- Sulfide phase (mantle)
- Iron phase (core)

1A (1)	2A (2)	3B (3)	4B (4)	5B (5)	6B (6)	7B (7)	8B (8)	8B (9)	8B (10)	1B (11)	2B (12)	3A (13)	4A (14)	5A (15)	6A (16)	7A (17)	8A (18)
H																	He
Li	Be											B	C	N	O	F	Ne
Na	Mg											Al	Si	P	S	Cl	Ar
K	Ca	Sc	Ti	V	Cr	Mn	Fe	Co	Ni	Cu	Zn	Ga	Ge	As	Se	Br	Kr
Rb	Sr	Y	Zr	Nb	Mo		Ru	Rh	Pd	Ag	Cd	In	Sn	Sb	Te	I	Xe
Cs	Ba	La	Hf	Ta	W	Re	Os	Ir	Pt	Au	Hg	Tl	Pb	Bi			

Ce	Pr	Nd	Pm	Sm	Eu	Gd	Tb	Dy	Ho	Er	Tm	Yb	Lu
Th		U											

Table 22.1 Abundance of Selected Elements in the Crust, Its Regions, and the Human Body as Representative of the Biosphere (Mass %)

Element	Crust	Crustal Regions: Lithosphere	Hydrosphere	Atmosphere	Human
O	49.5	45.5	85.8	23.0	65.0
C	0.08	0.018	—	0.01	18.0
H	0.87	0.15	10.7	0.02	10.0
N	0.03	0.002	—	75.5	3.0
P	0.12	0.11	—	—	1.0
Mg	1.9	2.76	0.13	—	0.50
K	2.4	1.84	0.04	—	0.34
Ca	3.4	4.66	0.05	—	2.4
S	0.06	0.034	—	—	0.26
Na	2.6	2.27	1.1	—	0.14
Cl	0.19	0.013	2.1	—	0.15
Fe	4.7	6.2	—	—	0.005
Zn	0.013	0.008	—	—	0.003
Cr	0.02	0.012	—	—	3×10^{-6}
Co	0.003	0.003	—	—	3×10^{-6}
Cu	0.007	0.007	—	—	4×10^{-4}
Mn	0.09	0.11	—	—	1×10^{-4}
Ni	0.008	0.010	—	—	3×10^{-6}
V	0.015	0.014	—	—	3×10^{-6}

Sources of the Elements

Oxides
Halide salts or brines
Phosphates
Silicates
Carbonates/Sulfates
Sulfides
Uncombined

1A (1) | 2A (2) | 3B (3) | 4B (4) | 5B (5) | 6B (6) | 7B (7) | 8B (8) (9) (10) | 1B (11) | 2B (12) | 3A (13) | 4A (14) | 5A (15) | 6A (16) | 7A (17) | 8A 18

H He
Li Be B C N O F Ne
Na Mg Al Si P S Cl Ar
K Ca Sc Ti V Cr Mn Fe Co Ni Cu Zn Ga Ge As Se Br Kr
Rb Sr Y Zr Nb Mo Ag Cd In Sn Sb Te I Xe
Cs Ba La Hf Ta W Re Pt Au Hg Tl Pb Bi
Ce Pr Nd Pm Sm Eu Gd Tb Dy Ho Er Tm Yb Lu
U

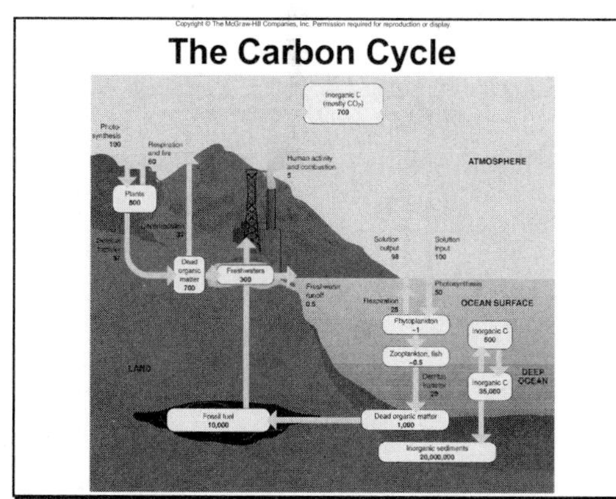

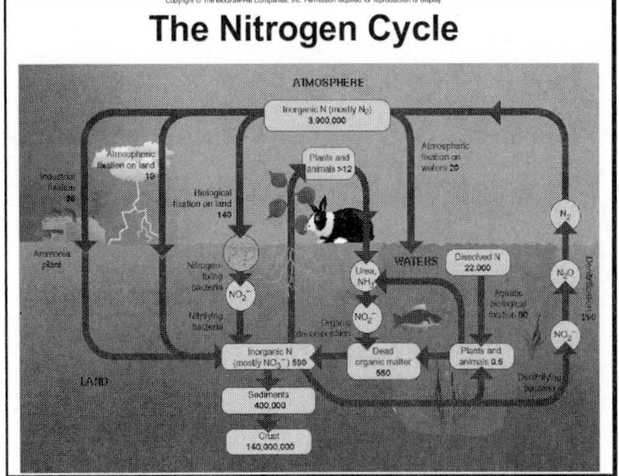
Copyright © The McGraw-Hill Companies, Inc. Permission required for reproduction or display
The Nitrogen Cycle
ATMOSPHERE
Inorganic N (mostly N_2) 3,900,000
Atmospheric fixation on land 10
Industrial fixation 86
Ammonia plant
Biological fixation on land 140
Plants and animals >12
Atmospheric fixation on waters 20
Nitrogen-fixing bacteria
NO_2^-
Nitrifying bacteria
Urea, NH_3
NO_2^-
WATERS
Dissolved N 22,000
Aquatic biological fixation 30
N_2
N_2O
NO_2^-
Inorganic N (mostly NO_3^-) 590
Dead organic matter 550
Plants and animals 0.6
LAND
Sediments 400,000
Crust 140,000,000

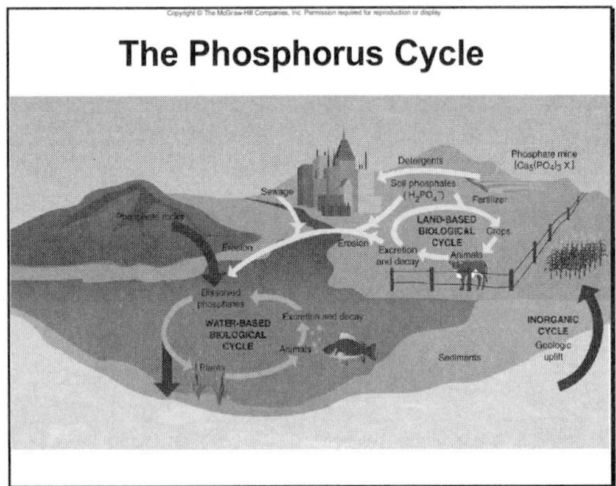
Copyright © The McGraw-Hill Companies, Inc. Permission required for reproduction or display
The Phosphorus Cycle
Detergents
Phosphate mine $[Ca_5(PO_4)_3X]$
Sewage
Soil phosphates ($H_2PO_4^-$)
Fertilizer
LAND-BASED BIOLOGICAL CYCLE
Crops
Erosion
Erosion
Excretion and decay
Animals
Excretion and decay
WATER-BASED BIOLOGICAL CYCLE
Animals
Plants
Sediments
INORGANIC CYCLE
Geologic uplift

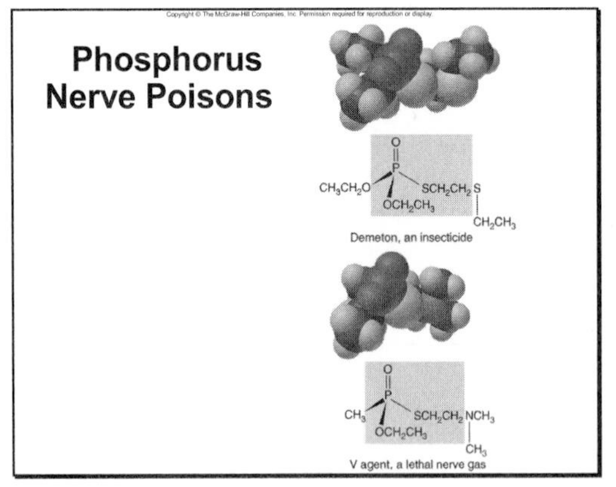
Copyright © The McGraw-Hill Companies, Inc. Permission required for reproduction or display
Phosphorus Nerve Poisons
CH_3CH_2O P(=O) SCH_2CH_2S OCH_2CH_3 CH_2CH_3
Demeton, an insecticide
CH_3 P(=O) $SCH_2CH_2NCH_3$ OCH_2CH_3 CH_3
V agent, a lethal nerve gas

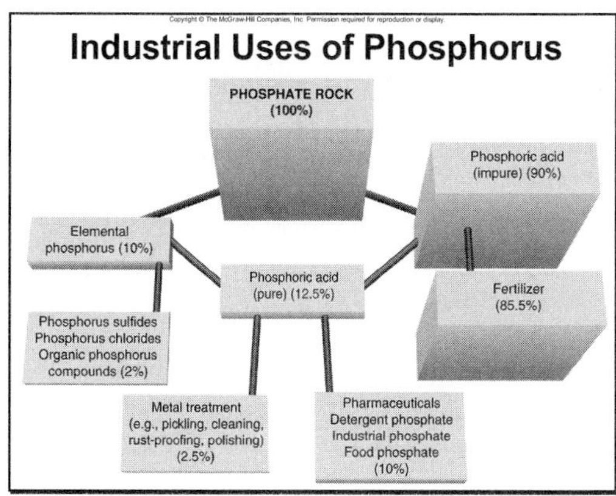

Table 22.2 Common Mineral Sources of Some Elements

Element	Mineral, Formula
Al	Gibbsite (in bauxite), $Al(OH)_3$
Ba	Barite, $BaSO_4$
Be	Beryl, $Be_3Al_2Si_6O_{18}$
Ca	Limestone, $CaCO_3$
Fe	Hematite, Fe_2O_3
Hg	Cinnabar, HgS
Na	Halite, NaCl
Pb	Galena, PbS
Sn	Cassiterite, SnO_2
Zn	Sphalerite, ZnS

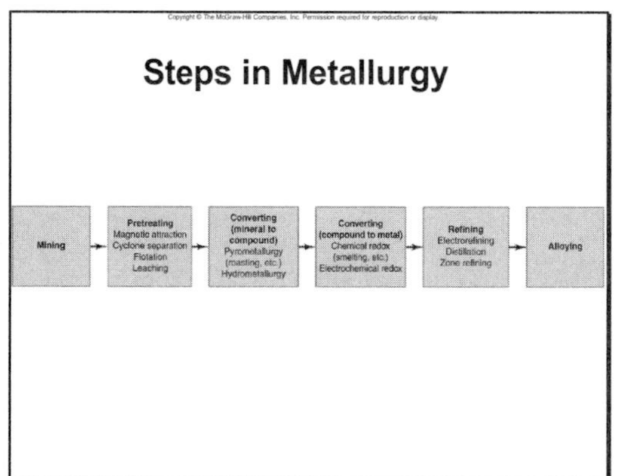

The Cyclone Separator

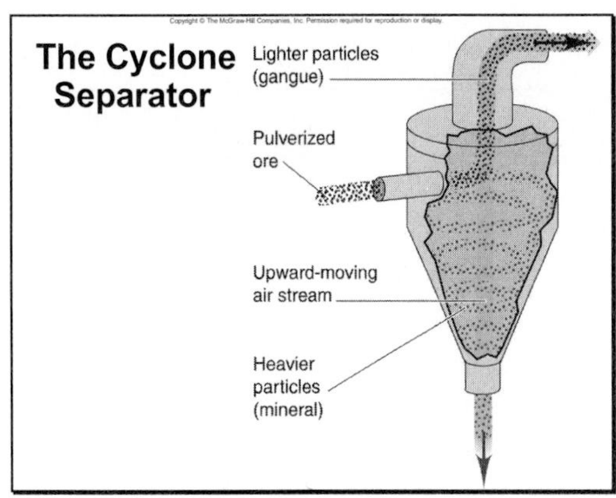

The Flotation Process

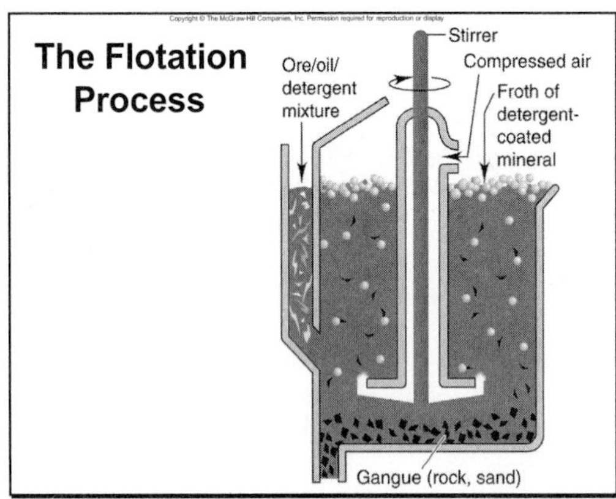

The Redox Step in Converting a Mineral to the Element

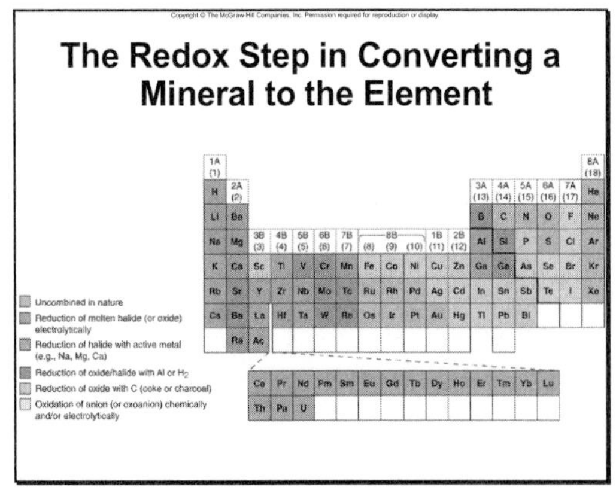

Table 22.3 Some Familiar Alloys and Their Composition

Name	Composition (Mass %)	Uses
Stainless steel	73–79 Fe, 14–18 Cr, 7–9 Ni	Cutlery, instruments
Nickel steel	96–98 Fe, 2–4 Ni	Cables, gears
High-speed steels	80–94 Fe, 14–20 W (or 6–12 Mo)	Cutting tools
Permalloy	78 Ni, 22 Fe	Ocean cables
Bronzes	70–95 Cu, 1–25 Zn, 1–18 Sn	Statues, castings
Brasses	50–80 Cu, 20–50 Zn	Plating, ornamental objects
Sterling silver	92.5 Ag, 7.5 Cu	Jewelry, tableware
14-Carat gold	58 Au, 4–28 Ag, 14–28 Cu	Jewelry
18-Carat white gold	75 Au, 12.5 Ag, 12.5 Cu	Jewelry
Typical tin solder	67 Pb, 33 Sn	Electrical connections
Dental amalgam	69 Ag, 18 Sn, 12 Cu, 1 Zn (dissolved in Hg)	Dental fillings

Three Binary Alloys

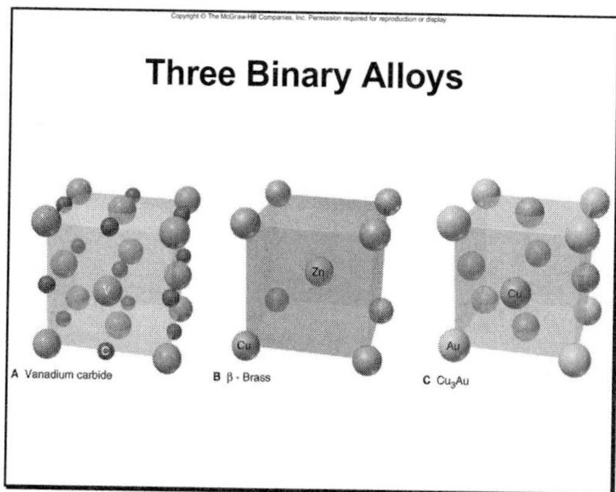

The Downs Cell for Production of Sodium

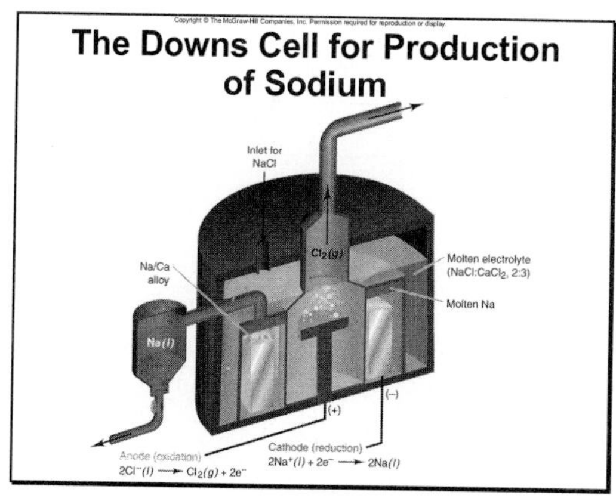

Copyright © The McGraw-Hill Companies, Inc. Permission required for reproduction or display.

Table 22.4 Important Minerals of Iron

Mineral Type	Mineral, Formula
Oxide	Hematite, Fe_2O_3
	Magnetite, Fe_3O_4
	Ilmenite, $FeTiO_3$
Carbonate	Siderite, $FeCO_3$
Sulfide	Pyrite, FeS_2
	Pyrrhotite, FeS

Copyright © The McGraw-Hill Companies, Inc. Permission required for reproduction or display.

The Major Reaction In a Blast Furnace

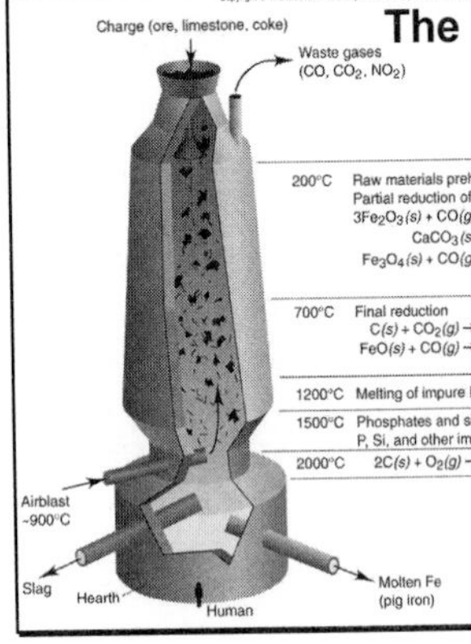
Charge (ore, limestone, coke)
Waste gases
(CO, CO_2, NO_2)
Airblast
~900°C
Slag
Hearth
Human
Molten Fe
(pig iron)

200°C	Raw materials preheated Partial reduction of iron ore $3Fe_2O_3(s) + CO(g) \rightarrow 2Fe_3O_4(s) + CO_2(g)$ $CaCO_3(s) \rightarrow CaO(s) + CO_2(g)$ $Fe_3O_4(s) + CO(g) \rightarrow 3FeO(s) + CO_2(g)$
700°C	Final reduction $C(s) + CO_2(g) \rightarrow 2CO(g)$ $FeO(s) + CO(g) \rightarrow Fe(l) + CO_2(g)$
1200°C	Melting of impure Fe and slag
1500°C	Phosphates and silicates reduced; P, Si, and other impurities enter molten Fe
2000°C	$2C(s) + O_2(g) \rightarrow 2CO(g)$

Copyright © The McGraw-Hill Companies, Inc. Permission required for reproduction or display.

The Basic-Oxygen Process for Making Steel

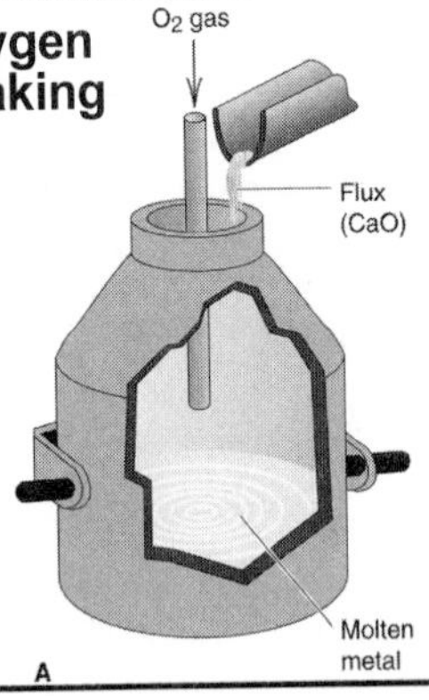
O_2 gas
Flux
(CaO)
Molten
metal
A

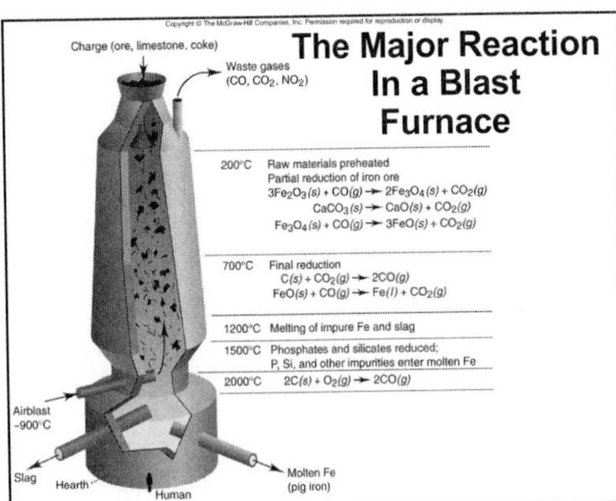

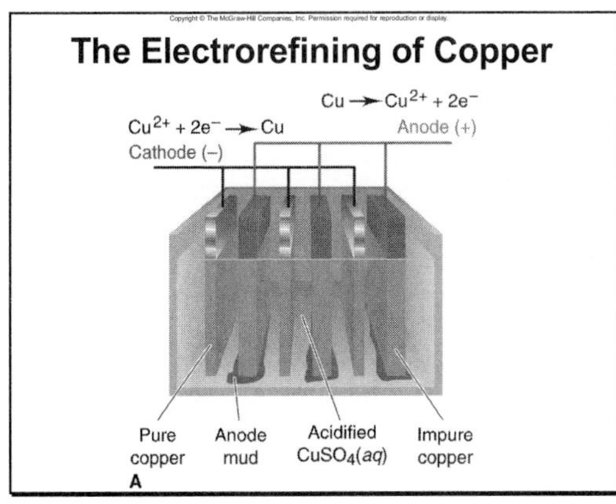
Copyright © The McGraw-Hill Companies, Inc. Permission required for reproduction or display.
The Electrorefining of Copper
Cu → Cu2+ + 2e−
Anode (+)
Cu2+ + 2e− → Cu
Cathode (−)
Pure copper
Anode mud
Acidified CuSO4(aq)
Impure copper
A

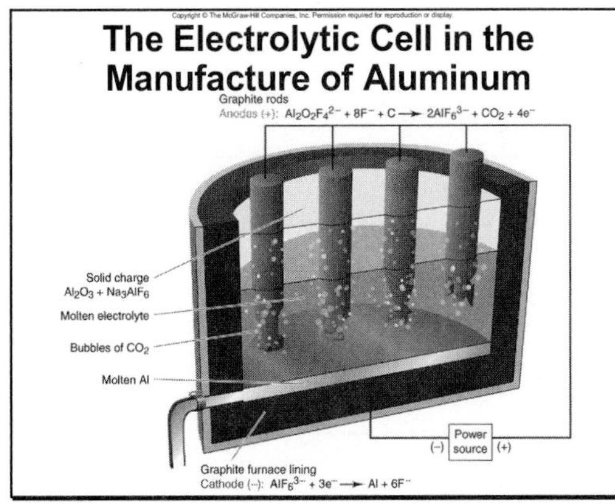
Copyright © The McGraw-Hill Companies, Inc. Permission required for reproduction or display.
The Electrolytic Cell in the Manufacture of Aluminum
Graphite rods
Anodes (+): Al2O2F4 2− + 8F− + C → 2AlF6 3− + CO2 + 4e−
Solid charge Al2O3 + Na3AlF6
Molten electrolyte
Bubbles of CO2
Molten Al
Power source
(−)
(+)
Graphite furnace lining
Cathode (−): AlF6 3− + 3e− → Al + 6F−

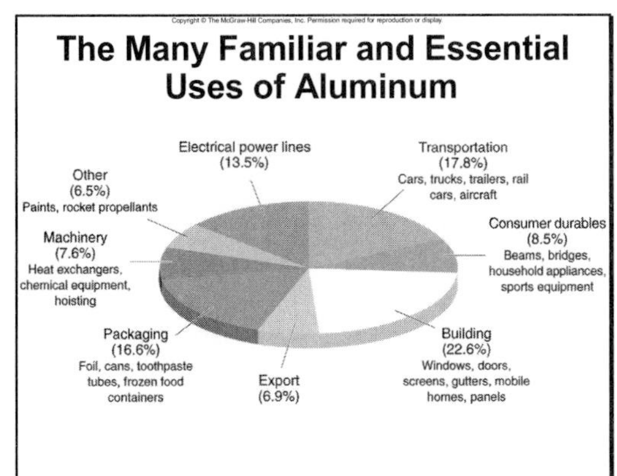
Copyright © The McGraw-Hill Companies, Inc. Permission required for reproduction or display.
The Many Familiar and Essential Uses of Aluminum
Electrical power lines (13.5%)
Transportation (17.8%)
Cars, trucks, trailers, rail cars, aircraft
Other (6.5%)
Paints, rocket propellants
Consumer durables (8.5%)
Beams, bridges, household appliances, sports equipment
Machinery (7.6%)
Heat exchangers, chemical equipment, hoisting
Packaging (16.6%)
Foil, cans, toothpaste tubes, frozen food containers
Export (6.9%)
Building (22.6%)
Windows, doors, screens, gutters, mobile homes, panels

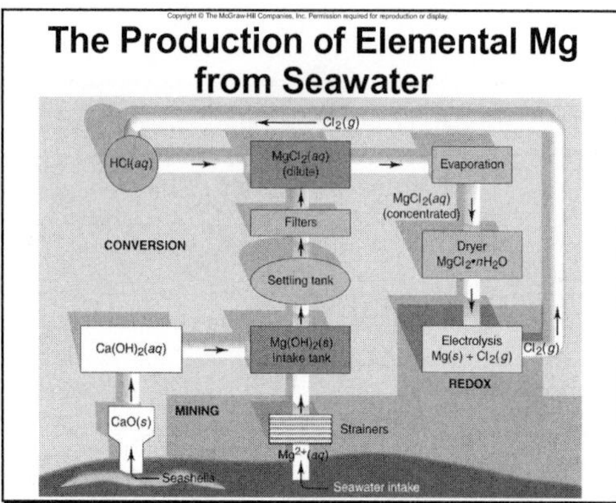

Table 22.5 Some Molecular and Physical Properties of Diatomic Protium, Deuterium, and Tritium

Property	H_2	D_2	T_2
Molar mass (g/mol)	2.016	4.028	6.032
Bond length (pm)	74.14	74.14	74.14
Melting point (K)	13.96	18.73	20.62
Boiling point (K)	20.39	23.67	25.04
ΔH^0_{fus} (kJ/mol)	0.117	0.197	0.250
ΔH^0_{vap} (kJ/mol)	0.904	1.226	1.393
Bond energy (kJ/mol at 298 K)	432	443	447

Table 22.6A Sources, Isolation, and Uses of Group 1A(1): The Alkali Metals

Element	Source	Isolation	Uses
Lithium	Spodumene [$LiAl(Si_2O_6)$]	Preparation and electrolysis of molten LiCl	In strong, low-density Mg and Al alloys for armor and aerospace parts; in Li batteries for computers, electric cars
Sodium	NaCl in rock salt (halite); $NaNO_3$ (saltpeter)	Electrolysis of molten NaCl (Downs cell; see text)	Reducing agent for isolation of Ti, Zr, and others; heat exchanger in nuclear reactors
Potassium	KCl (sylvite) in seawater	Na reduction of molten KCl (see text)	Reducing agent: production of KO_2 (see text)
Rubidium	Minor component of Li ores	Ca reduction of molten RbCl; by-product of Li isolation	Reducing agent
Cesium	Minor component of Li ores; pollucite ($Cs_4Al_4Si_9O_{26} \cdot H_2O$)	Ca reduction of molten CsCl; by-product of Li isolation	Reducing agent
Francium	Minute traces from ^{235}U decay		

Table 22.6B Sources, Isolation, and Uses of Group 2A(2): The Alkaline Earth Metals

Element	Source	Isolation	Uses
Beryllium	Beryl ($Be_3Al_2Si_6O_{18}$)	Electrolysis of molten $BeCl_2$; reduction of BeF_2 with Mg	In high-strength alloys of Cu and Ni for aerospace engines and electronics; neutron moderator and reflector in nuclear reactors (Section 24.7); window in x-ray tubes
Magnesium	Magnesite ($MgCO_3$), dolomite ($MgCO_3 \cdot CaCO_3$), seawater	Electrolysis of molten $MgCl_2$ (see text); silicothermal method, $2(MgO \cdot CaO) + FeSi \longrightarrow 2Mg + Ca_2SiO_4 + Fe$	Lightweight alloys
Calcium	Limestone and aragonite ($CaCO_3$)	Electrolysis of molten $CaCl_2$ formed by HCl on $CaCO_3$	Strengthener in Al alloys; reducing agent to produce Cr, Zr, and U; scavenger of traces of O_2, P, and S in steel
Strontium	Strontianite ($SrCO_3$); celestite ($SrSO_4$)	Thermal decomposition, then Al reduction of SrO	Scavenger of O_2 and N_2 in electronic devices
Barium	Barite ($BaSO_4$)	Al reduction of BaO	Scavenger of O_2 and N_2 in electronic devices
Radium	Minor (0.1 ppb) component in pitchblende (uranium ore)	Electrolysis of molten $RaCl_2$ after extensive extraction (Section 24.1)	Formerly used in cancer therapy

Table 22.6C Sources, Isolation, and Uses of the Period 4 Transition Metals [Groups 3B(3) to 2B(12)]

Element	Source	Isolation	Uses
Scandium	Thortveitite (40% Sc_2O_3); by-product of U extraction	Reduction of Sc_2O_3 with C	None
Titanium	Rutile (TiO_2); ilmenite ($FeTiO_3$)	Conversion to $TiCl_4$, then reduction with Mg	Very abundant; stronger than steel but half as dense; high-temperature, lightweight alloys for rocket and jet engines and for train and car parts
Vanadium	Carnotite [$K(UO_2)(VO_4) \cdot 1.5H_2O$]	Conversion to $NaVO_3$, then reduction with Al (thermite) or FeSi	Combines with C in steel to make very strong alloy for truck springs and axles
Chromium	Chromite ($FeCr_2O_4$)	Conversion to Cr_2O_3, then reduction with Al	Nonferrous alloys; chrome plating; stainless steels
Manganese	Pyrolusite (MnO_2); many other ores; in future, Mn "nodules" on ocean floor	Conversion to Mn_3O_4, then reduction with Al; conversion to $MnSO_4$, then electrolysis of aqueous Mn(II)	Scavenger of O and S in steel; high-strength steel alloys of excavators, rail crossings
Iron	Hematite (Fe_2O_3); magnetite (Fe_3O_4)	Reduction using C (see text)	Steel (see text)
Cobalt	Smaltite ($CoAs_2$); many sulfides with Ni, Cu, and Pb	Roasting in O_2, leaching with H_2SO_4, precipitating $Co(OH)_3$ with ClO^-, heating to form CoO, and reducing with C	Cobalt blue glass and pottery; pigments for paints and inks; catalysts for organic reactions; specialty alloys with Cr and W for drill bits, lathe tools, and surgical instruments; magnetic alloys (Alnico)
Nickel	Pentlandite [$(Ni,Fe)_9S_8$]	Roasting in O_2 to NiO, reducing with C; Mond process, $Ni(CO)_4(g) \rightleftharpoons Ni(s) + 4CO(g)$	Nickel steels for armor; stainless steel and Alnico; nonferrous alloys (tableware) with Ag; Monel with Cu for handling F_2; nichrome; undercoat for chrome plating; hydrogenation catalyst
Copper	Chalcopyrite ($CuFeS_2$)	See text	Wiring, plumbing, coins (see text)
Zinc	Zinc blende (ZnS); sphalerite	Roasting in O_2 to form ZnO, then reducing with C	Brasses (50% to 80% Cu); galvanizing steel to prevent corrosion; batteries (Section 21.5)

Table 22.6D Sources, Isolation, and Uses of Group 3A(13): The Boron Family

Element	Source	Isolation	Uses
Boron	Borax ($Na_2[B_4O_5(OH)_4] \cdot 8H_2O$); kernite ($Na_2[B_4O_5(OH)_4] \cdot 2H_2O$)	Mg reduction of B_2O_3; electrolysis of KBF_4	M_xB_y turbine blades, rocket nozzles, heat shields
Aluminum	Bauxite [contains gibbsite, $Al(OH)_3$]	Electrolysis of Al_2O_3 in Na_3AlF_6 (see text)	Many familiar alloys; electric transmission lines (see text)
Gallium	Trace element in bauxite	Obtained as trace impurity in Al purification	High-speed semiconductors; in photovoltaic solar panels
Indium	Trace element in Zn/Pb sulfide ores	Recovered from sulfide roasting flue dusts	Semiconductors with P or Sb; low-melting alloys in sprinklers
Thallium	Trace element in Zn/Pb sulfide ores	Recovered from sulfide roasting flue dusts	Very toxic; few uses

Table 22.6E Sources, Isolation, and Uses of Group 4A(14): The Carbon Family

Element	Source	Isolation	Uses
Carbon	Diamond; graphite; petroleum; coal; carbonates; CO_2	Used as found, or isolated from petroleum or coal by heating in the absence of air	Graphite: composites; electrodes; control rods in nuclear reactors Diamond: jewelry; abrasives; films Coke, carbon black: reductant in metallurgy; rubber tire strengthener; pigment; decolorizer for sugar
Silicon	Silica (SiO_2); silicate minerals	Reduction of K_2SiF_6 with Al; reduction of SiO_2 with Mg, then zone refining	Semiconductors; glass; ceramics
Germanium	Germanite (mixture of Cu, Fe, and Ge sulfides)	Roasting in O_2, then reducing GeO_2 with H_2, and zone refining	Semiconductors; infrared spectrometer windows and lenses
Tin	Cassiterite (SnO_2)	Thermal reduction of SnO_2 with C	Prevents corrosion in steel cans; alloys (e.g., solder, bronze, pewter)
Lead	Galena (PbS)	Roasting in O_2 to PbO, then reducing with C, and electrorefining	Automotive batteries; solder; ammunition

Table 22.6F Sources, Isolation, and Uses of Group 5A(15): The Nitrogen Family

Element	Source	Isolation	Uses
Nitrogen	Air	Fractional distillation of liquefied air	$N_2(g)$: inert atmosphere in metallurgical and petrochemical processing; reactant in NH_3 production $N_2(l)$: freeze-drying food; grinding meat for hamburger; biological preservation; future use in superconductors
Phosphorus	Phosphate ores, e.g., fluoroapatite [$Ca_5(PO_4)_3F$] (see text)	Reducing phosphate rock with C	Starting material for synthesis of H_3PO_4 (90%), PCl_3, P_4S_3 (matches), and P_4S_{10} (pesticide) (see text)
Arsenic	Arsenopyrite (FeAsS); flue dust in Cu and Pb extraction	Heating in absence of air	Films, light-emitting (photo) diodes; lead alloys
Antimony	Stibnite (Sb_2S_3); flue dust in Cu and Pb extraction	Roasting in air to Sb_2O_3, then reducing with C	In lead-acid batteries (5% Sb)
Bismuth	Bismuthinite (Bi_2S_3)	Roasting to Bi_2O_3, then reducing with C or Fe	Alloys; medicines

Table 22.6G Sources, Isolation, and Uses of Group 6A(16): The Oxygen Family

Element	Source	Isolation	Uses
Oxygen	Air	Fractional distillation of liquefied air	Oxidizing agent in steelmaking (see text), sewage treatment, paper-pulp bleaching, rocket fuel; medical applications
Sulfur	Underground S deposits; sour natural gas or petroleum	Frasch process (see text); catalytic oxidation of H_2S	Production of H_2SO_4 (see text); vulcanization of rubber; chemicals for pharmaceuticals, textiles, and pesticides
Selenium	Impurity in sulfide ores; anode muds of Cu refining	Reducing H_2SeO_3 with SO_2	Electronics; xerography; cadmium pigments
Tellurium	Mixed tellurides and sulfides of Group 8 to 11 metals; anode muds of Cu refining	Oxidizing to Na_2TeO_3, then electrolysis	Steelmaking
Polonium	Pitchblende; trace element formed in radium decay	Isolated in trace amounts	Future use as heat source in space satellites and lunar stations

Table 22.6H Sources, Isolation, and Uses of Group 7A(17): The Halogens

Element	Source	Isolation	Uses
Fluorine	Fluorite; fluorspar (CaF_2)	Electrolysis of KF in molten anhydrous HF	Synthesis of UF_6 (for nuclear fuel) and SF_6 (electrical insulator); fluorinating agents; Teflon monomer
Chlorine	Halite (NaCl); seawater	Electrolysis of molten NaCl (see text); electrolysis of concentrated seawater (Section 22.5)	Oxidizing agent in bleach and disinfectant; production of poly(vinyl chloride) monomer; major biological anion
Bromine	Brine wells; seawater	Oxidation of Br^- salts by Cl_2 (see text)	Preparation of organic bromides; AgBr in photography
Iodine	Brine wells; Chilean saltpeter ($NaIO_3$)	Oxidation of I^- salts by Cl_2; reduction of IO_3^- with HSO_3^-	In table salt as essential trace element for thyroid hormones; disinfectant
Astatine	Extremely rare radioisotope	Obtained only in trace quantities	None

Table 22.6I Sources, Isolation, and Uses of Group 8A(18): The Noble Gases

Element	Source	Isolation	Uses
Helium	In natural gas (>0.4 mass %)	Distillation of condensed natural gas or differential diffusion of natural gas	Coolant for superconducting magnets; substitute for N_2 in deep-sea breathing mixture; mobile phase in gas chromatography
Neon	Air	Fractional distillation of liquefied air	Luminous gas in signs
Argon	Air	Fractional distillation of liquefied air	Arc welding
Krypton	Air	Fractional distillation of liquefied air	None
Xenon	Air	Fractional distillation of liquefied air	None
Radon	Air	Fractional distillation of liquefied air	None; radioactive air pollutant

The Frasch Process for Mining Elemental Sulfur

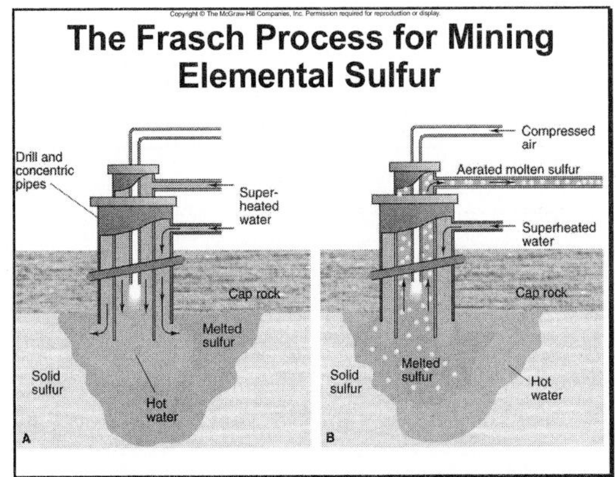

Disulfuric Acid

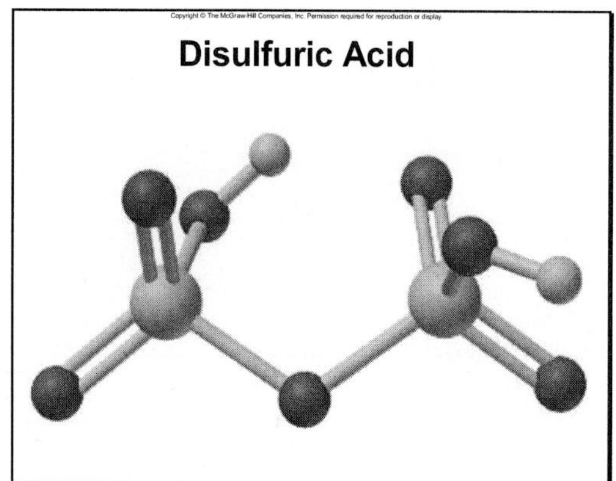

The Many Indispensable Applications of Sulfuric Acid

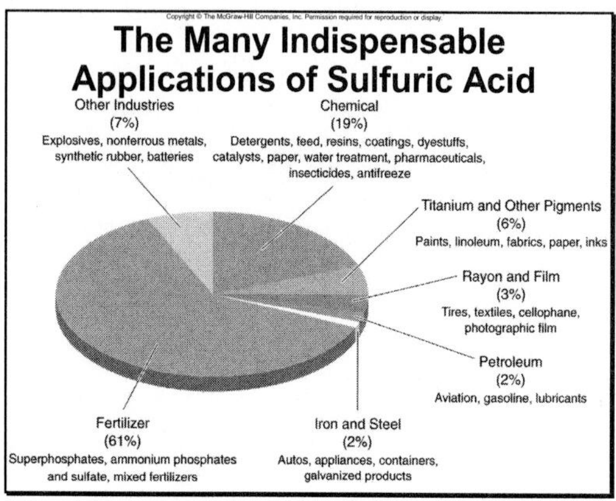

A Diaphragm Chloralkali Cell

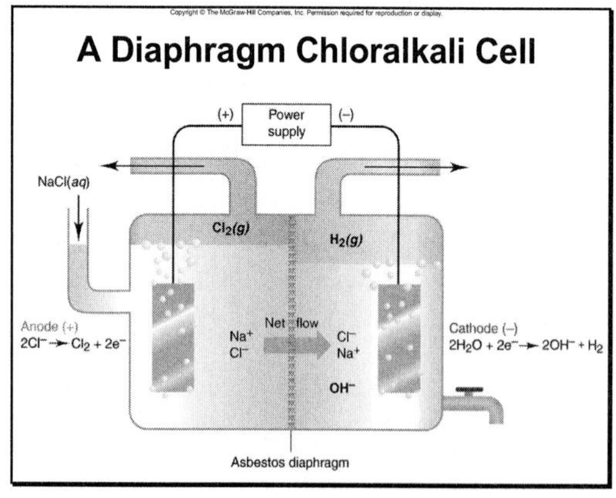

Chapter 23

Chemistry: The Molecular Nature of Matter and Change

Third Edition

Martin S. Silberberg

The Transition Elements (*d* Block) and Inner Transition Elements (*f* Block) in the Periodic Table

TRANSITION ELEMENTS *d* block

INNER TRANSITION ELEMENTS *f* block

Period 4 Transition Metals — Part 1

Scandium, Sc; 3B(3)

Titanium, Ti; 4B(4)

Vanadium, V; 5B(5)

Chromium, Cr; 6B(6)

Manganese, Mn; 7B(7)

Period 4 Transition Metals — Part 2

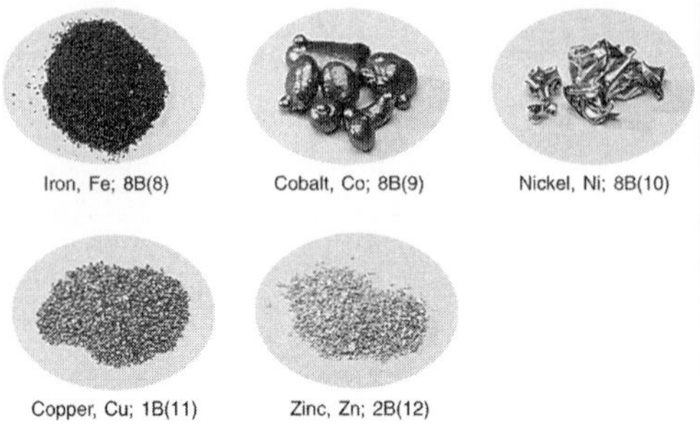

Table 23.1 Orbital Occupancy of the Period 4 Transition Metals

Element	Partial Orbital Diagram 4s	3d	4p	Unpaired Electrons
Sc	↑↓	↑		1
Ti	↑↓	↑ ↑		2
V	↑↓	↑ ↑ ↑		3
Cr	↑	↑ ↑ ↑ ↑ ↑		6
Mn	↑↓	↑ ↑ ↑ ↑ ↑		5
Fe	↑↓	↑↓ ↑ ↑ ↑ ↑		4
Co	↑↓	↑↓ ↑↓ ↑ ↑ ↑		3
Ni	↑↓	↑↓ ↑↓ ↑↓ ↑ ↑		2
Cu	↑	↑↓ ↑↓ ↑↓ ↑↓ ↑↓		1
Zn	↑↓	↑↓ ↑↓ ↑↓ ↑↓ ↑↓		0

Horizontal Trends in Key Atomic Properties of the Period 4 Elements

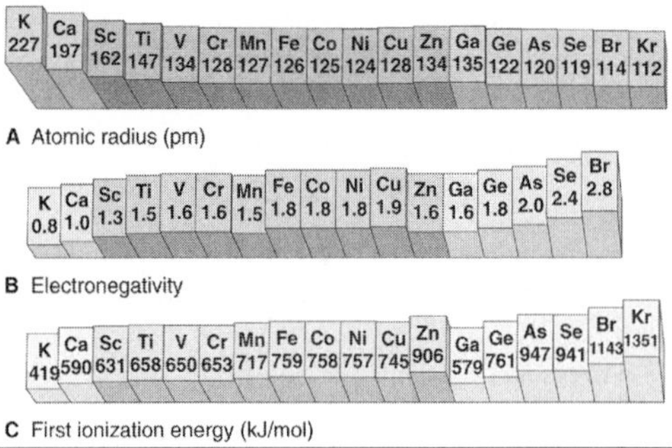

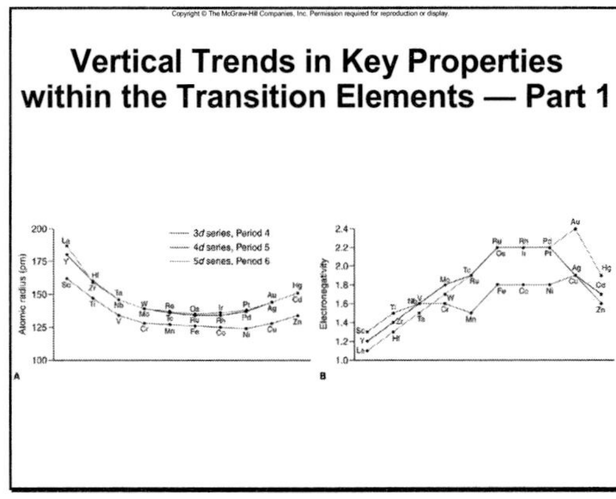

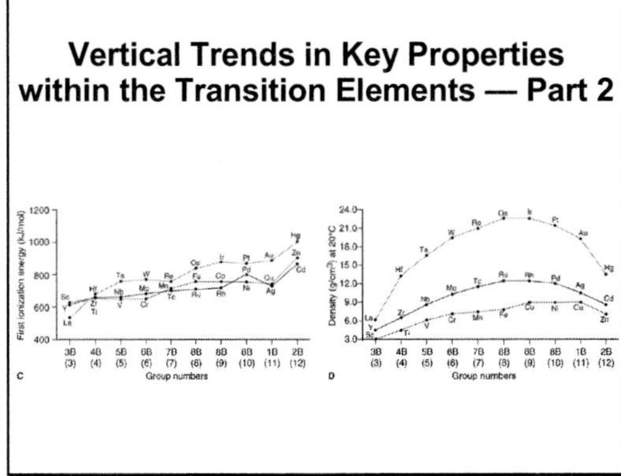

Table 23.2 Oxidation States and *d*-Orbital Occupancy of the Period 4 Transition Metals*

Oxidation State	3B (3) Sc	4B (4) Ti	5B (5) V	6B (6) Cr	7B (7) Mn	8B (8) Fe	8B (9) Co	8B (10) Ni	1B (11) Cu	2B (12) Zn
0	d^1	d^2	d^3	d^5	d^5	d^6	d^7	d^8	d^{10}	d^{10}
+1			d^3	d^5	d^5	d^6	d^7	d^8	d^{10}	
+2		d^2	d^3	d^4	d^5	d^6	d^7	d^8	d^9	d^{10}
+3	d^0	d^1	d^2	d^3	d^4	d^5	d^6	d^7	d^8	
+4		d^0	d^1	d^2	d^3	d^4	d^5	d^6		
+5			d^0	d^1	d^2		d^4			
+6				d^0	d^1	d^2				
+7					d^0					

*Most important in color.

Table 23.3 Standard Electrode Potentials of Period 4 M^{2+} Ions

Half-Reaction	E^0 (V)
$Ti^{2+}(aq) + 2e^- \rightleftharpoons Ti(s)$	−1.63
$V^{2+}(aq) + 2e^- \rightleftharpoons V(s)$	−1.19
$Cr^{2+}(aq) + 2e^- \rightleftharpoons Cr(s)$	−0.91
$Mn^{2+}(aq) + 2e^- \rightleftharpoons Mn(s)$	−1.18
$Fe^{2+}(aq) + 2e^- \rightleftharpoons Fe(s)$	−0.44
$Co^{2+}(aq) + 2e^- \rightleftharpoons Co(s)$	−0.28
$Ni^{2+}(aq) + 2e^- \rightleftharpoons Ni(s)$	−0.25
$Cu^{2+}(aq) + 2e^- \rightleftharpoons Cu(s)$	0.34
$Zn^{2+}(aq) + 2e^- \rightleftharpoons Zn(s)$	−0.76

Colors of Representative Compounds of the Period 4 Transition Metals

The Bright Colors of Chromium(VI) Compounds

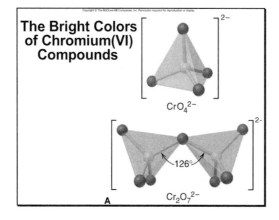

2−

CrO_4^{2-}

2-

126°

A

$Cr_2O_7^{2-}$

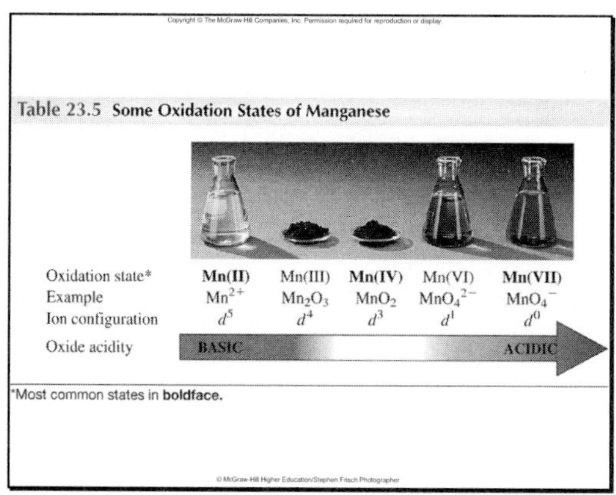
Copyright © The McGraw-Hill Companies, Inc. Permission required for reproduction or display.
Table 23.5 Some Oxidation States of Manganese
Oxidation state* Mn(II) Mn(III) Mn(IV) Mn(VI) Mn(VII)
Example Mn^{2+} Mn_2O_3 MnO_2 MnO_4^{2-} MnO_4^-
Ion configuration d^5 d^4 d^3 d^1 d^0
Oxide acidity BASIC ACIDIC
*Most common states in boldface.
© McGraw-Hill Higher Education/Stephen Frisch Photographer

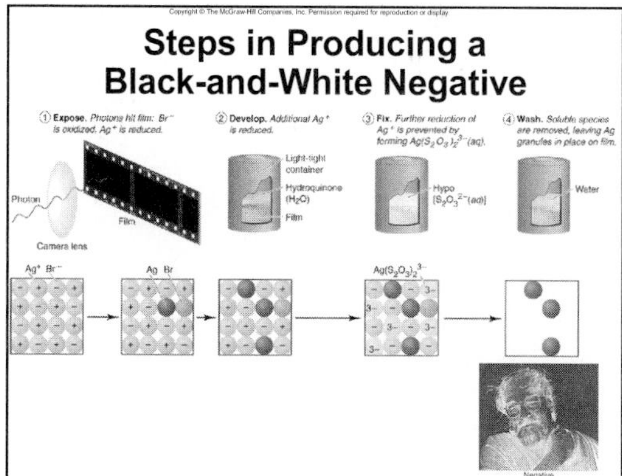
Copyright © The McGraw-Hill Companies, Inc. Permission required for reproduction or display.
Steps in Producing a Black-and-White Negative
① Expose. Photons hit film: Br^- is oxidized, Ag^+ is reduced.
② Develop. Additional Ag^+ is reduced.
③ Fix. Further reduction of Ag^+ is prevented by forming $Ag(S_2O_3)_2^{3-}(aq)$.
④ Wash. Soluble species are removed, leaving Ag granules in place on film.
Photon
Camera lens
Film
Light-tight container
Hydroquinone (H_2O)
Film
Hypo [$S_2O_3^{2-}(aq)$]
Water
Ag^+ Br^-
Ag Br
$Ag(S_2O_3)_2^{3-}$
Negative

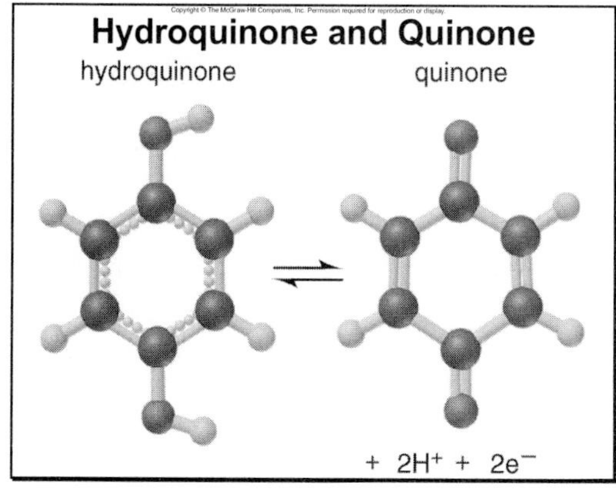
Copyright © The McGraw-Hill Companies, Inc. Permission required for reproduction or display.
Hydroquinone and Quinone
hydroquinone
quinone
+ $2H^+$ + $2e^-$

Components of a Coordination Compound

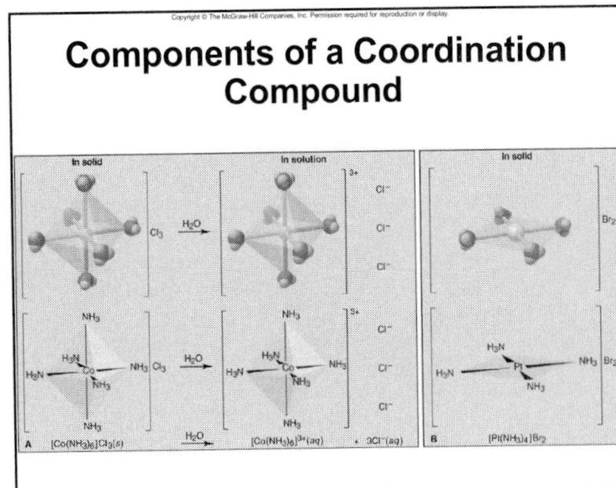

Copyright © The McGraw-Hill Companies, Inc. Permission required for reproduction or display.

Table 23.6 Coordination Numbers and Shapes of Some Complex Ions

Coordination Number	Shape	Examples
2	Linear	$[CuCl_2]^-$, $[Ag(NH_3)_2]^+$, $[AuCl_2]^-$
4	Square planar	$[Ni(CN)_4]^{2-}$, $[PdCl_4]^{2-}$, $[Pt(NH_3)_4]^{2+}$, $[Cu(NH_3)_4]^{2+}$
4	Tetrahedral	$[Cu(CN)_4]^{3-}$, $[Zn(NH_3)_4]^{2+}$, $[CdCl_4]^{2-}$, $[MnCl_4]^{2-}$
6	Octahedral	$[Ti(H_2O)_6]^{3+}$, $[V(CN)_6]^{4-}$, $[Cr(NH_3)_4Cl_2]^+$, $[Mn(H_2O)_6]^{2+}$, $[FeCl_6]^{3-}$, $[Co(en)_3]^{3+}$

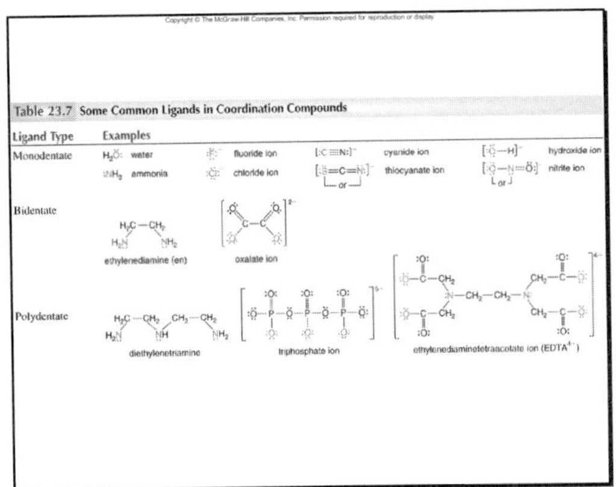

Copyright © The McGraw-Hill Companies, Inc. Permission required for reproduction or display.

Table 23.7 Some Common Ligands in Coordination Compounds

Ligand Type	Examples
Monodentate	H_2O water; F^- fluoride ion; $[C{\equiv}N]^-$ cyanide ion; $[O{-}H]^-$ hydroxide ion; NH_3 ammonia; Cl^- chloride ion; $[S{=}C{=}N]^-$ thiocyanate ion (or); $[O{-}N{=}O]^-$ nitrite ion (or)
Bidentate	ethylenediamine (en); oxalate ion
Polydentate	diethylenetriamine; triphosphate ion; ethylenediaminetetraacetate ion ($EDTA^{4-}$)

Grabbing Ions

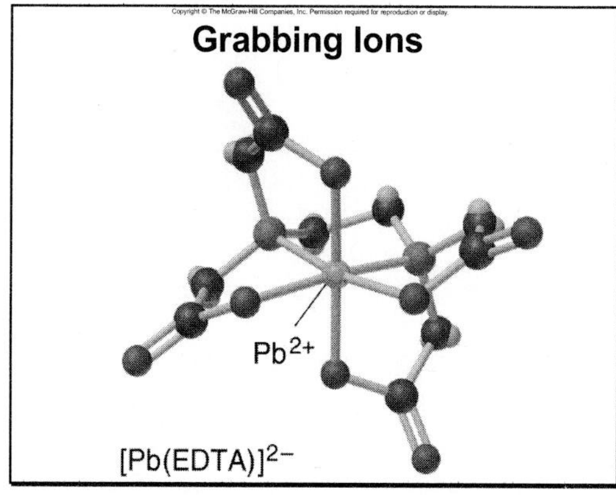

Table 23.8 Names of Some Neutral and Anionic Ligands

Neutral		Anionic	
Name	**Formula**	**Name**	**Formula**
Aqua	H_2O	Fluoro	F^-
Ammine	NH_3	Chloro	Cl^-
Carbonyl	CO	Bromo	Br^-
Nitrosyl	NO	Iodo	I^-
		Hydroxo	OH^-
		Cyano	CN^-

Table 23.9 Names of Some Metal Ions in Complex Anions

Metal	Name in Anion
Iron	Ferrate
Copper	Cuprate
Lead	Plumbate
Silver	Argentate
Gold	Aurate
Tin	Stannate

Table 23.10 Some Coordination Compounds of Cobalt Studied by Werner

Traditional Formula	Werner's Data* Total Ions	Free Cl^-	Modern Formula	Charge of Complex Ion
$CoCl_3 \cdot 6NH_3$	4	3	$[Co(NH_3)_6]Cl_3$	3+
$CoCl_3 \cdot 5NH_3$	3	2	$[Co(NH_3)_5Cl]Cl_2$	2+
$CoCl_3 \cdot 4NH_3$	2	1	$[Co(NH_3)_4Cl_2]Cl$	1+
$CoCl_3 \cdot 3NH_3$	0	0	$[Co(NH_3)_3Cl_3]$	—

*Moles per mole of compound.

Important Types of Isomerism in Coordination Compounds

ISOMERS
Same chemical formula, but different properties

Constitutional (structural) isomers
Atoms connected differently

Coordination isomers
Ligand and counter-ion exchange

Linkage isomers
Different donor atom

Stereoisomers
Different spatial arrangement

Geometric (*cis-trans*) isomers (diastereomers)
Different arrangement around metal ion

Optical isomers (enantiomers)
Nonsuperimposable mirror images

Geometric (*cis-trans*) Isomerism

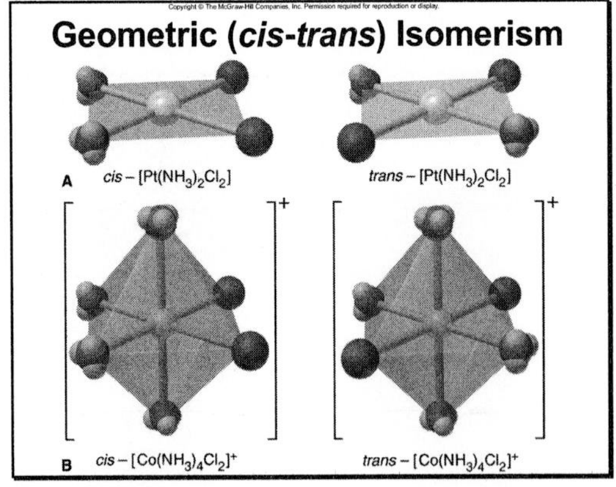

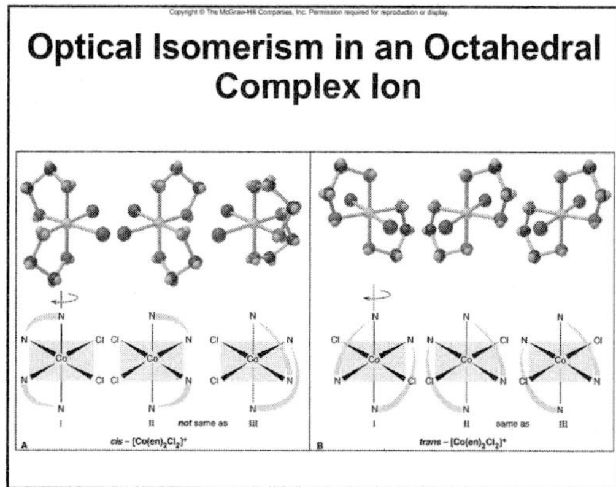
Optical Isomerism in an Octahedral Complex Ion

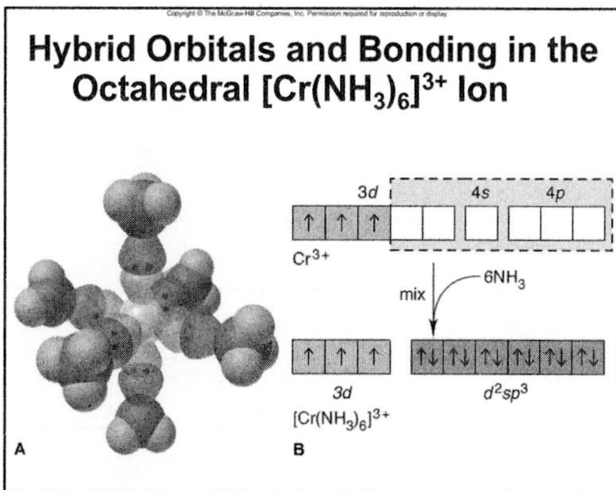
Hybrid Orbitals and Bonding in the Octahedral $[Cr(NH_3)_6]^{3+}$ Ion
3d
4s
4p
Cr^{3+}
mix
$6NH_3$
3d
d^2sp^3
$[Cr(NH_3)_6]^{3+}$
A
B

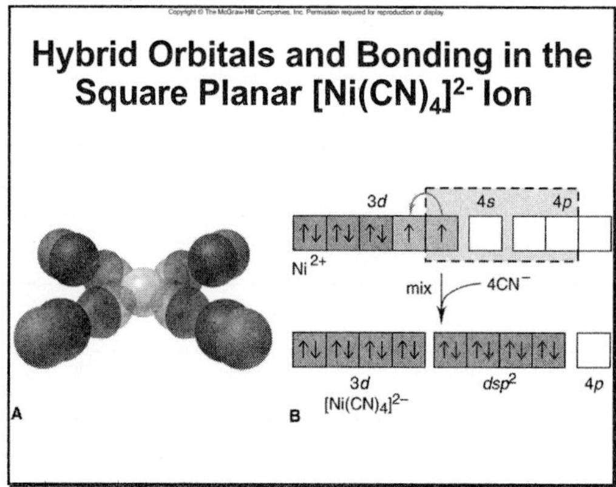
Hybrid Orbitals and Bonding in the Square Planar $[Ni(CN)_4]^{2-}$ Ion
3d
4s
4p
Ni^{2+}
mix
$4CN^-$
3d
dsp^2
4p
$[Ni(CN)_4]^{2-}$
A
B

Hybrid Orbitals and Bonding in the Tetrahedral $[Zn(OH)_4]^{2-}$ Ion

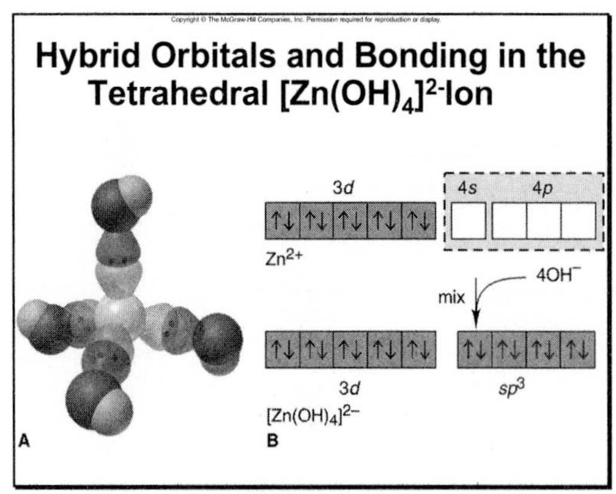

An Artist's Wheel

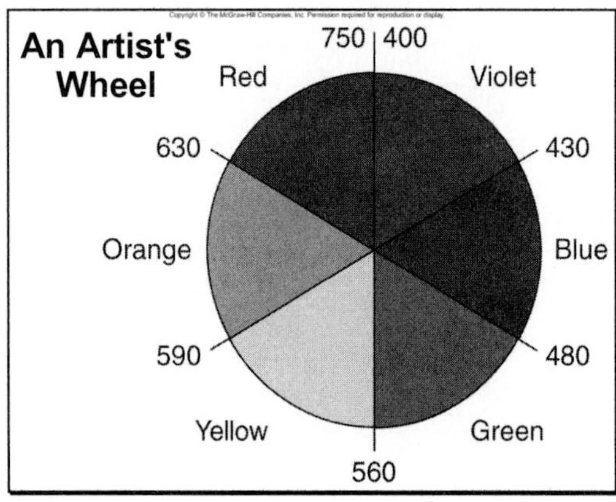

Table 23.11 Relation Between Absorbed and Observed Colors

Absorbed Color	λ (nm)	Observed Color	λ (nm)
Violet	400	Green-yellow	560
Blue	450	Yellow	600
Blue-green	490	Red	620
Yellow-green	570	Violet	410
Yellow	580	Dark blue	430
Orange	600	Blue	450
Red	650	Green	520

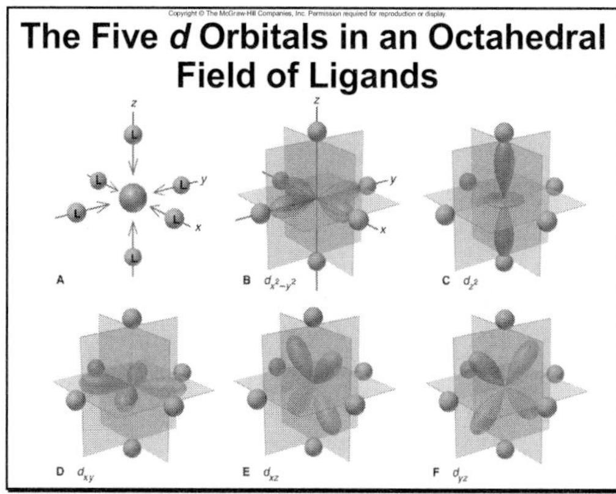
Copyright © The McGraw-Hill Companies, Inc. Permission required for reproduction or display.
The Five d Orbitals in an Octahedral Field of Ligands
A
B $d_{x^2-y^2}$
C d_{z^2}
D d_{xy}
E d_{xz}
F d_{yz}

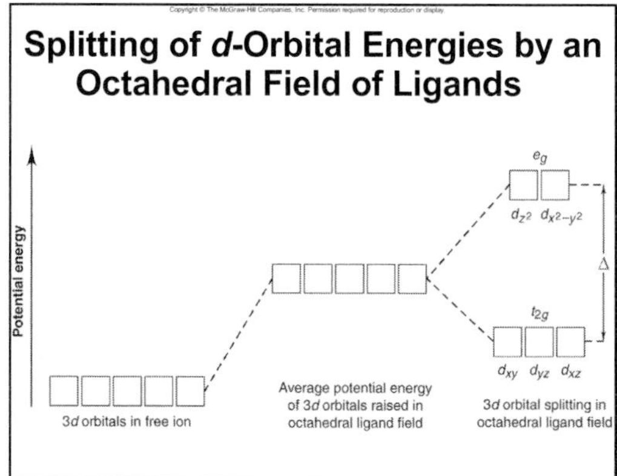
Copyright © The McGraw-Hill Companies, Inc. Permission required for reproduction or display.
Splitting of d-Orbital Energies by an Octahedral Field of Ligands
Potential energy
e_g
d_{z^2} $d_{x^2-y^2}$
Δ
t_{2g}
d_{xy} d_{yz} d_{xz}
3d orbitals in free ion
Average potential energy of 3d orbitals raised in octahedral ligand field
3d orbital splitting in octahedral ligand field

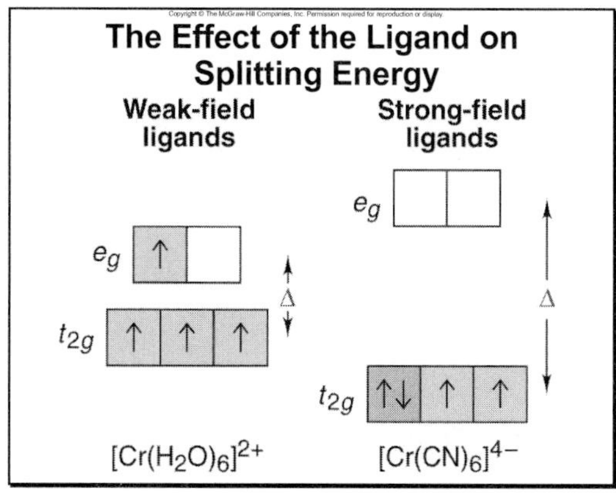
Copyright © The McGraw-Hill Companies, Inc. Permission required for reproduction or display.
The Effect of the Ligand on Splitting Energy
Weak-field ligands
Strong-field ligands
e_g
t_{2g}
Δ
$[Cr(H_2O)_6]^{2+}$
$[Cr(CN)_6]^{4-}$

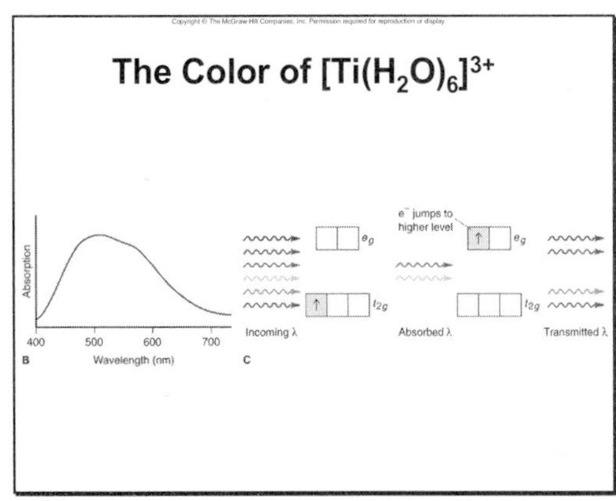

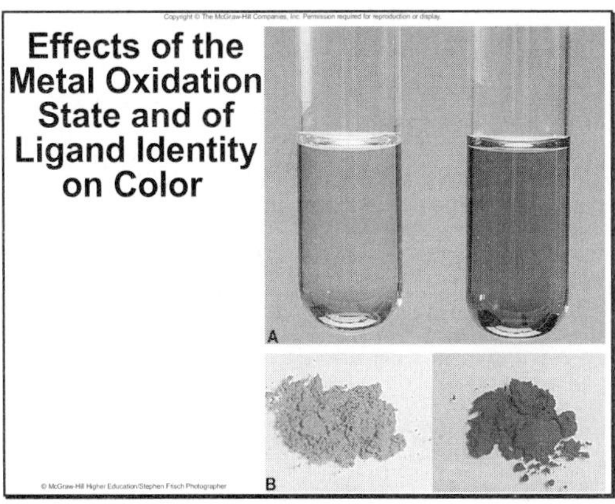

The Spectrochemical Series

$I^- < Cl^- < F^- < OH^- < H_2O < SCN^- < NH_3 < en < NO_2^- < CN^- < CO$

WEAKER FIELD	STRONGER FIELD
SMALLER Δ	LARGER Δ
LONGER λ	SHORTER λ

High-Spin and Low-Spin Complex Ions of Mn^{2+}

No field

Maximum number of unpaired electrons

↑ ↑ ↑ ↑ ↑

A Free Mn^{2+} ion

Weak-field ligand

High-spin complex

$E_{pairing} > \Delta$

e_g ↑ ↑

t_{2g} ↑ ↑ ↑

Δ

B $[Mn(H_2O)_6]^{2+}$

Strong-field ligand

Low-spin complex

$E_{pairing} < \Delta$

e_g

t_{2g} ↑↓ ↑↓ ↑

Δ

C $[Mn(CN)_6]^{4-}$

Orbital Occupancy for High-and Low-Spin Complexes of d^4 through d^7 Metal Ions

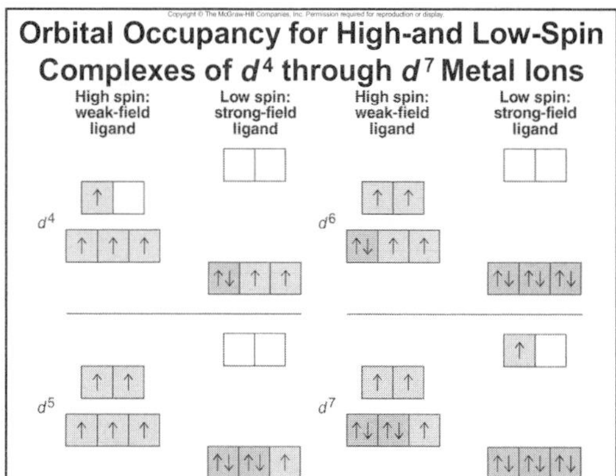

High-Spin vs. Low-Spin Complexes

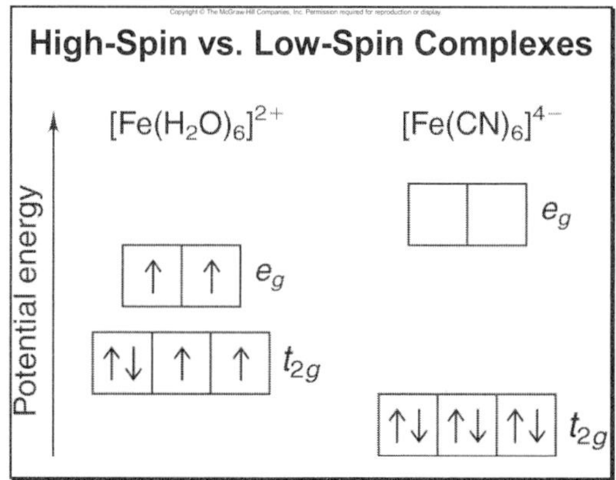

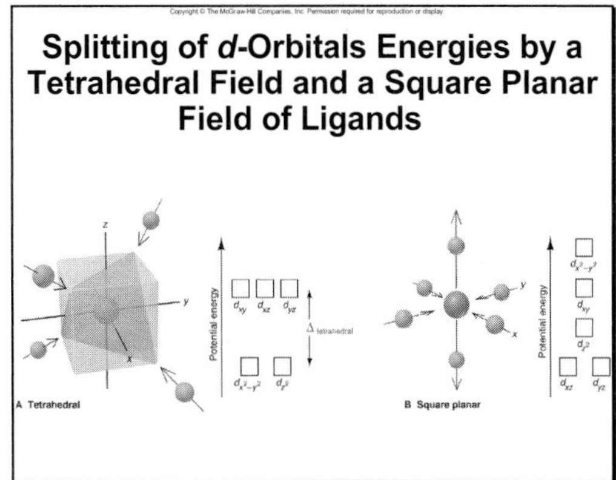

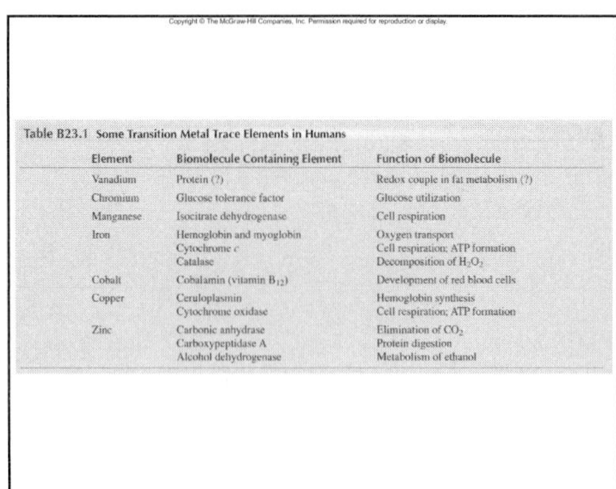

Table B23.1 Some Transition Metal Trace Elements in Humans

Element	Biomolecule Containing Element	Function of Biomolecule
Vanadium	Protein (?)	Redox couple in fat metabolism (?)
Chromium	Glucose tolerance factor	Glucose utilization
Manganese	Isocitrate dehydrogenase	Cell respiration
Iron	Hemoglobin and myoglobin	Oxygen transport
	Cytochrome *c*	Cell respiration; ATP formation
	Catalase	Decomposition of H_2O_2
Cobalt	Cobalamin (vitamin B_{12})	Development of red blood cells
Copper	Ceruloplasmin	Hemoglobin synthesis
	Cytochrome oxidase	Cell respiration; ATP formation
Zinc	Carbonic anhydrase	Elimination of CO_2
	Carboxypeptidase A	Protein digestion
	Alcohol dehydrogenase	Metabolism of ethanol

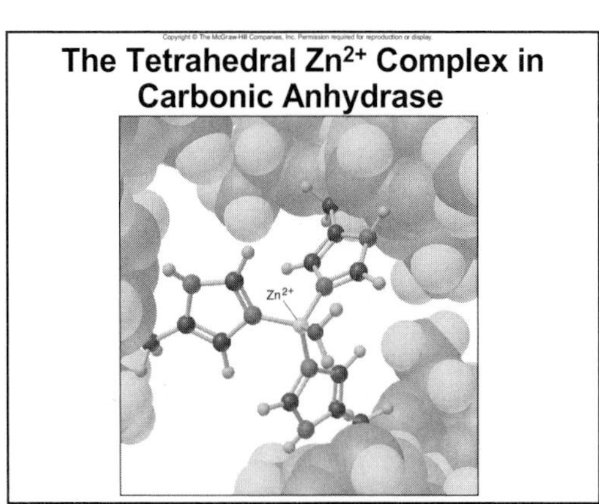

Chapter 24

Chemistry: The Molecular Nature of Matter and Change

Third Edition

Martin S. Silberberg

Copyright © The McGraw-Hill Companies, Inc. Permission required for reproduction or display.

Table 24.1 Comparison of Chemical and Nuclear Reactions

Chemical Reactions	Nuclear Reactions
1. One substance is converted into another, but atoms never change identity.	1. Atoms of one element typically are converted into atoms of another element.
2. Orbital electrons are involved as bonds break and form; nuclear particles do not take part.	2. Protons, neutrons, and other particles are involved; orbital electrons rarely take part.
3. Reactions are accompanied by relatively small changes in energy and no measurable changes in mass.	3. Reactions are accompanied by relatively large changes in energy and measurable changes in mass.
4. Reaction rates are influenced by temperature, concentration, catalysts, and the compound in which an element occurs.	4. Reaction rates are affected by number of nuclei, but not by temperature, catalysts, or, normally, the compound in which an element occurs.

Copyright © The McGraw-Hill Companies, Inc. Permission required for reproduction or display.

The Behavior of Three Types of Radioactive Emissions in an Electric Field

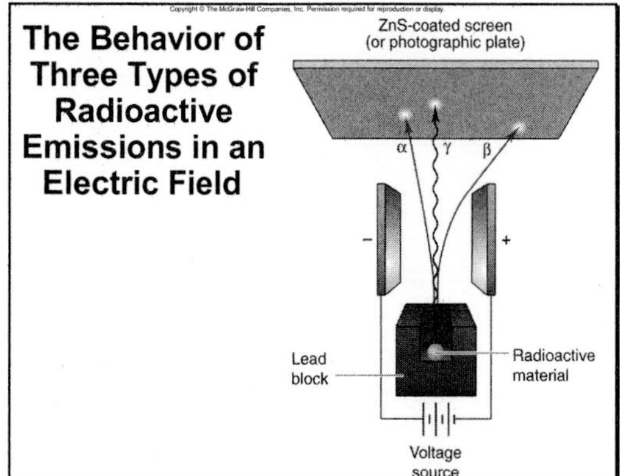

Table 24.2 Modes of Radioactive Decay*

Mode	Emission	Decay Process	Change in A	Change in Z	Change in N
α Decay	α (^4_2He)	Reactant (parent) → Product (daughter) + α expelled	−4	−2	−2
β Decay	$^{0}_{-1}\beta$	^1_0n in nucleus → ^1_1p in nucleus + $^{0}_{-1}\beta$ β expelled	0	+1	−1
Positron emission	$^0_1\beta$	$h\nu$ high-energy photon + nucleus with x p⁺ and y n⁰ → nucleus with $(x-1)$ p⁺ and $(y+1)$ n⁰ + $^0_1\beta$ positron expelled	0	−1	+1
Electron capture	x-ray photon	$^{0}_{-1}e$ absorbed from low-energy orbital + ^1_1p in nucleus → ^1_0n in nucleus	0	−1	+1
γ Emission	$^0_0\gamma$	excited nucleus → stable nucleus + $^0_0\gamma$ γ photon radiated	0	0	0

*Neutrinos (ν) are involved in several of these processes but are not shown.

A Plot of Neutrons vs. Protons for the Stable Nuclides

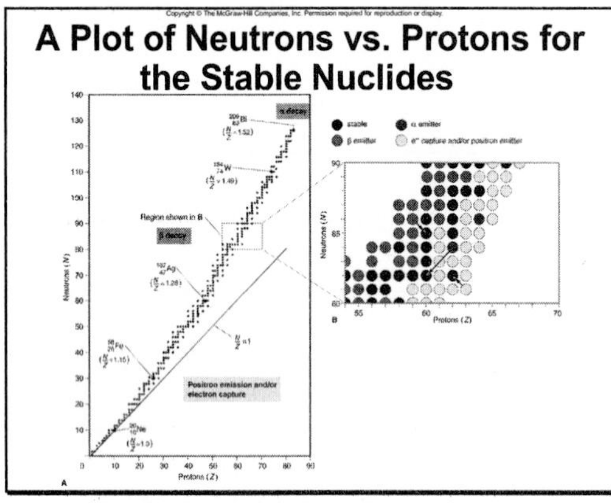

Table 24.3 Number of Stable Nuclides for Elements 48 Through 54*

Element	Atomic No. (Z)	No. of Nuclides
Cd	**48**	**8**
In	49	2
Sn	**50**	**10**
Sb	51	2
Te	**52**	**8**
I	53	1
Xe	**54**	**9**

*Even Z shown in boldface.

Table 24.4 An Even-Odd Classification of the Stable Nuclides

Z	*N*	Number of Nuclides
Even	Even	157
Even	Odd	53
Odd	Even	50
Odd	Odd	7
	TOTAL	267

The ^{238}U Decay Series

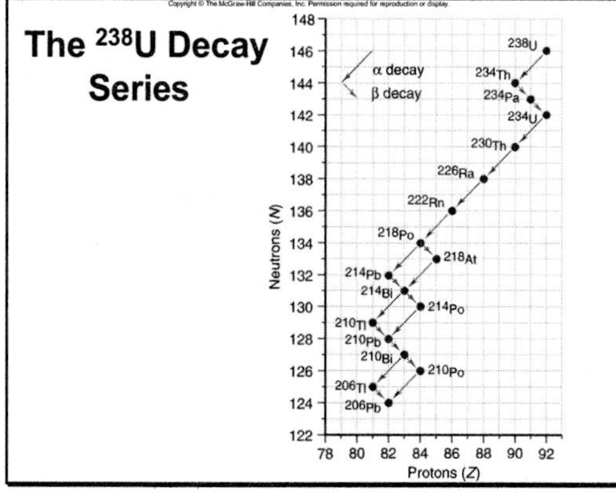

Detection of Radioactivity by an Ionization Counter

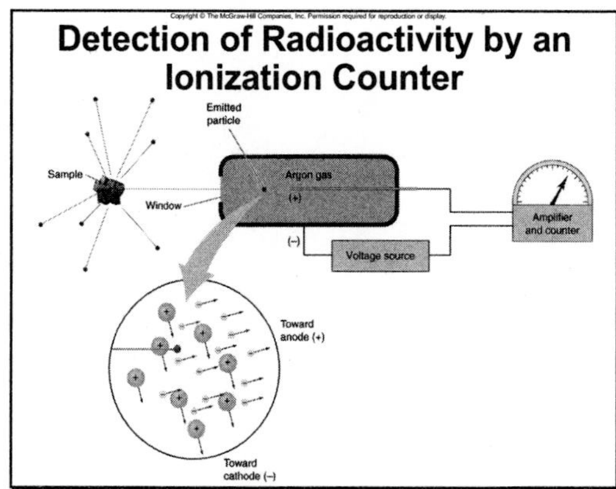

Decrease in Number of ^{14}C Nuclei Over Time

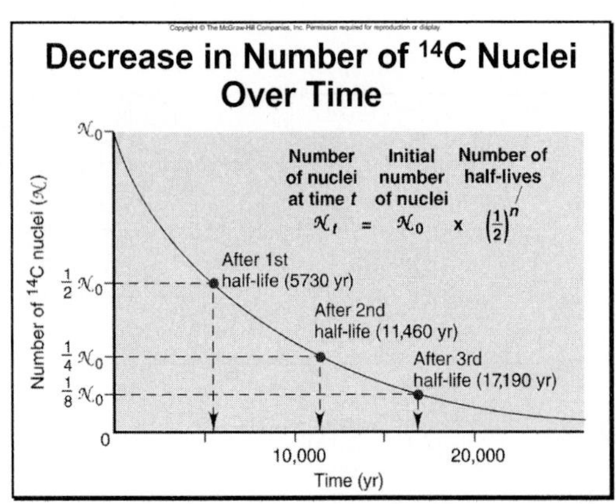

Table 24.5 Decay Constants (k) and Half-Lives ($t_{1/2}$) of Beryllium Isotopes

Nuclide	k	$t_{1/2}$
$^{7}_{4}Be$	1.30×10^{-2}/day	53.3 days
$^{8}_{4}Be$	1.0×10^{16}/s	6.7×10^{-17} s
$^{9}_{4}Be$	Stable	
$^{10}_{4}Be$	4.3×10^{-7}/yr	1.6×10^{6} yr
$^{11}_{4}Be$	5.02×10^{-2}/s	13.8 s

Radiocarbon Dating For Determining the Age of Artifacts

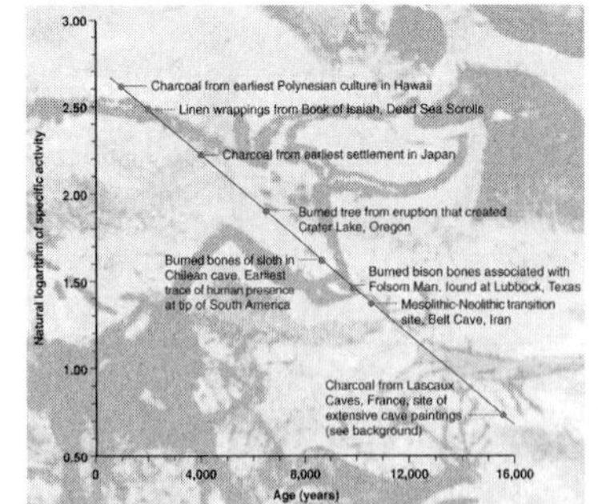

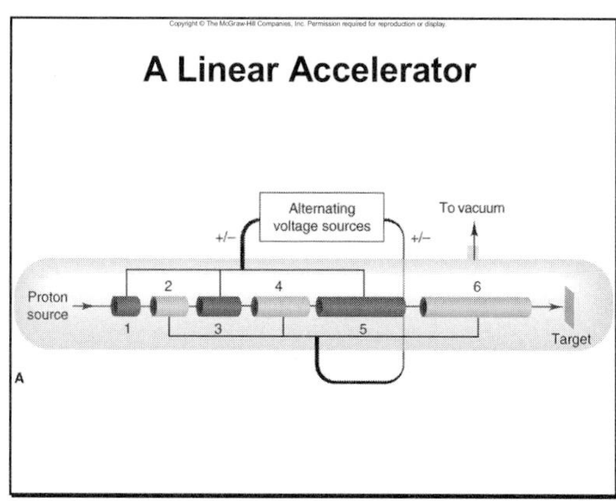

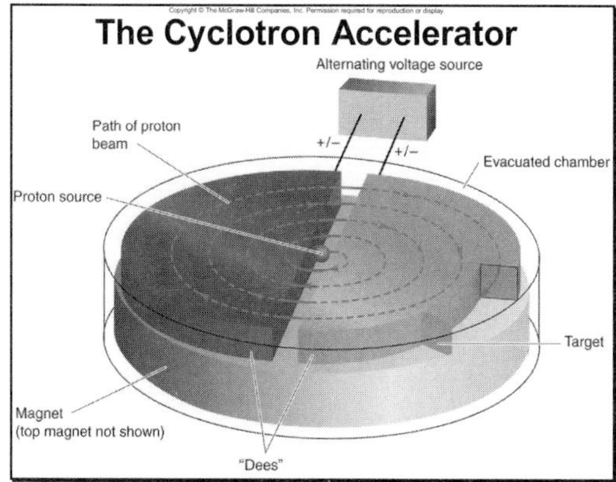

Table 24.6 Formation of Some Transuranium Nuclides

Reaction	Half-life of Product
$^{239}_{94}Pu + ^{4}_{2}He \longrightarrow ^{240}_{95}Am + ^{1}_{1}H + 2^{1}_{0}n$	50.9 h
$^{239}_{94}Pu + ^{4}_{2}He \longrightarrow ^{242}_{96}Cm + ^{1}_{0}n$	163 days
$^{244}_{96}Cm + ^{4}_{2}He \longrightarrow ^{245}_{97}Bk + ^{1}_{1}H + 2^{1}_{0}n$	4.94 days
$^{238}_{92}U + ^{12}_{6}C \longrightarrow ^{246}_{98}Cf + 4^{1}_{0}n$	36 h
$^{253}_{99}Es + ^{4}_{2}He \longrightarrow ^{256}_{101}Md + ^{1}_{0}n$	76 min
$^{252}_{98}Cf + ^{10}_{5}B \longrightarrow ^{256}_{103}Lr + 6^{1}_{0}n$	28 s

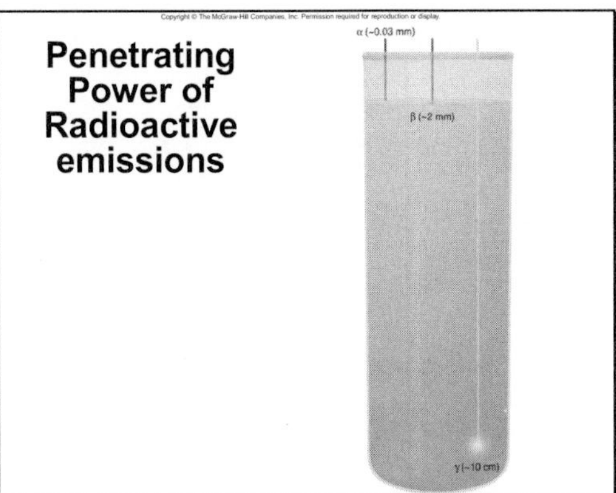

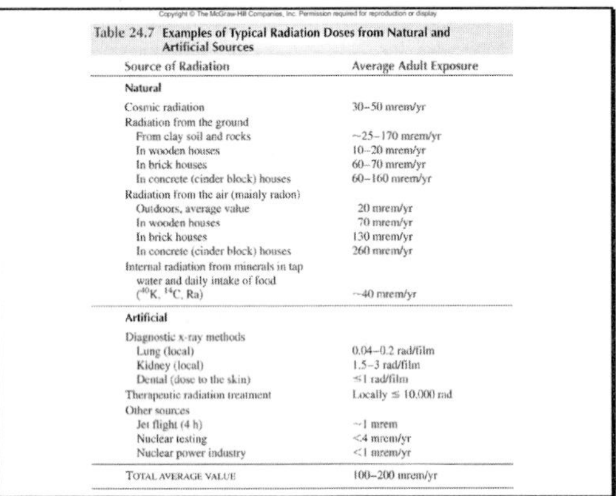

Table 24.7 **Examples of Typical Radiation Doses from Natural and Artificial Sources**

Source of Radiation	Average Adult Exposure
Natural	
Cosmic radiation	30–50 mrem/yr
Radiation from the ground	
From clay soil and rocks	~25–170 mrem/yr
In wooden houses	10–20 mrem/yr
In brick houses	60–70 mrem/yr
In concrete (cinder block) houses	60–160 mrem/yr
Radiation from the air (mainly radon)	
Outdoors, average value	20 mrem/yr
In wooden houses	70 mrem/yr
In brick houses	130 mrem/yr
In concrete (cinder block) houses	260 mrem/yr
Internal radiation from minerals in tap water and daily intake of food (^{40}K, ^{14}C, Ra)	~40 mrem/yr
Artificial	
Diagnostic x-ray methods	
Lung (local)	0.04–0.2 rad/film
Kidney (local)	1.5–3 rad/film
Dental (dose to the skin)	≤1 rad/film
Therapeutic radiation treatment	Locally ≤ 10,000 rad
Other sources	
Jet flight (4 h)	~1 mrem
Nuclear testing	<4 mrem/yr
Nuclear power industry	<1 mrem/yr
TOTAL AVERAGE VALUE	100–200 mrem/yr

Table 24.8 **Acute Effects of a Single Dose of Whole-Body Irradiation**

Dose (rem)	Effect	Lethal Dose: Population (%)	Lethal Dose: No. of Days
5–20	Possible late effect; possible chromosomal aberrations	—	—
20–100	Temporary reduction in white blood cells	—	—
50+	Temporary sterility in men (100+ rem = 1 yr duration)	—	—
100–200	"Mild radiation sickness": vomiting, diarrhea, tiredness in a few hours Reduction in infection resistance Possible bone growth retardation in children	—	—
300+	Permanent sterility in women	—	—
500	"Serious radiation sickness": marrow/intestine destruction	50–70	30
400–1000	Acute illness, early deaths	60–95	30
3000+	Acute illness, death in hours to days	100	2

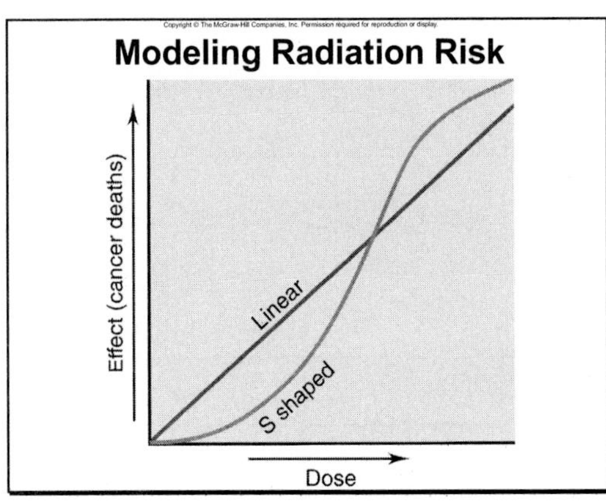

Table 24.9 Some Radioisotopes Used as Medical Tracers

Isotope	Body Part or Process
^{11}C, ^{18}F, ^{13}N, ^{15}O	PET studies of brain, heart
^{60}Co, ^{192}Ir	Cancer therapy
^{64}Cu	Metabolism of copper
^{59}Fe	Blood flow, spleen
^{67}Ga	Tumor imaging
^{123}I, ^{131}I	Thyroid
^{111}In	Brain, colon
^{42}K	Blood flow
^{81m}Kr	Lung
^{99}Tc	Heart, thyroid, liver, lung, bone
^{201}Tl	Heart muscle
^{90}Y	Cancer, arthritis

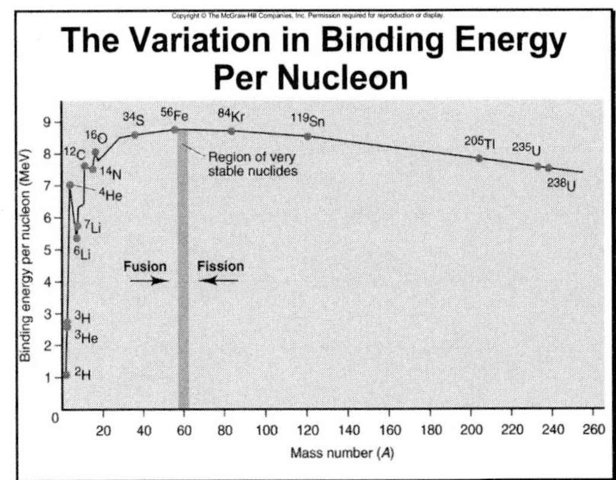

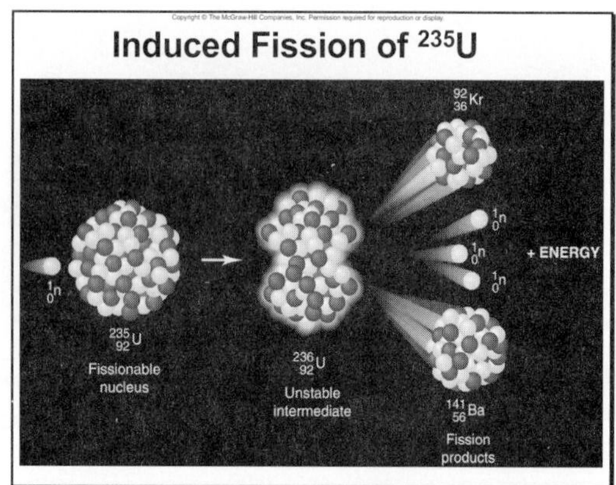
Induced Fission of ^{235}U
$^{92}_{36}Kr$
$^{1}_{0}n$
+ ENERGY
$^{235}_{92}U$
Fissionable nucleus
$^{236}_{92}U$
Unstable intermediate
$^{141}_{56}Ba$
Fission products

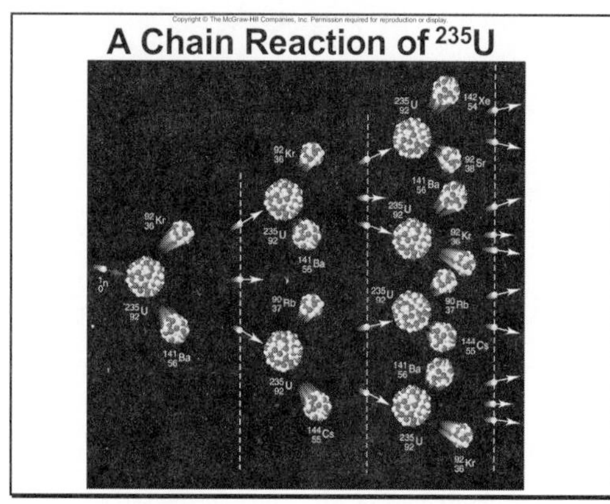
A Chain Reaction of ^{235}U

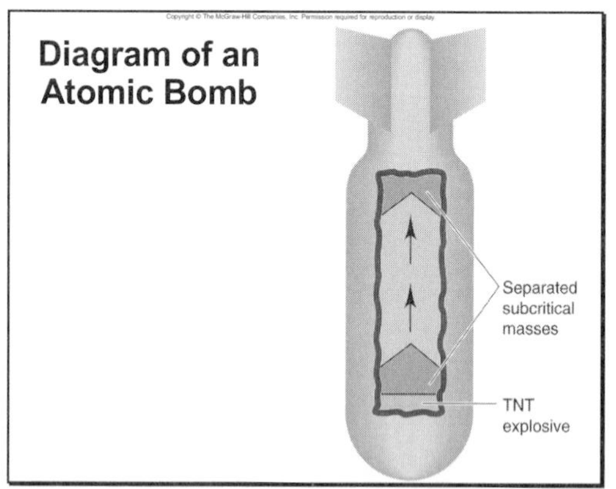
Diagram of an Atomic Bomb
Separated subcritical masses
TNT explosive

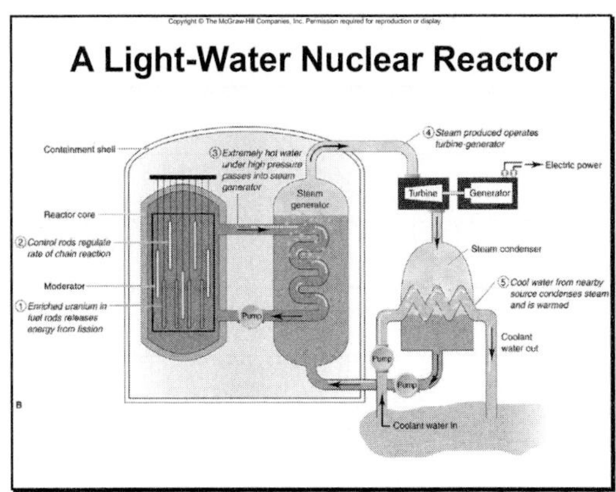
Copyright © The McGraw-Hill Companies, Inc. Permission required for reproduction or display.
A Light-Water Nuclear Reactor
Containment shell
③ Extremely hot water under high pressure passes into steam generator
④ Steam produced operates turbine generator
Electric power
Turbine
Generator
Steam generator
Reactor core
② Control rods regulate rate of chain reaction
Moderator
① Enriched uranium in fuel rods releases energy from fission
Pump
Steam condenser
⑤ Cool water from nearby source condenses steam and is warmed
Coolant water out
Coolant water in
B

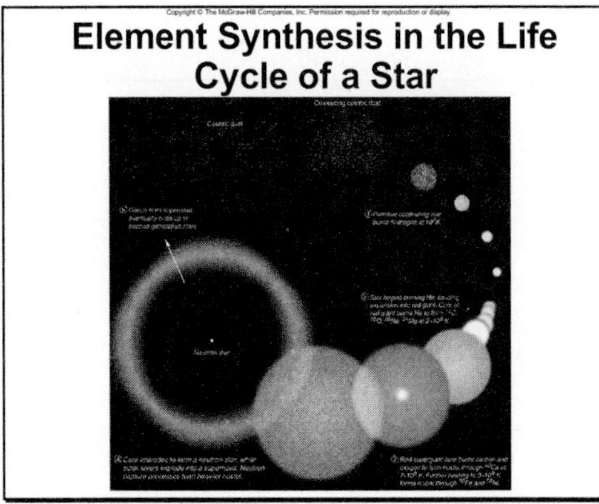
Copyright © The McGraw-Hill Companies, Inc. Permission required for reproduction or display.
Element Synthesis in the Life Cycle of a Star

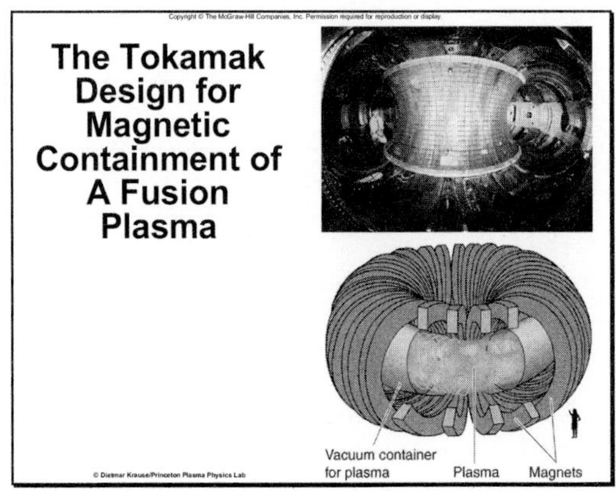
Copyright © The McGraw-Hill Companies, Inc. Permission required for reproduction or display.
The Tokamak Design for Magnetic Containment of A Fusion Plasma
Vacuum container for plasma
Plasma
Magnets
© Dietmar Krause/Princeton Plasma Physics Lab

Endsheets

Chemistry: The Molecular Nature of Matter and Change

Third Edition

Martin S. Silberberg

Fundamental Physical Constants (six significant figures)

Avogadro's number	N_A	$= 6.02214\times10^{23}$/mol
atomic mass unit	amu	$= 1.66054\times10^{-27}$ kg
charge of the electron (or proton)	e	$= 1.60218\times10^{-19}$ C
Faraday constant	F	$= 9.64853\times10^{4}$ C/mol
mass of the electron	m_e	$= 9.10939\times10^{-31}$ kg
mass of the neutron	m_n	$= 1.67493\times10^{-27}$ kg
mass of the proton	m_p	$= 1.67262\times10^{-27}$ kg
Planck's constant	h	$= 6.62608\times10^{-34}$ J·s
speed of light in a vacuum	c	$= 2.99792\times10^{8}$ m/s
standard acceleration of gravity	g	$= 9.80665$ m/s^2
universal gas constant	R	$= 8.31447$ J/(mol·K)
		$= 8.20578\times10^{-2}$ (atm·L)/(mol·K)

SI Unit Prefixes

p	n	μ	m	c	d	k	M	G
pico-	nano-	micro-	milli-	centi-	deci-	kilo-	mega-	giga-
10^{-12}	10^{-9}	10^{-6}	10^{-3}	10^{-2}	10^{-1}	10^{3}	10^{6}	10^{9}

Conversions and Relationships

Length
SI unit: meter, m

1 km = 1000 m
= 0.62 mile (mi)
1 inch (in) = 2.54 cm
1 m = 1.094 yards (yd)
1 pm = 10^{-12} m = 0.01 Å

Volume
SI unit: cubic meter, m^3

1 dm^3 = 10^{-3} m^3
= 1 liter (L)
= 1.057 quarts (qt)
1 cm^3 = 1 mL
1 m^3 = 35.3 ft^3

Pressure
SI unit: pascal, Pa

1 Pa = 1 N/m^2
= 1 $kg/m{\cdot}s^2$
1 atm = $1.01325{\times}10^5$ Pa
= 760 torr
1 bar = $1{\times}10^5$ Pa

Mass
SI unit: kilogram, kg

1 kg = 10^3 g
= 2.205 lb
1 metric ton (t) = 10^3 kg

Energy
SI unit: joule, J

1 J = 1 $kg{\cdot}m^2/s^2$
= 1 coulomb·volt (1 C·V)
1 cal = 4.184 J
1 eV = $1.602{\times}10^{-19}$ J

Math relationships

$\pi = 3.1416$
volume of sphere = $\frac{4}{3}\pi r^3$
volume of cylinder = $\pi r^2 h$

Temperature
SI unit: kelvin, K

0 K = −273.15°C
mp of H_2O = 0°C (273.15 K)
bp of H_2O = 100°C (373.15 K)
T (K) = T (°C) + 273.15
T (°C) = [T (°F) − 32]$\frac{5}{9}$
T (°F) = $\frac{9}{5}T$ (°C) + 32

Notes

Notes

Notes

Notes

Notes

Notes

Notes

Notes

Notes

Notes

Notes